Advances in
PARASITOLOGY

VOLUME 3

Advances in
PARASITOLOGY

Edited by
BEN DAWES

Department of Zoology, King's College,
University of London, England

VOLUME 3

1965

ACADEMIC PRESS
London and New York

ACADEMIC PRESS INC. (LONDON) LTD.
Berkeley Square House
Berkeley Square
London, W.1

U.S. Edition published by
ACADEMIC PRESS INC.
111 Fifth Avenue
New York, New York 10003

Library of Congress Catalog Card Number: 62–22124

PRINTED IN GREAT BRITAIN
BY WILLMER BROTHERS LIMITED, BIRKENHEAD

CONTRIBUTORS TO VOLUME 3

JOSEPH E. ALICATA, *Department of Parasitology, University of Hawaii Agricultural Experiment Station, Honolulu, Hawaii, U.S.A.* (p. 223)

DON R. ARTHUR, *Department of Zoology and Animal Biology, King's College, University of London, England* (p. 249)

S. B. KENDALL, *Central Veterinary Laboratory, Ministry of Agriculture, Fisheries and Food, New Haw, Weybridge, England* (p. 59)

W. H. R. LUMSDEN, *Bacteriology Department, University of Edinburgh Medical School, Edinburgh, Scotland* (p. 1)

PAUL H. SILVERMAN, *Department of Zoology, University of Illinois, Urbana-Champaign, Illinois, U.S.A.* (p. 159)

MUNEO YOKOGAWA, *Department of Parasitology, School of Medicine, Chiba University, Chiba, Japan* (p. 99)

CONTRIBUTORS TO VOLUME

PREFACE

The appearance of a third volume in this series indicates the aim of the Editor to obtain from specialists critical reviews which extend the scope and interest of the series by covering "fresh woods and pastures new" in a sustained attempt to survey the parasitological landscape in a world of invigorated biological effort. Without disrespect to willing authors and contemplating only the order in which contributions appear, it must be admitted that the Editor's own preferences materialize only in so far as contributors are able to meet some specified closing date for receiving manuscripts. This may imply that a satisfactory balance of contributions can hardly be sustained volume by volume and must be achieved by overall effort. However, no time has been lost in supplying contributions on the biological aspects of trypanosomiasis research, the relationship between species of *Fasciola* and their molluscan hosts, *Paragonimus* and paragonimiasis, *in vitro* cultivation procedures for parasitic helminths, the biology and distribution of the rat lungworm, *Angiostrongylus cantonensis*, and its relation to eosinophilic meningoencephalitis, and feeding in ectoparasitic Acari, with special reference to ticks.

W. H. R. Lumsden reveals new concepts arising from improved methods of investigation, notably the use of "stabilates"—viable biological materials protected against changes in antigenicity and other properties by low temperature storage and other techniques. New structural differences between trypanosomes recovered from blood and cultures have been revealed by electron microscopy and related to physiological states. Various criteria on which classification is based have been clarified by new methods of counting, measuring infectivity, preserving viability and facilitating culture. Arthropodan vectors have been considered in relation to feeding and maintenance in the laboratory and host–parasite relationships in the field, and an account of the biology of vertebrate hosts mentions the relevant habits and occupations of man. The development of trypanosomes within the gut and the haemocoele of the vectors and methods of isolation are discussed. Parasitism in the mammalian body during the infective period and in established infections, and features of susceptibility and distribution are treated. Immunological concepts are well defined and there is a working hypothesis of trypanosomal antigens of internal and external (released) types. The relationships between parasites, arthropodan vectors and mammalian hosts are considered against both laboratory and field settings and there is some account of African sleeping sickness. In a concluding section, Lumsden indicates that the great breadth of trypanosomiasis research makes difficult the application of ecological methods and concepts. Tests for the detection of antibodies indicative of past infections are as yet hardly applicable. Many species and strains of trypanosomes are

transmitted simultaneously in the field and serum antibodies cannot yet be referred precisely to pathogens of major interest. New methods are needed for
gaining quantitative information about situations in the field, and we are
shown where future effort can best be expended in trying to improve our knowledge of mechanisms of survival and transmission of the trypanosomes, which
will probably come about by the deployment of various biological disciplines
in combined efforts not possible just a few years ago.

Writing on species of *Fasciola*, S. B. Kendall suggests that *F. hepatica* and
F. gigantica are probably the only valid species and that they predominate respectively in temperate and tropical regions of the earth. After reviewing the
general features of the life cycle, development of the eggs, penetration into
snail hosts and normal development in the body of the snail, he compares larval development in these two trematode species and discusses the question of
snail hosts. The conclusion is reached that transmission seems to depend on
a limited number of snail species, only one species being involved in a given
area. Problems associated with the classification of the Lymnaeidae provide
difficulties of identification, but snails which transmit *F. hepatica* are resistant
to *F. gigantica*, and vice versa. The hosts of *F. hepatica* are amphibious snails
living on wet mud, rarely inhabiting moving water and never living in deep
permanent water; conversely, the hosts of *F. gigantica* are truly aquatic snails
nearly always living in permanent waters having much vegetation. In dealing
with questions of host specificity, however, we have to recognize the possible
existence of physiological races of both flukes and snails in different geographical regions. Even in some restricted areas, differences of susceptibility may
characterize different strains of snails. Some of the factors which influence
the development of larval flukes within the snail host are reviewed. Variability of temperature is notable, because it may bring about in either species
of fluke the production of either rediae or cercariae from first generation
rediae, giving reason for the belief that daughter rediae can offset the effects
of adverse conditions by "overwintering" in the snail's body. It is noted also
that few observations have been made on the possible effect of the nutritional
states of snails on the development of larval flukes. Snails of all sizes, and
both well fed and ill nourished snails, are likely to be susceptible to infection.
It is subsequent development that is affected by the low nutritional state of
some snails. Aestivation of snail hosts can be regarded as a special effect
produced by malnutrition. Host-resistance is also considered in relation to
initial infection and later development, and the special case of repeated infection is discussed. Finally, Kendall discusses the pathogenicity of snail infections and factors which affect the emergence and survival of cercariae, and
he provides epidemiological notes which show how it has become possible in
Britain to forecast reasonably accurately the likely incidence of serious outbreaks of fascioliasis so that timely control measures can be carried out.

Muneo Yokogawa's account of *Paragonimus* and paragonimiasis has great
breadth and depth, and far more than one hundred original papers referred
to were published in Japanese and are therefore not readily available to most
readers. This genus of lung flukes has seventeen species, two of which were
discovered more than a century ago—*P. rudis*, from the lungs of an otter, and

P. compactum, from the lungs of an Indian mongoose. The only species which is known to develop in man, *P. westermani*, was found in the lungs of a tiger which died in the Zoo at Amsterdam in 1877 and was described in 1878. At about this time, ovoid bodies found in the sputum of suspected tuberculosis patients were regarded as the spores of some gregarine, but subsequently identified as the eggs of *P. westermani*. This was the first appearance of the trematode in man. Some other species of *Paragonimus* are probably invalid, and after considering species differentiation in terms of the structure of cercariae, metacercariae (which are more properly called juveniles after excystment) and adults, Yokogawa describes the life cycles of four indubitable species, *P. westermani, P. kellicotti, P. ohirai* and *P. iloktuenensis*. Attention is then directed to various biological and physiological characteristics—the development of miracidia, resistance and excystment of metacercariae, development of juveniles *in vitro*, and egg production. Histochemical research bearing on the metabolism of *P. westermani* is also considered. Development in the final host takes into account migratory routes, the way in which cysts are formed and the duration of adult life. The life span may exceed ten years, although maturity is attained in a few weeks or months. The lung fluke thus resembles *Fasciola hepatica*, and likewise is capable of self-fertilization, because *P. ohirai* can produce fertile eggs in isolation, although *P. westermani* seems to require a "mate". In experimental infections of dogs and cats, two or three flukes usually occur within a single cyst in the lungs but cysts may contain only one worm because one of a pair or two of a trio die and degenerate.

In considering geographical distribution, Yokogawa shows that human paragonimiasis is restricted to localities where food habits favour infection. The chief endemic areas include Korea, Japan, Formosa, central China and the Philippines, although a few scattered cases occur in Manchuria and Indo-China. Infection generally results from eating raw or imperfectly cooked crabs, usually species of *Eriocheir*. However, in some countries only well cooked crabs are eaten, and some other mode of infection must prevail. Yokogawa observed that in the preparation of crab soup cysts may remain on various utensils subsequently used to prepare pickles and spices favoured as food and that infection may result from such use of a contaminated chopping block or strainer, or the hands of the cook. In dealing with the pathology of pulmonary and extrapulmonary paragonimiasis much detail is given which should prove to be of great value to the medical profession. The development of pathological states in parasitism has not been sufficiently studied, although as the outcome of the host's reaction to its parasites it is deserving of close attention from the moment of its inception. In paragonimiasis there are many points of resemblance with pathological states in fascioliasis, for instance, hyperplasia of epithelia, the development of fibrosis and the formation of Charcot-Leyden crystals. Diagnostic techniques are broader in paragonimiasis than in fascioliasis and include examination of sputum as well as faeces, sero-immunological procedures and X-ray analysis, but the confounding of diagnoses of paragonimiasis and tuberculosis suggests the need for closer scrutiny of pathological states and the ways in which they develop. In respect of treatment and control of paragonimiasis, control is likely to be the more difficult. Methods directed against snail hosts are of limited application, those against crabs not easy to carry out in endemic areas. Biological education of the populace will facilitate greater circumspection in the preparation of food and chemotherapy will be of great service in destroying adult flukes. After considering chemotherapeutic studies in great detail, Yogogawa concluded that mass treatment with bithionol will work well in endemic areas. Food scarcity and the movements of people to rural districts during and since the Second World War has increased the incidence of paragonimiasis in Japan so that during the past ten years it has remained a serious public health problem in certain areas, but there is hope that the disease may die out where mass treatment with bithionol has been practised.

Paul H. Silverman considers that, in spite of limitations, *in vitro* cultivation procedures facilitate the assessment of essential physiological requirements of helminths and are complementary to *in vivo* methods in the elucidation of some aspects of the host–parasite relationships. Such procedures are involved, calling for physiologically homogeneous biological materials, which must be sterilized and maintained under aseptic conditions and suitable media which simulate *in vivo* conditions, although these are not invariably advantageous and have sometimes been deleterious. Trial and error methods have largely been used which include the testing of balanced salines, complex tissue culture media, natural liquids such as plasma and serum, and some other tissue extracts, either separately or in conjunction. Various criteria used for assessing the value of *in vitro* procedures—motility and reaction to stimuli, increase in size, evidence of development, utilization of substrates and mitotic activity—are not always valid and must be used with caution. Dying worms may show motility, and maturation phenomena may appear because of available nutritional reserves rather than conditions of culture. However, *in vitro* studies have contributed to our knowledge of metabolism, antigenicity, behaviour, growth and development, and they have acquired their own terminology, although after defining such terms as "axenic culture" Silverman considers the use of other terms as yet unnecessary. He then deals with matters of techniques and media in such necessary detail as will prove helpful to many investigators, and also discusses findings and conclusions in orderly fashion under the headings nematodes, cestodes, trematodes and acanthocephalans. Starting with the classical work of Glaser and of Stoll and his pupils on *Neoaplectana* and of Weinstein and Jones on *Nippostrongylus*, he continues with the work of Lapage on *Haemonchus* and deals with researches involving *Hyostrongylus*, *Ostertagia*, *Cooperia* and *Trichostrongylus*, *Oesophagostomum* and *Stephanurus*, *Dictyocaulus*, *Trichinella*, *Ancylostoma* and some Ascaridoidea and Filarioidea. In considering the tapeworms he deals with the work of Smyth on *Schistocephalus* and *Ligula*, of Mueller on *Spirometra* and of Mendelsohn, Robinson, Taylor and others on *Taenia*. Also considered are important works by Schiller, Taylor, Berntzen and others on *Hymenolepis* and of Rausch and Jentoft, Yamashita, Smyth, Webster and Cameron, Parker and others on *Echinococcus*. In dealing with the trematodes he discussed the researches of Ferguson on *Posthodiplostomum* and *Diplostomum* and related work by Bell and Hopkins, Bell and Smyth, Williams and others. The meagre research on *Fasciola* is mentioned, as is the more sustained work on *Fascio-loides* by Freidl, and on *Schistosoma* by Lee and Chu, Ross and Bueding, Newsome and Robinson, Ito and Komiya, Senft and his colleagues and Clegg. Mention is made also of the work of Ingersoll on *Cyclocoelium* and of Yoko-gawa and his colleagues on *Paragonimus*. The research of Dunagan stands as significant in respect of the Acanthocephala. This catalogue of names is a poor indication of the task which Silverman has carried out of combining information and ideas on techniques, media and other matters with a kind of progress report of researches within this field. In a Discussion section points of vital importance to investigators are noted in respect of preculture treat-ment, sterilization, media and culture conditions, and future developments. Silverman considers the immediate aims in this field to be the development of chemically defined media, the use of axenic conditions which avoid the ad-verse effects of antibiotics, and the need to consider limiting as well as abso-lute dietary requirements. He stresses also the point that a developing parasite may be undergoing metabolic as well as metamorphic changes, so that peri-odic transfer to new conditions of culture at critical times might be necessary to ensure some success.

Joseph E. Alicata's contribution is concerned with a nematode parasite of rats which was little known until the 1960's. The life cycle of this lungworm, *Angiostrongylus cantonensis*, was elucidated only ten years ago, but this event inaugurated researches on cerebral angiostrongylosis in man in a number of areas, including south-east Asia and the islands of the Pacific, and "has opened up a new chapter in the field of human parasitology". In some areas this syndrome, characterized by eosinophilia of the cerebrospinal liquid of mammals, appears in some non-helminthic and helminthic diseases but cases have appeared in areas where these diseases are not endemic and here the rat lungworm is probably the aetiological agent. Adult worms occur in the pul-monary arteries and right ventricle of the heart. Eggs travel by the blood stream, lodge in emboli in small vessels of the lungs and develop in about 6 days. First stage larvae migrate to the trachea, are swallowed and when about 0·3 mm long leave the host's body in the faeces. In fresh water such larvae can remain alive for about 6 days (3 days in sea water) but usually they enter some mollusc, either through the mouth or by active penetration of the integument, undergo two moults and become infective third stage larvae. Rats are infected by eating infected molluscs, or drinking contaminated water, and the larvae penetrate the intestinal wall and enter the blood circulatory system. Within 17 h some of the larvae have entered the cerebrum, where they pass through two further moults within the next 2 weeks and become juvenile worms. These emerge and lodge in the subarachnoid spaces for 2 more weeks until when 11–12 mm long they travel by the blood stream to the final location 29–32 days after infection. After 1 week more they begin to lay eggs and 42–48 days after infection first stage larvae appear in the faeces. Recent in-vestigations reveal a wide variety of terrestrial snails and slugs which serve as intermediate hosts and freshwater prawns, land crabs and land planarians, pigs and calves also transmit the parasite to human and simian hosts which acquire eosinophilic meningoencephalitis during the migratory stages of its development. Alicata has traced out parallels in the geographical distribution of human cases of this disease and rodent hosts, and he has shown that transmission of the parasite is by ingestion of uncooked carrier hosts and molluscan intermediaries. He stresses the point that so far only basic information has been acquired and indicates that we need better methods of diagnosis, more information about carrier hosts and the effects produced by the parasite in mammalian hosts, particularly their relation to neurological disorders which arise.

Don R. Arthur is concerned principally with the feeding operations of ticks —the feeding mechanism, the sites of saliva deposition and the histopathology of trauma which are produced by the mouth parts and skin reactions evoked by the salivary secretion. However, he starts by considering feeding in larval Trombiculid mites, some of which are important pests or vectors of parasitic disease, because these redbugs or scrub mites illustrate a possible stage in the evolution of the blood sucking habit of ticks. Initial penetration by the cheliceral claws lacerates the skin and compresses, ruptures and displaces epithelial cells. Salivary secretions of a dual nature lead to histolysis of the cells in the deeper layer of the skin and a host reaction is evoked which produces new surrounding tissue. After ingestion of cytolysed tissue further injections of saliva and imbibitions of digested materials by the larva occur repeatedly until a hyaline stylostome, or feeding tube, is formed, and through this tissue fluids or liquefied tissue elements are sucked. In ticks, the feeding process is initiated by the chelicerae and the mechanical action is augmented by salivary secretions. The second type of saliva is more liquid than the first but so far feeding in ticks approximates to that of Trombiculid larvae, indicating a possible origin of the two forms from some common progenitor which fed on extravascular tissue liquids. However, by a lengthening of the chelicerae feeding on deeper tissues was facilitated, so that ticks became able to feed upon blood, although a diet of blood is not essential for the development of immature forms. Going into great detail on problems associated with the feeding of ticks, Arthur has shown that significant amounts of tissue other than blood make up the diet. Being much larger than mites, ticks deeply insert the hypostome and chelicerae into the host's tissues and these organs form channels for the conveyance of saliva and food to and from the host's body. The saliva is more potent than that of mites, producing greater liquefaction of the host's tissues. Ixodid ticks are therefore able to penetrate deeply and obtain blood, which is the main constituent of the diet during the later stages of feeding. However, it is possible for such ticks to feed on tissue liquid which accumulates from microtrauma during lengthy periods of slow feeding. Other topics discussed include features of digestion and absorption, the removal of undigested residues, engorgement under field conditions, rhythmicity in detachment of repleted ticks, factors influencing attachment to the host, and feeding sites on natural hosts. Many indications are given of areas which remain for further investigation in this field of research.

Once again, my gratitude is expressed in sincere thanks to authors who in a spirit of service have willingly undertaken severe tasks to assist in the dissemination of parasitological knowledge and ideas. Other worthy writers may now have acquired a greater desire to participate in this far-seeing venture. Other volumes are at present in preparation but the broad landscape of parasitology includes many vistas still to be explored in the modern world of biology and any plans to enrich this effort will be welcomed. It is my pleasure also to express my thanks to the staff of the Academic Press for the great care which has been exercised in the production of this book.

BEN DAWES
Professor of Zoology
(Parasitology)
May 1965

KING'S COLLEGE
UNIVERSITY OF LONDON
STRAND, LONDON, W.C.2

CONTENTS

Biological Aspects of Trypanosomiasis Research

W. H. R. LUMSDEN

Relationships between the Species of *Fasciola* and their Molluscan Hosts

S. B. KENDALL

xv

Paragonimus and Paragonimiasis

MUNEO YOKOGAWA

In vitro Cultivation Procedures for Parasitic Helminths

PAUL H. SILVERMAN

Biology and Distribution of the Rat Lungworm, *Angiostrongylus cantonensis*, and its Relationship to Eosinophilic Meningoencephalitis and other Neurological Disorders of Man and Animals

JOSEPH E. ALICATA

Feeding in Ectoparasitic Acari with Special Reference to Ticks

DON R. ARTHUR

Biological Aspects of Trypanosomiasis Research

W. H. R. LUMSDEN*

Bacteriology Department, University of Edinburgh Medical School,
Edinburgh, Scotland

I. INTRODUCTION

This review is written from the standpoint of a director of research which has the practical aim of reducing the incidence of pathogenic trypanosomiasis in man and domestic animals of tropical Africa. This objective can be achieved along any one of at least four approaches which involve respectively chemotherapy, reduction or eradication of the arthropodan vector, manipulation or removal of the vertebrate host, or methods involving immunology. In recent years chemotherapy and vector control by the introduction of residual insecticides have produced most change in field practice. In other ways, research results have brought about only marginal alteration of control methods (Lumsden, 1964a). However, chemotherapy or chemoprophylaxis and vector control by means of insecticides do not lead independently to inherent

*Formerly Director, East African Trypanosomiasis Research Organization, Tororo, Uganda.

1

B

stable conditions, so that they do not alone proffer solutions which are ultimately satisfactory. The lines of research most likely to lead to improved field practices are still not clearly defined, so that wide-ranging studies have been indicated in order to gain a more complete understanding of the ecology of trypanosomiasis, mechanisms of mammalian immunity or adjustment to infection, and interactions between these mechanisms and drug treatment.

Interest has been wide ranging but also selective, tending to be concentrated in areas most likely to yield improvements in field applications by greater epidemiological understanding. Such unevenness is reflected in this effort to deal mainly with recent research in Africa and only selectively with research elsewhere in so far as it is applicable to African problems. Trypanosomiasis impinges on so many aspects of African life and economics that its main problems are difficult to define. Attention will be drawn to new concepts and approaches which promise to be fruitful of results, because the principal pre-requisite for more rapid advance of knowledge seems to be improvements in methods of study. Hitherto, these have been classified as medical, veterinary and entomological, but this is no longer practicable. Lumsden (1964a) classified trypanosomiasis research according to the number of components in it—the parasite or vector alone or more complicated areas involving more than one component and leading on to areas which involve the entire epidemiological complex of parasite, vector, wild animal hosts and man or his domesticated animals. Such a scheme has the advantage of grouping studies that are basically similar, thus facilitating discussion, and it is followed in this review.

The following authorities, conventions and definitions will be cited: Buxton (1955) on entomological questions; Hoare (1957) for the parasites and Allen (1939) for the nomenclature of wild animal hosts. It has not been considered necessary in this general survey to quote the authors of the specific names mentioned.

With regard to the trypanosome materials, the term "strain" will be applied in situations in which the trypanosomes are maintained available for experi-mentation by continuous passage, either cyclical or mechanical. Such passage involves the possibility of antigenic and other change on the part of the organisms, and such material is characteristically unstable. A separate term is required to distinguish material in which change has been arrested, at least to some extent, by viable preservation. The term "stabilate" has been proposed (Lumsden and Hardy, 1965) and is defined as an individual trypanosome (or other biological material) preserved in viable condition on a unique occasion; there will be, of course, only as many examples of a stabilate available for experimentation or reference purposes, as individual samples of the material laid down on the unique occasion. It will be convenient also to have some way of defining the degree of "deep freezing" by which trypanosomes are preserved; the easiest practice seems simply to state the temperature used, as for example, " −80° C freezing". Logarithms quoted are calculated to the base 10.

II. The Trypanosome

In recent years the deficiencies of the methods available for the study of trypanosomes have become increasingly realized. The ease with which trypanosomes are seen by light microscopy and the beauty and variety of their structure encouraged morphological and biometrical studies. Experimental and inductive approaches were discouraged by the variability of the material during serial passage in laboratory animals or, in cases in which the organisms were established in culture, by their losing characteristics of essential experimental interest, such as infectivity to the vertebrate host. These difficulties have probably contributed to the delay in the development of standard methods for the manipulation of trypanosomes; for example, a multiplicity of different diluents have been used for suspending trypanosomes in experimental procedures (Lumsden, 1963). Also, although it was known, in some situations at least, that trypanosomes were not uniform in their characteristic of prime interest—their capability to establish and multiply in a new susceptible host—quantitative studies were based usually on the concentrations of organisms existing in suspensions, not on the infectivity of the suspensions. Also, enumeration of trypanosomes by means of haemacytometer counts or, more approximately, by scoring organisms in microscope fields, afford data without drudgery only in the upper ranges of the concentrations occurring. For instance, trypanosomes can readily be counted in the haemacytometer only when their concentrations exceed about antilog 4 per ml; in fluids such as blood, which require dilution before counting, the threshold is correspondingly higher. Even fulminant parasitaemias rarely exceed antilog 8·5 trypanosomes per ml, so that counting by visual methods is largely confined to the upper range of trypanosome concentrations.

It is to Weinman and McAllister (1947) that the credit is due for first drawing attention to the fundamental significance of the low temperature storage of viable organisms in affording material in which antigenic and other change is arrested, now called stabilate material. The improvement of methods for this purpose by Polge and Soltys (1957) and their simplification by Cunningham *et al.* (1963) have made it worthwhile to attempt the development of more sophisticated laboratory procedures.

A. STRUCTURE

The remarkable advances in knowledge of the morphology of trypanosomes, mainly relating to the *Trypanosoma brucei* subgroup, which electron microscopy has provided, are summarized by Vickerman (1962, 1963).

Fibrils of about 20 mμ diam. extend lengthwise under the pellicle of the trypanosome over its entire surface; these fibrils are presumed to be contractile and responsible for changes in body shape. The flagellum has an axial filament composed of two central and nine double peripheral fibrils; a structure which occurs widely in the locomotory organelles of plants and animals. The flagellum appears to be without the anchoring attachment to the trypanosome body presumed by the classical "undulating membrane" concept; it seems simply to be applied to the trypanosome pellicle. There is, however, alongside the axial filament in the flagellum, an additional accessory filament of lattice-like ultrastructure, which may contribute to the "undulating membrane" appearance. Pinocytosis has been demonstrated in the culture forms of *Trypanosoma mega* by using colloidal ferritin as an electron-dense marker; ferritin was ingested into vacuoles through a cystotome near the point of emergence of the flagellum.

Differences shown by electron microscopy between the blood and culture forms of trypanosomes have been strikingly related to physiological differences between these forms (Vickerman, 1962, 1963). In the blood forms of the *T. brucei* subgroup there is a simple tubular anterior mitochondrion arising from the kinetoplast but no posterior mitochondrion. In the culture forms (assumed to represent developmental stages found in the midgut of *Glossina*) there are extensive and elaborate anterior mitochondria and a sinuous posterior mitochondrion extending from the kinetoplast to the posterior end of the organism. The development of the posterior mitochondrion may account for the forward displacement of the kinetoplast in the insect form, as compared with the blood form, which displacement results ultimately in the crithidial state. The blood forms live in a medium rich in glucose and oxygen and are notable for their high rates of oxygen consumption. They do not, however, metabolize glucose beyond pyruvate and their terminal respiration is mediated by a system associated with a L-α-glycerophosphate oxidase, not by a cytochrome system (Grant and Sargent, 1960, 1961; Grant et al., 1961). In the culture forms, on the other hand, Krebs' cycle intermediaries are utilized, respiration is mediated by cytochrome systems and metabolism proceeds beyond pyruvate (Ryley, 1961). In other cells the Krebs' cycle systems are located in the mitochrondria and so this switch in respiratory metabolism is likely to be associated with the mitochondrial proliferation described (Vickerman, 1962, 1963). Conversely, perhaps, conversion of crithidial to metacyclic infective forms at the end of the developmental cycle in *Glossina* is associated with involution of the posterior mitochondrion in preparation for the reverse change in respiratory metabolism.

B. TAXONOMY

The most important change in the list of the trypanosomes of African mammals is the rediscovery of *Trypanosoma suis* by Peel and Chardome (1954). The species is monomorphic and pathogenic to pigs; its development in *Glossina* terminates in the salivary glands.

In certain papers and reviews Hoare (1956a,b, 1959) has shown intensive interest in the taxonomy of the mammal-infecting species of the genus *Trypanosoma*. His latest revision of the genus (1964) is set out in Table I. He advanced this as a natural classification, based on the probable phylogeny of the organisms. It will be followed in the present review, except that the "*T. brucei* subgroup" of Hoare's earlier classifications still has an application—to designate *T. (T.) brucei, gambiense* and *rhodesiense*—and will be retained.

1. *Taxonomic Criteria*

The identification of trypanosomes still offers difficulties in many situations and it is appropriate to discuss recent opinions regarding the value of the different taxonomic criteria.

a. Biometry. The application of statistical methods to the comparison of measurements of trypanosomes has sometimes been of value, e.g. in the

TABLE I

Classification and Characters of the Genus Trypanosoma (*from Hoare,*
1956a, 1959, 1964)

The type species of each subgenus is cited first.

A. STERCORARIA

Free flagellum present; kinetoplast large, not terminal; posterior end of body pointed; multiplication in mammal discontinuous, typically in crithidial or leishmanial stages; typically non-pathogenic; development in vector in posterior station, transmission contaminative

Subgenus *Megatrypanum*	Large species; kinetoplast typically near nucleus, far from posterior end of body; includes *T. (M.) theileri, tragelaphi, ingens, melophagium* and others
Subgenus *Herpetosoma*	Medium-sized species; kinetoplast subterminal; includes *T. (H.) lewisi, duttoni, nabiasi,* and others
Subgenus *Schizotrypanum*	Small species, typically curved; kinetoplast voluminous, close to posterior end of body; includes *T. (S.) cruzi, vespertilionis, pipistrelli* and others
Subgenus *Endotrypanum*	Endoglobular crithidial and trypanosome forms; includes only *T. (E.) schaudinni*

B. SALIVARIA

Free flagellum present or absent; kinetoplast terminal or subterminal; posterior end of body usually blunt; multiplication in mammal continuous in trypanosomal stage; typically pathogenic; development in vector in anterior station and transmission inoculative; includes also some atypical species transmitted non-cyclically by arthropod vectors, or by coitus

Subgenus *Duttonella*	Monomorphic species; posterior end of body rounded; kinetoplast large, terminal; free flagellum present; development in vector (*Glossina*) in proboscis only; includes *T. (D.) vivax, uniforme*
Subgenus *Nannomonas*	Small species; monomorphic or polymorphic; kinetoplast of medium size, typically marginal; free flagellum usually absent; development in vector (*Glossina*) in midgut and proboscis; includes *T. (N.) congolense, dimorphon, simiae*
Subgenus *Pycnomonas*	Short, stout species; monomorphic; kinetoplast small, subterminal; free flagellum short; development in vector (*Glossina*) in midgut and salivary glands; includes *T. (P.) suis*
Subgenus *Trypanozoon*	Typically polymorphic species with small subterminal kinetoplast; development in vector (*Glossina*) in midgut and salivary glands; includes some aberrant species transmitted non-cyclically or by coitus; includes *T. (T.) brucei, gambiense, rhodesiense, evansi, equinum, equiperdum*

differentiation of *Trypanosoma vivax* and *Trypanosoma uniforme* (Hoare, 1956b). The validity of the differentiation of *Trypanosoma congolense* from *T. dimorphon* on grounds of differing mean lengths (Hoare, 1959) has been questioned by Godfrey (1960). Godfrey distinguished *T. congolense*, intermediate, and *T. dimorphon* types among only five isolations. He pointed out that comparisons between different populations should be made in the same species of host; the biometrics of isolations in normal hosts were, on the whole, consistent but they were very variable in rats. The ranges of the mean lengths of the three types in cattle and sheep, however, formed a continuous series with no gaps between the types and Godfrey (1960) saw no valid reason for classifying *T. dimorphon* as a separate species, preferring to regard *T. congolense* as a series of types separable by mean length measurements of many samples. Godfrey (1961) correlated the shorter *T. congolense* and longer *T. dimorphon* with different intensities of infection in experimental animals.

Other attempts to relate differences of virulence between trypanosome strains and strains or intraspecific races defined by biometrical methods have been less satisfactory. In a study of *Trypanosoma evansi*, Hoare (1956a) showed that the mean length of strains (even of substrains of the same strain) varied considerably, the differences between samples being statistically significant in about 50% of the pairs compared. He concluded that the statistical significance of such variations does not necessarily provide criteria for distinguishing strains taxonomically. Godfrey (1961) suggested that the exact terminology of minor taxons should be left until full serological and physiological studies can be made.

Clearly, biometry must be used with circumspection and its application is likely to be severely limited by an inherent laboriousness. If statistically significant differences between, for instance, the mean lengths of individuals of different trypanosome populations, or in the representation of different forms, are to be accepted as also biologically significant, standard procedures for preparing the material, for making a random sample, free from any subjective bias, from the population for measurement and for measurement itself are clearly primary requirements. Even when these requirements are fulfilled, difficulties may arise from the heterogeneity of the populations of trypanosomes available or from variations in the characteristics of the organisms at different stages in an infection or in different hosts. An example of this kind of difficulty is afforded by the phenomenon of polymorphism. Although the validity of the division of populations of trypanosomes of the *T. brucei* subgroup into three separate forms, "long-slender", "intermediate" and "short-stumpy", has long been a subject of controversy, the comprehensive study of the matter by Wijers (1960) indicates that the question is still unresolved.

b. Morphology. Hoare (1956b, 1957) has emphasized that we have exact criteria for the diagnosis of trypanosome species in the mammalian host so long as thin blood films suitably stained are available. But it is true, also, that experienced observers may sometimes be misled on morphological assessments. Hoare (1956b) cited an example of the difficulties entailed in the diagnosis of mixed infections. He concluded that a strain reported from Portuguese East Africa in which the characteristics of *T. simiae* and *T. brucei* were combined was in fact a mixture of the two species, one or other becoming predominant in the course of a series of passages, depending on the susceptibility of the hosts and alternation of the periods of predominance of the two species.

Hoare (1956b) pointed out that, with the recognition of the occurrence of polymorphism in *T. simiae*, the term "polymorphic trypanosomes" cannot now be used without qualification to designate the three species, *T. brucei*, *T. gambiense* and *T. rhodesiense*, as has been the custom in the past.

In the vector all the species of the trypanosome groups resemble each other and it is possible in this situation to distinguish on morphological grounds only the taxonomic groups, not the individual species (Hoare, 1956b).

   c. Physiology. Williamson (1963) has reviewed present knowledge of the chemical composition of trypanosomes; the information available covers trypanosomes differing in type of existence, host and tissue preference, mode of development in the intermediate host, drug sensitivity, virulence and morphology. The amino-acid constitution of trypanosome proteins conforms to the general pattern of most known proteins and is closely similar to that of bovine plasma albumin, differing mainly in having a higher proportion of glycine and a lower proportion of cysteine/cystine. The amino-acid constitution shows little variation between species or strains; a significant difference was found between the alanine content of *T. cruzi* (19·1%) and that of *T. lewisi* (8·4%) and a difference of borderline significance between the lysine/arginine content of normal and stilbamidine-resistant strains of *T. rhodesiense* (Williamson and Desowitz, 1961). The Ouchterlony agar gel diffusion method has been used as a convenient indicator of antigenic activity in trypanosome preparations. Two widely different strains of *T. brucei* subgroup organisms and a number of serological variants derived from them all showed the same basic precipitin pattern (Williamson, 1963).

Differences between trypanosome populations in respect of their capability to infect particular mammal hosts and their susceptibility to the effect of anti-trypanosomal drugs may not be due solely, or even mainly, to physiological differences, but in so far as such differences are relatable to taxonomy they are conveniently discussed here.

The differential effects on the *Trypanosoma* spp. of economic importance of the various anti-trypanosomal drugs in common use are discussed by Davey (1957). Some drugs, e.g. tryparsamide (a neutral aromatic arsenical) and suramin (a sulphonated naphthylamine derivative) are effective mainly or only against *T.* (*Trypanozoon*) spp., others, e.g. homidium (a phenanthridinium derivative) and quinapyramine (a 6-aminoquinaldine compound) have wider "spectra" of activity but are active primarily against *Duttonella* and *Nannomonas* infections. In a recent comprehensive and informative review of the chemotherapy of African trypanosomiasis, Williamson (1962) states that the mode of action of the active drugs "is in no case known with any precision". He discusses the general activity of aromatic arsenicals and antimonials against *T.* (*Trypanozoon*) spp. and their general inactivity against species of the subgenera *Duttonella* and *Nannomonas*. He points out that all the parasites show active aerobic glycolysis and hence might be expected to show comparable sensitivities to the organometallic drugs. He suggests, therefore, that it may be the non-metallic part of the drug molecule which determines its lethal action and that the determination of the arsenic-refractory character may be due to the pattern of enzyme protein receptors in the region of the active thiol centres. Williamson discusses many other of the implications of drug action on trypanosome metabolism and emphasizes the importance of this approach in arriving not only at an understanding of the mode of action of drugs but also of the fundamental differences between trypanosome groups or species. For instance, he quotes work (Yarmolinsky and Haba, 1959) which suggests that puromycin (an antibiotic obtained from *Streptomyces*) inhibits the soluble ribonucleic acid-amino acid transfer mechanism in protein synthesis and suggests that further elucidation of the structure of the related compound, nucleocidin, should shed light on the metabolic differences between species of the subgenus *Trypanozoon* and those of the subgenera *Duttonella* and *Nannomonas*; puromycin is active mainly in the first context, nucleocidin only in the latter. Differences appear, so far, to be in the modes of nucleic acid and protein synthesis, rather than in respiration and glycolysis.

The "spectrum" of hosts which can be infected by a given trypanosome population is sometimes taken as indicative of the specific identity of the population. For instance, the absence of parasitaemia following the inoculation of *T. brucei* subgroup organisms into man is held to indicate that the inoculation was of *T. brucei sensu stricto*. The susceptibility of hosts to trypanosomes will be discussed later in this paper and attention at present is limited to the consideration of the possible influence of physiological factors in this context. The subject has been reviewed by Desowitz (1963). The nutritional status of the host may affect the course of the infection. For instance, Lincicome (1958, 1959) has shown with *T. lewisi* in the mouse that starvation of the host may allow multiplication of the parasite, so leading to high parasitaemias, sometimes lethal, which do not occur in the normally-fed host. Godfrey (1958) has shown that suppression of the parasitaemia of *T. vivax* in rats fed on a high cod-liver oil diet was reversed by vitamin E. There are many examples of vitamin-deficient diets being associated with the occurrence of more severe parasitaemias in the mammal host (Desowitz, 1963); e.g. diets deficient in pantothenate or biotin lead to severe infections of *T. lewisi* in rats (Becker *et al.*, 1947; Caldwell and Gyorgy, 1947), and diets deficient in thiamine, pantothenate or pyridoxine, but not in riboflavin, enhanced the parasitaemias caused by *T. cruzi* in rats (Yaeger and Miller, 1960a–d). How far such effects are due to direct physiological effects on the parasites or due to indirect effects due to alterations of host physiology or antibody production is not known; Desowitz (1963) comments that we are "still in the position where only hypotheses can be offered". It is clear, however, that the susceptibility of a given host to a given trypanosome material, whether determined by physiological or immunological factors, is not an immutable characteristic and that the "spectrum" of host susceptibility should be used with circumspection for taxonomic purposes.

d. *Cultural characteristics.* Lehmann (1960, 1961, 1962) has compared the behaviour of *T.* (*Nannomonas*) group and *T. brucei* subgroup species in various diphasic cultures with a view to using behavioural differences as a taxonomic tool. In diphasic media of the usual type, in which the blood component is added after autoclaving, he found that *T. congolense* (2 strains) and *T. rhodesiense* (2 strains) almost always established, while *T. brucei* (1 strain) almost always failed to do so. On the other hand, with diphasic media in which the blood component was autoclaved, there was some indication that *T. brucei* established more frequently than did *T. rhodesiense*. There was indication also, of morphological differences between *T. brucei* and *T. rhodesiense* in the characteristics of the rosettes and in the proportion of slender forms in the population in cultures aged 24–48 h. In comparisons of the effect of the constitution of the overlay Lehmann found that *T. congolense* and *T. rhodesiense* would both grow in cultures in which the overlay added was distilled water but that only *T. congolense* survived when it was 1·8% NaCl. Lehmann pointed out some of the difficulties in the way of work of this sort, in particular that "strains" as usually isolated may be heterogeneous in their type, even in their specific, constitution. There is need for a considerable collection of stabilates firmly established by repeated demonstration of their incapacity to infect man, as of *T. brucei sensu stricto*, for extension of this type of work (Lumsden, 1963).

2. *The Identification of Trypanosomes*

Hoare has drawn attention (1956b) to the shortcomings of the specific determinations of trypanosomes by certain workers and to the confusion arising therefrom. He points out that medical men and veterinarians, preoccupied with the prevention or the [treatment of disease, have tended to disregard the parasites themselves and concentrate on epidemiological or clinical approaches, lumping all the different species of parasite together under the inclusive term "trypanosomiasis". The writer wishes to reinforce Hoare's comment. Clearly each trypanosome species is likely to represent a population occupying a particular ecological niche and so almost certainly existing by means of mechanisms differing in some way from those serving other trypanosome species for survival; differences may be expected to occur as regards both vectors and wild mammal hosts. It is likely, therefore, ultimately to be unprofitable to attempt epidemiological analysis of trypanosomiasis as a whole. Accurate taxonomic determination will therefore be a prerequisite for any sophisticated study.

Although in many cases a taxonomic decision can be made, there are clearly still many situations in which extended study of populations rather than individuals is required for this purpose. There is great need for methods for the rapid recognition of populations or better, of individuals, of the biological forms in which interest is greatest because of their pathogenic properties. The development of such methods implies the long-term availability of standard precisely-designated trypanosome materials for comparative study. This can now be afforded by the use of stabilates. For homogeneity of population, stabilates set up from single organisms, perhaps metacyclic trypanosomes, have obvious recommendations but have so far been little used.

C. EXPERIMENTAL

1. Counting Organisms

A method for counting living trypanosomes and at the same time allowing the study of their cytoplasmic inclusions by phase-contrast microscopy, has been described by Ormerod *et al.* (1963). The blood of which the trypanosome content is to be estimated is applied as a spot to the surface of a thin layer of agar on a microscope slide and covered by a glass slip. The trapped blood spreads under the slip to form a single layer of erythrocytes lying edge to edge, termed a "phalanx". Trypanosomes are counted and examined in successive and contiguous fields round the periphery of the phalanx and the mean number occurring per field estimated. A close relation exists between that value and the absolute estimate made with the haemacytometer; a conversion factor is used.

2. Measuring the Infectivity of Trypanosome Suspensions

As trypanosomes can be seen, and therefore counted, by light microscopy, it was natural, when quantitative studies of them were required, that they should first be based on numbers of organisms. In the virus field, where the direct visual approach was not generally available, methods were developed to measure infectivity as an index of virus content. The second approach is applicable also to trypanosomes and may be applied simultaneously with the first. The two approaches are independent and comparison of their results will indicate what proportion of the organisms present are potentially infective.

The experimental methods evolved for this purpose have been described and discussed by Lumsden *et al.* (1963). The concentration of trypanosomes in a suspension was estimated by means of the haemacytometer. The infectivity of the suspension was estimated by serially diluting it and inoculating standard quantities of several of the serial dilutions into mice. The response of any individual animal was regarded as "all or none", infected or not-infected, on the basis of a standard microscopical examination. On the results of these examinations, an end-point was estimated, at which a given proportion of the animals responded.

In comparing the infectivity of a trypanosome suspension with the concentration of organisms in it, when differences occur, two interpretations are possible: (a) the trypanosome population is heterogeneous, some individuals being capable of initiating an infection when inoculated, and some not; (b) the trypanosome population is homogeneous but more than one individual must be inoculated to allow one to establish. The first model is known to obtain on some occasions—animals may be infected experimentally with single trypanosomes—and so it was selected. On this model 63% of recipient animals are expected to become infected at such a dilution of the suspension that the mean number of infective organisms in each inoculum is one. The 63% end-point is therefore a convenient one, being directly comparable with the visual count of trypanosomes in the same material.

In developing the method it was necessary to make an arbitrary start, standardizing as many factors as possible and operating so that any factors necessarily left uncontrolled were likely to be of negligible effect. Initial assessment of the usefulness of the method depended on demonstration that it yielded results which were consistent and of such precision, in relation to the total range of variation occurring, that differences between estimates might be recognized as significant. These requirements were established by carrying out ten replicate estimations of the same trypanosome suspension (Lumsden *et al.*, 1963). No statistically significant differences occurred among the ten estimates and the estimates were of such precision, using tenfold dilution intervals and six recipient animals at each dilution, that differences of about tenfold and upward could be recognized as significant. As the infectivity of the *T. brucei* subgroup suspension used was of the order of antilog 8·0 63% infective doses (ID_{63}) per ml, this degree of precision was sufficient for many applications.

In the work described above (Lumsden *et al.*, 1963) the estimates of numbers of trypanosomes per unit volume of suspension were, on an average, 0·45 on the log scale higher than the estimates of infectivity. This result was interpreted as indicating that about 1 trypanosome in 3 was potentially infective when inoculated into another host. This relationship has, however, been found not to be constant. Lumsden *et al.* (1965) studied both fresh and stabilate material and found that the optimum pH of the suspending medium for the maintenance of both numbers of trypanosomes and infectivity was about 8·0. At low pH values, particularly below 6·0, infectivity was rapidly and drastically reduced; an exposure of 10 min to low pH might reduce infectivity to 1/2500 of its initial value even though trypanosome numbers were undiminished. It has been shown, also, that the relationship between the concentration of trypanosomes in, and the infectivity of, the blood of laboratory rodents is not constant through the course of a *T. brucei* subgroup infection (see below, pp. 26-27).

Infectivity titration has been used, also, to study the effects of various experimental procedures. Infectivity was maintained with little loss for several hours at tonicity equivalent values as low as 0·58% NaCl; there were, however, rapid losses at tonicity equivalents of below 0·41% NaCl (Webber *et al.*, in EATRO, 1961).

None of several antibiotics investigated—penicillin, streptomycin, these two combined, terramycin, polymyxin—significantly affected the infectivity of a *T. brucei* subgroup suspension over a period of 2 h, as compared with a control suspension without any antibiotics (Lumsden *et al.*, in EATRO, 1961). A similar result was obtained with *T. congolense* (Cunningham and van Hoeve, in EATRO, 1962–63).

T. brucei subgroup organisms in infected rat blood were washed by repeated centrifugation and resuspension in diluent at 0–5° C, so that the final concentration of rat plasma was about 1:200 000, without significantly affecting either trypanosome numbers or infectivity. These washed organisms did not, however, withstand preservation by cooling; after that process no trypanosome could be seen in the suspensions nor were the suspensions infective. With the addition to the suspensions of 0·75% bovine plasma albumin, or of 10% precolostral calf serum, but not of glucose solution, however, the trypanosomes did survive $-80°$ C freezing although both numbers and infectivity were reduced (Lumsden et al., in EATRO, 1962–63).

These examples indicate the value of the method of infectivity titration in yielding quantitative information on trypanosome potentiality independent of trypanosome numbers. It may be expected also to be a more sensitive tool than counts of the numbers of organisms. Infectivity measurement should be applicable down to levels of a few infective organisms per ml of suspension. Trypanosomes can only be easily and accurately counted when they are fairly concentrated, say more than antilog 5 organisms per ml.

3. *The Viable Preservation of Trypanosomes*

Polge and Soltys (1957) showed that the addition of glycerol to the trypanosome suspension to be preserved, and cooling the suspension slowly, improved survival rates. Since then methods have been further improved, simplified and standardized (Cunningham et al., 1963). The principles governing the use of low temperature preservation for laying down stabilate material of trypanosomes have been discussed by Cunningham and Lumsden (1965).

(a) The material should be bacteriologically sterile. In short-term operations such as the simple passage of large inocula of infected blood the possibility of contamination can be neglected, but if longer term *in vitro* experimentation is contemplated it is essential to exclude bacteria which may be expected adventitiously to affect the food materials or metabolic products present in the medium, its pH and other factors. All procedures should be carried out with aseptic precaution; antibiotics may be added.

(b) The material should contain as little as possible of any foreign substance. The ideal of trypanosomes suspended in a medium devoid of other antigenic material is probably unattainable (Lumsden et al., in EATRO, 1962–63), but it is clearly desirable to avoid unnecessary addition of foreign, particularly antigenic, substances.

(c) The preserved material should be altered as little as possible from its original condition by the treatment before preservation. Manipulation should be carried through as quickly as possible and as continuously as possible at $0°$ C.

(d) If the trypanosomes for preservation are to be suspended in fluids other than those of the body of their host a medium of experimentally-established suitability is necessary. A protein-containing balanced salts solution of pH $8·0$ appears suitable for *T. brucei* subgroup organisms (Lumsden et al., 1965; Lumsden et al., in EATRO, 1962–63).

(e) The method of cooling for preservation should be standard and established as satisfactory by experiment. The rates of cooling permissible, without significantly reducing the infectivity of the trypanosome suspension treated, have been defined (Webber et al., in EATRO, 1961). The infectivities of two samples of a trypanosome suspension not cooled below $0°$ C were estimated and compared with similar estimates made for pairs of samples of the same material cooled to $-80°$ C at different rates, and maintained at that temperature for 24 h. No significant loss of infectivity occurred at such rates of cooling that $-60°$ C was not reached more quickly than after 8 min. At more rapid rates of cooling infectivity was markedly reduced.

(f) Where frequent recourse is to be made to the material as a standard for reference purposes it is necessary to lay down large numbers of samples of each material, and so individual samples should be small. Glass lymph tubes, each containing about 25 μl of trypanosome suspension, are suitable.

(g) The samples of standard material should be so arranged in the store that individual samples can be removed without disturbing the conditions of storage of the remainder. Metal, methanol-filled, systematically-arranged, containers fulfil this requirement.

The long-term storage of standard material for reference purposes (now called stabilate material) is by far the most important implication of the process of preservation of trypanosomes at low temperature. Desirably, future experimental work should be related to a specific stabilate, not to trypanosome "strains". The long-term stability of $-80°$ C frozen material has been demonstrated; no significant differences in infectivity between individual samples of the same material, nor significant deterioration in infectivity, were found after periods of storage of 576 days (*T. congolense*), 960 days (*T. rhodesiense*) and 438 days (*T. brucei* subgroup) (Cunningham *et al.*, in EATRO, 1962–63). Some standardization of the documentation for stabilate material would be advantageous; this has been discussed by Cunningham and Lumsden (EATRO, 1962–63).

Subsidiary advantages of the low temperature preservation of trypanosomes are the ease with which stabilates may be transferred between laboratories, the economy in the use of laboratory animals and the avoidance of error which is difficult to exclude in any long series of passages. Also, the method facilitates experimentation with material closely representative of wild trypanosomes; material may be preserved at as low a passage level as desired, even at the first mammal passage from fly. Even metacyclic trypanosomes from *Glossina* may be preserved in this way. Cunningham and Harley (1962) allowed wild *G. pallidipes* to feed on a lake of defibrinated bovine blood through a membrane. Immediately after they had fed the blood was shown to be infective to mice (*T. brucei* subgroup) by intraperitoneal inoculation and was, therefore, presumed to contain metacyclic forms derived from the flies. Part of the same lake, $-80°$ C frozen for 21 days, tested in the same way, was found to be infective.

4. *Trypanosome Culture*

Lehmann (1960, 1961, 1962) indicated which culture media are most suitable for the several species of African pathogenic trypanosomes and drew attention to culture as a possible method for distinguishing *T. brucei* from *T. rhodesiense* (see above).

Trager (1959) obtained initial outgrowth and long-term survival of several kinds of tissue from the pupa of *Glossina palpalis* in a medium containing salts, lactalbumin hydrolysate, sheep serum and an extract of *Glossina* pupae. *Trypanosoma vivax* was established in these tissue cultures by inoculating them with blood from a sheep with a long-term chronic infection and then incubating the cultures at 30–32° C. Trager considered that the success of the cultures was related to their being incubated at that temperature rather than the usual one of 28° C. Very profuse trypanosome multiplication was obtained and the insect tissue appeared to be unharmed by the presence of the organisms. Trager made several attempts to infect sheep with the culture trypanosomes and succeeded on two occasions, with trypanosomes which had been maintained *in vitro* for 39 and 16 days, respectively. The infected cultures were held for 19 h at 38° C just before being inoculated into sheep; both the infective cultures showed exceptional activity after this treatment. Metacyclic-like forms were noted in both cultures which were shown to be infective and also in non-infective cultures. *T. brucei* and *T. congolense* were also found to establish readily in these tissue cultures but, in a short series of experiments, infection of animals with the culture forms of these species was not accomplished.

Trager (1959) summarized previous work in which culture trypanosomes have been found infective to mammals. Grainge (in EATRO, 1961) has reported another example, of *T. rhodesiense* which was found infective to mice in the fifteenth culture passage, after 8 months maintenance *in vitro*. The subject is of great general interest and importance and Trager's (1959) work is a very significant contribution to it.

III. THE ARTHROPODAN VECTOR

A. *Glossina*

Recent work on the ecology of *Glossina* has been ably summarized by Langridge *et al.* (1963); also Glasgow (1963) has contributed an interesting book mainly concerned with the distribution and abundance of the genus. The present treatment may, therefore, be limited to additions to these reviews, to some aspects of special interest in the context of trypanosomiasis and to some general comment.

1. *In the Laboratory*

a. Physiology. The process of feeding in *Glossina morsitans* has been studied by Gordon *et al.* (1956) by direct observation of the behaviour of the haustellum in the ear of the mouse and by histological study of the host tissues at the site of the bite. Essentially, the insertion of the haustellum (labrum, hypopharynx and labium) is mediated by the rapid eversion and inversion of the labial labella and their attached rasps, though the action of this cutting tool may be assisted by thrusts of the head of the fly, particularly during the stage of penetration of the stratum corneum. The haustellum is highly flexible and, once the stratum corneum has been pierced, a hemispherical space under the skin, of radius the haustellar range, may be rapidly searched by repeated probing. This search results in numerous capillary haemorrhages into the tissues. Most of these are small and are disregarded. Engorgement usually follows the rupture of a larger capillary but, then, the rate of removal of blood by the haustellum of the fly is close to the delivery of the ruptured vessel so that larger haemorrhages in the tissues ("pools"; Gordon and Lumsden, 1940) do not usually form until the withdrawal of the haustellum at the completion of feeding. "Pool"-feeding, on re-entering a haemorrhage caused by earlier haustellar movements, may, however, occur sometimes. Saliva is ejected intermittently throughout the feeding process and, considering the extensive tissue damage caused by the haustellum, may be expected to enter tissue spaces and capillary lumina, and also to be re-ingested by the fly.

Saunders (1962) described a method, based on changes occurring in the reproductive system during successive gonotrophic cycles, by which the age of the female *Glossina* may be determined to within a few days up to about 50 days, the age at which all four ovarioles have ovulated.

Bursell (1960a) has pointed out the need for a standard method for the measurement of size in *Glossina* for comparative physiological purposes; without such a standardized method, the quantities of materials used or produced by the metabolism of the organisms cannot be critically compared. He introduced a function of the dorsal thoracic surface for this purpose. The same author (1958, 1959, 1960b) has contributed valuable studies of the water and fat metabolism of the important developmental stages of *Glossina*. He (1959) found no correlation between the degree of resistance to desiccation of adult flies of the various species studied and the aridity of their typical habitats. He concluded, therefore, that the water balance of the adult tsetse is not the obstacle to their invasion of arid habitats. On the other hand, there was close correlation between resistance to desiccation of the puparia of different species and the typical habitat in which they occurred, suggesting that the water balance of the pupa might be the important limiting factor in the invasion of arid habitats (Bursell, 1958).

The amount of fat consumed in the pupal period by *G. morsitans* was least at 22–24° C. Above these temperatures the rate of fat consumption was increased without corresponding reduction in the length of the pupal period, and below them the pupal period was lengthened without corresponding decrease in the rate of fat consumption. Smaller individuals emerged from the pupa with less fat than did larger ones and this appeared to be because the amount of fat laid down at the beginning of pupal development was relatively small in small individuals. Estimates were made of the size which a fly must be if it is to complete its development and live to obtain its first blood meal. Comparisons of these estimates with the size distribution of two species in cold and hot seasons suggested that exhaustion of the pupal fat reserves might play a part in limiting the distribution under extreme climatic conditions (Bursell, 1960b).

b. Laboratory maintenance of Glossina. The difficulty of maintaining *Glossina* spp. in the laboratory in self-perpetuating colonies has continued to be a major impediment in the progress of trypanosomiasis research. Added emphasis on the need for such colonies has been provided recently by the interest in the possibility of the control of *Glossina* by the release of irradiated sterile males. The problems in general have been summarized by Nash (1963) and details of techniques used for *G. palpalis* are given by Nash *et al.* (1958) and for *G. morsitans* by Foster (1958).

Cockings (in EATRO, 1958, 1959, 1960) and Southon and Cockings (in

EATRO, 1959, 1961) have studied methods of feeding flies on blood lakes enclosed in membranes. With species, such as *G. pallidipes*, which may be readily trapped in large numbers, the method may be used for the production of puparia of known age by feeding wild-caught flies in the laboratory. It may also be applied to study the factors of importance in the blood meal. For instance, of anticoagulant techniques for maintaining the fluidity of the blood lake, defibrination was best; female flies fed by this method often survived as well as those fed directly on a cow. Ethylenediaminetetra-acetate disodium salt (EDTA) appeared to be toxic. The blood lakes were found convenient for the collection of metacyclic trypanosomes from infected flies. In studies of the factors determining the proportion of females becoming inseminated in the laboratory, the age of the males used and the relative proportions of the two sexes were found important; the fertility rate was increased by using 10- or 15-day-old males, as compared with 5-day-old males, and by using numbers of males equal to or greater than the numbers of females, as compared with numbers of males half those of females (Southon and Cockings, in EATRO, 1962–63).

Recently, de Azavedo (1964) has reported the maintenance of a *G. morsitans* colony in the laboratory for an uninterrupted period of 5 years without the addition of fresh individuals. He considered the maintenance of the puparia in a high atmospheric relative humidity was an important factor for this success.

c. Recognition of individual hosts used. Knight and Southon (1963) have developed a method by which the *Glossina* (and presumably other haematophagous insects) which have fed on an individual animal may be recognized. Trypan blue injected intravenously is used as a marker. This dye was detected by paper chromatography in the blood meals of all of 108 *G. morsitans* which fed on a marked ox up to 24 days after the injection of the dye and which were examined 2 or fewer days after feeding. The method has the advantage that it obviates any disturbance or handling of the insect, and so the likelihood of abnormally influencing its behaviour, before its final collection and examination.

2. *In the Field*

a. Study methods. Sampling methods for *Glossina* have come under critical study. Ford *et al.* (1959) introduced a more standardized way of carrying out the classical "fly-round" method of sampling the wild population; Glasgow (1963) discusses the causes of variation in the results of such rounds. Smith and Rennison (1961a–c) and Rennison and Smith (1961) have contributed critical studies of the results of different sampling methods as regards their comparative efficiency and the significance of their results. Essentially the results of sampling a *G. pallidipes* population simultaneously by means of baited catches on cattle of various colours and by traps of different colours were compared statistically in Latin square or similar designs and the results of these studies were then correlated with the results of fly-round studies in the same area over a period overlapping the other studies. Smith and Rennison analysed the wide and confusing numerical variations which occur in field studies of *Glossina* so as to allow the confident ascription of variation to the effect of particular factors. Light coloured traps were found more attractive than dark ones and dark cattle than pale. Such differences might, however, have been determined in part by olfactory factors. Catchers were found to vary significantly in their performance and so experimental designs are required in which isolation of such variation is possible. Fly-round catches were similar in both wet and dry seasons but both baited and trap catches were markedly reduced in the latter, indicating that it should not be assumed that fly-round data give a reliable measure of the risk of being infected with trypanosomes. Also the traps, despite the fact that they sampled throughout the day and took large numbers of females, were considered unlikely to afford a more sensitive measure of risk as there was no useful correlation between their catches and the baited catches on cattle. The best estimate of the risk of acquiring infection was concluded to be direct catches on exposed grazing cattle. In studies of the hunger stages of flies, it was found that individual workers differed markedly in their assessments so that experimental designs must allow for such bias to be discounted. The proportion of hungry flies in catches of males on various oxen were all similar but varied widely among catches in traps which appeared identical structurally. Further experimentation on the influence of frequency of emptying, of the size of the entry slot, of deficiencies in their closing, and of predation, on the performance of traps, failed to explain the variation between them.

An observation, perhaps of importance for the improvement of sampling procedures but not yet followed up, is that the release of carbon dioxide within the trap significantly increased the yield of *Glossina pallidipes* from traps (Rennison and Robertson, in EATRO, 1958).

The work of Saunders (1962) on the determination of the age of female *Glossina* in the field has contributed to understanding of the significance of the sample taken by different methods. In the case of *G. pallidipes* in Uganda, the oldest flies and those most advanced in pregnancy are caught in traps, the youngest and least so advanced, by the fly-round. Flies taken on a bait animal are intermediate in these respects. In the case of *G. palpalis fuscipes*, the oldest flies were taken on the bait animal, the youngest in the traps. These differences emphasize the need to understand the behaviour of *Glossina* in the field if sampling methods are to be informative in any particular way desired. Different methods of sampling collect different sections of the population. The causes of these differences are not known but they are likely to be important epidemiologically.

b. Host relationships. The major contribution in this sphere comes not from direct study but from the serological identification of blood meals of *Glossina* collected in the field (see a comprehensive survey of the subject by Weitz, 1963d). All the species studied attack a wide variety of hosts but in most the main attack is on only a few species. Weitz divides the fifteen species studied into five groups depending on whether they feed mainly on suids (*G. fuscipleuris, G. tabaniformis, G. swynnertoni, G. austeni*), mainly on suids or bovids (*G. morsitans* sspp.), mainly on bovids (*G. fusca, G. longipalpis, G. pallidipes*), mainly on mammals other than suids or bovids (*G. brevipalpis, G.*

o

longipennis) or on a variety of hosts including man (*G. palpalis, G. fuscipes, G. tachinoides*). It is interesting to note that the distribution of feeding habits does not follow the taxonomic grouping of *Glossina*; both the *fusca* and the *morsitans* groups, for instance, include representatives of several of the host categories.

The demonstration of these characteristic feeding patterns is of great interest and leads to a consideration of how such patterns are determined. That they are not simply determined by the relative abundance of the various animal species was shown clearly by Lamprey *et al.* (1962), who found in simultaneous studies of the potential and actual food sources of *G. swynnertoni* in Tanganyika that 77% of the blood meals were derived from *Phacochoerus* (warthog) which composed less than 3% of the animals in the area.

Ford (1962b) points out that the main hosts of those economically important *Glossina* spp. which have been most studied are characteristically animals which exist in small groups confined to small territories, rather than animals which form large herds and migrate large distances. Ford divides up the hosts into categories:

Important hosts: *Potamochoerus* (bushpig), *Phacochoerus* (warthog).

Locally or seasonally important hosts: *Loxodonta* (elephant), *Diceros* (black rhinoceros), *Hippopotamus, Syncerus* (buffalo), *Redunca* (reedbuck).

Less important hosts: *Giraffa, Limnotragus* (situtunga), *Taurotragus* (eland), *Kobus* (waterbuck), *Hippotragus* (antelope).

Probably never important: *Equus* (zebra), *Cephalophus* (duiker), *Onotragus* (lechwe), *Adenota* (kob), *Oryx, Damaliscus* (topi), *Alcelaphus* (hartebeest), *Gorgon* (wildebeest), *Ourebia* (oribi), *Raphicerus* (steinbok), *Rhynchotragus* (dikdik), *Aepyceros* (impala), *Gazella*.

Incidentally, Ford points out that the animals likely to be important for "game-cropping", the economic exploitation of wild African artiodactyls as a food source, are all of little or no importance as hosts of *Glossina*, except *Hippopotamus* and *Syncerus*.

The mechanisms determining these choices of host are obscure. Harley (in EATRO, 1962–63) has shown that significantly more *G. pallidipes* were caught on black than on brown or white cattle, and also that more flies were caught on larger than on smaller animals. Glover and his colleagues (e.g. Langridge, 1960) have shown that some of the constituents of the skin of pigs attract *Glossina*. The release of carbon dioxide in traps has been shown significantly to increase their performance (Rennison and Robertson, in EATRO, 1958). Besides such obvious factors there are other considerations which may influence host selection; the most likely of these is coincidence of habitat and behaviour. Perhaps the predominance of the fly-round as a sampling method for *Glossina* has contributed to a conception of flies ranging rather freely to locate their hosts. But it may be the case that mechanisms exist to keep flies in more continuous contact with the parts of the environment frequented by their main hosts. Glasgow (1961b), in a study of the distribution of *G. pallidipes* over an area of 180 acres, found, occasionally, that 50% or more of the catch was concentrated in a small area, less than 5% of the total, and that sometimes such concentrations could be related to the passage of herds of animals. Glasgow (1961a) has shown that *G. swynnertoni* tends to feed on a host in shade rather than on one in full sunlight. Bursell (1961) compared the hunger cycle stages represented, and the fat and water content of flies, in samples of *G. swynnertoni* collected by several different methods: those attracted to a catching party, to an ox and to a moving lorry and those found in resting sites. He recognized four stages of behaviour in the male hunger cycle: inactivity, sexual appetitive behaviour and two stages of appetitive behaviour in relation to feeding, the first indifferent, the second responsive, to the stimulus of moving objects. He emphasized the selective advantage to *Glossina* of securing early fertilization and suggested that the male behaviour may be adapted to this end. He drew attention to the possibility that quiescence and shade may be significant factors in determining "host preference"; preferred hosts are often species which lie up in shade for a large part of the day.

Morris (1960d) has noticed a similar effect; from the evidence of the distribution of *G. pallidipes* in traps he deduced that a herd of elephant may be accompanied by a "swarm" of *Glossina* and that the "swarm" may follow the elephant into open grassland or other environment outside the habitat they usually occupy.

Harley (in EATRO, 1961) has investigated the periodicity of biting attack by *Glossina* spp. and other biting Diptera. The maximum attack by male *G. pallidipes* occurred between 15.00 and 16.00 h (sun time); females showed a more regular level of attack through the day from 11.00 to 17.00 h and few attacked at night. Both sexes of *G. palpalis fuscipes* attacked most commonly in the middle of the day. Both sexes of *G. brevipalpis* attacked most in the hours following sunrise and sunset but the species was taken at all hours of both day and night. The species most affected by weather conditions was *G. pallidipes*; evening rain depressed or suppressed the evening activity wave. *G. brevipalpis* was most commonly caught during the day when the weather was overcast, or at shaded catching stations; it frequently showed a sudden wave of activity just before an afternoon or evening storm and this replaced the usual wave of activity near sunset. Most *G. palpalis fuscipes* biting activity was over before the usual time of storms (the late afternoon or evening). As regards the age of flies coming to bite, as established by ovarian examination: higher proportions of young *G. pallidipes* occurred during the first and last hours of daylight than in the middle of the day; *G. brevipalpis* showed much lower proportions of young flies during the waves of activity near sunrise and sunset and during the night than in the middle of the day. No differences in the age constitution of the catch related to time of day were detected in the case of *G. palpalis fuscipes* (Harley, in EATRO, 1962–63).

Glover and his co-workers (Kenya, 1957; Power, 1964) found *G. longipennis* to be active just before sunset and at dawn, particularly the former, largely inactive during the day. Thus catches confined to the day are unlikely to indicate the true prevalence of the species. Yvoré (1962) found that *G. fusca* bit man as much as animals and that it bit man particularly in the forest at night. On cattle, biting took place throughout the day but with a main peak of activity in the early morning.

Of great interest are the differences in distribution of attack by *Glossina* on the several parts of the body in different mammal species. Harley (in EATRO, 1958) has recorded that *G. swynnertoni* feeding on *Phacochoerus* (warthog) bite it predominantly on the head, but that when feeding on a calf they bite it mainly on the legs and flanks. Associated with this kind of observation is assessment of the efficiency of host species as blood supplier for *Glossina*. In Harley's work both the warthog and the calf became irritable under prolonged attack and became less efficient as hosts. The demonstration of the selectiveness of *Glossina* in its utilization of hosts, and of the irritability of hosts under attack, point to the possibility that individual competition between flies for food may be a factor in limiting *Glossina* populations. Lamprey *et al.* (1962) were able to estimate the blood loss suffered by individual animals bitten by tsetse; it was 18–38 g/day, a not insignificant amount.

c. Resting sites. The biased nature of the population sample obtained by the fly-round, particularly the low proportion of gorged flies, stimulated the search for resting flies (Isherwood, 1957). He found that *G. swynnertoni* at Shinyanga, Tanganyika, rested mainly on the undersides of the branches of small trees, usually on trees whose lower branches were not obscured by foliage except above. He found 59% of non-teneral resting females gorged, as compared with 6% of active females. Similar resting sites were used by *G. morsitans* in Ankole, Uganda (Harley, in EATRO, 1959).

Ford (1962a) describes studies in which the distribution of *Glossina morsitans* and *pallidipes* resting on the branches and boles of trees in Southern Rhodesia was correlated with microclimatic determinations. In hot weather flies tended to seek resting places at a lower level in the middle of the day than they did early in the morning, or in the evening. This behaviour was interpreted as a mechanism by which lethal temperatures in resting places might be avoided. The lethal temperatures for *G. morsitans* is in the region of 39° C. Mean temperatures of over 39° C were reached on branch sites by noon by which time these sites had been evacuated by *Glossina*; reoccupation of these sites began again after 17.00 h. The mean temperature of bole sites, and of a rot-hole much favoured as a resting site, would have been unlikely to exceed the temperature tolerated by *Glossina*. These findings were correlated with earlier work which showed a negative response to light by *Glossina* at temperatures over 30° C; this reaction would provide *Glossina* with an escape mechanism from lethal midday temperatures. Reaction to humidity differences may be important in motivating the avoidance by *Glossina* of lethal conditions. Bursell (1957) demonstrated that the activity of hungry flies is greater in dry than in wet air except at low light intensities. Thus, at least hungry flies would be expected to move more frequently in the lower humidities of the hot season but, having found a resting place in deep shade, would be inhibited to move.

Two methods have been evolved for the location of *Glossina* at night. One employs paints which fluoresce in ultraviolet light (Jewell, 1956, 1958), the other, reflective paints of the type used for road signs, whose effect depends on the reflection of light by minute glass beads, 100–400 μ in diam. (Rennison *et al.*, 1958; Southon, 1958). Both these methods were efficient in locating *Glossina* in night-time resting places. The method using reflective beads has some advantage over that using fluorescent paints in that it requires only a simple beam-projecting hand torch for its field application, not a special source of ultraviolet light. It was established that, at dusk, *G. swynnertoni* and *G. pallidipes* leave their daytime resting places on the trunks and branches of trees and take up positions on the leaves. The reverse movement takes place at dawn. Most *G. swynnertoni* observed were resting on the upper surfaces of the leaves between 1½ and 10 ft from the ground. Flies resting on the leaves can be removed by the hand with ease (Southon, 1958). McDonald (1960) found *G. morsitans* rested at night on twigs, leaves and small creepers, mostly more than 7 ft from the ground; *G. palpalis* also settled on leaves or small twigs but within 1 ft of the ground.

d. *Glossina populations*. The interrelations between *Glossina* and its environment are of great complexity. Glasgow and Bursell (1961) showed that wild *Glossina* populations were characterized by fluctuations in mean size and in fat content and that such fluctuations could be related to periods of nutritional stress. They discussed previous work in which these changes had been related to a single meteorological factor—the 14.00 h saturation deficit of 2 months earlier. They pointed out, rightly, that such changes are not likely to be controlled by single factors and that the seasons differ in many ways not susceptible of direct measurement—for instance, in the prevalence of grass fires, the shedding of the leaves of trees, disappearance of temporary water, movements of animals and so on.

Long-term and seasonal variations in the numbers of *G. swynnertoni* taken by fly-round in an area of woodland near Shinyanga, Tanganyika, over a period of about 23 years up to 1959 were studied by Glasgow and Welch (1962). This study has done much to bring conceptions of the regularity and extent of fluctuations of *Glossina* numbers into proportion. These workers concluded that the amplitude of the fluctuations found were small in comparison with those recorded for many other animal populations; maxima were about 18 times minima. Only one of the fluctuations could be associated with any known causative event.

Temporal fluctuations in population density of *Glossina* spp. are to be related to changes in their distribution. Glasgow (1963) has devoted much attention to this interrelation, taking as the start of his argument a statement of Andrewartha and Birch (1954) that distribution and abundance are the obverse and reverse aspects of the same problem. The point is of importance in relation to the well-known "advances" of tsetse fly into areas believed previously to be unoccupied by it. Such advances are usually discussed only on the basis that a species of fly is extending its absolute range, and indeed practical control measures are usually planned on this basis and on a concept of stemming a flood of flies invading a previously unoccupied area (e.g. Willett, 1962b). There is great difficulty in recognizing the presence of fly at low population densities. To the examples quoted by Buxton (1955), Lovemore (1958) has added another: *G. pallidipes*, only recently recognized as present in the fly-belt of Southern Rhodesia, is, in fact, almost as widely distributed as *G. morsitans*. It is conceivable, then, that apparent invasions of tsetse may sometimes be the result of the build-up of populations, already existing, to levels capable of detection by the sampling methods used.

It seems equally difficult to arrive at categorical decisions with respect to the wider distribution of *Glossina* spp. Glasgow (1963) instances as anomalies the absence of any member of the *palpalis* group from the Indian Ocean drainage of Africa and the restriction of *G. austeni* of the *morsitans* group to that drainage. He regards this situation as solely determined by lack of opportunity for these species reciprocally to colonize each other's territory, because of the existence of a geographical barrier, the watershed between the two drainage basins. He goes on to say that if *G. palpalis* were introduced on the East African coast it could live on any part of the permanent rivers and if *G. austeni* were taken to Uganda it could live in the secondary thickets of that country and spread far to the west. Glasgow's conviction in this matter appears to be based on general similarities of habitat but these may be more apparent than real. Glasgow himself (1963) has discussed several subtle ways in which *Glossina* may be controlled by its environment. He emphasizes that competition for food may be a factor of importance in determining populations even in situations in which the wild mammal hosts would appear to casual observation to be amply sufficient. Other factors which he considers likely to be of influence are the aridity of the habitat and the prevalence of predators. It seems, then, that ecological factors are as likely to be an explanation of the distributions of *G. palpalis* and *G. austeni* as are geographical accidents. The decision would seem to rest only on the experiment of reciprocal introduction, not likely to be performed. But comparable examples are furnished by *G. brevipalpis* and *G. longipennis* of both of which Glasgow (1963) records that it is not known why they do not extend west of their present distributions in East Africa. The coincidence of geographical barriers with distribution margins need not necessarily imply that only they are factors determinant of the distributions.

B. VECTORS OTHER THAN *Glossina*

Although the "mechanical" transmission of trypanosomiasis is frequently discussed in relation to trypanosomiasis in cattle, few specific studies have been made. Harley (in EATRO, 1961, 1962–63) has studied the attack on cattle of haematophagous insects other than *Glossina*. One of two species of *Stomoxys* showed a biting activity peak soon after midday, the other in the evening. *Tabanus taeniola* attacked mainly in the hour preceding midday.

The frequency with which a haematophagous species derives its blood meal from more than one individual host, either because of its own propensity to do so or because of inducing such a reaction of the host that its feeding is interrupted, should be indicative of its likelihood to act as a non-cyclical vector. The method of marking animals individually with antibodies specific to different trypanosome antigenic types (Cunningham *et al.*, in EATRO, 1961) may be applicable for study of this point. A high incidence of meals derived from more than one host would be indicative of potentiality to act as a direct vector.

IV. The Vertebrate Host

A. BIOLOGY OF WILD ANIMALS

The correspondence between the biting habits of *Aedes africanus* in the canopy of tropical forest (Haddow and Mahaffy, 1949) and the night-resting habits of monkeys in the same environment (Lumsden, 1951) is well known in relation to the survival of yellow fever virus in Africa. We know less of the patterns of behaviour of African artiodactyls in relation to the *Glossina* spp. attacking them because the conditions of direct study in these situations are more difficult than they are with mosquitoes and monkeys. The most informative work in this sphere has so far been derived not from direct observation but from the serological identification of *Glossina* blood meals (see above).

More specific information on the habits of African artiodactyls in the *Glossina*–trypanosome context is desirable, for instance, in relation to such observations as that of Bursell (1961) that quiescence and shade-frequenting on the part of the host may be significant factors in the determination of *Glossina* "host-preference".

B. BIOLOGY OF CATTLE

A series of papers (Harker *et al.*, 1954, 1956, 1961; Rollinson *et al.*, 1955, 1956; Taylor *et al.*, 1955) gives very comprehensive information on the behaviour of *Bos indicus* Nkedi Zebu cattle in the lacustrine area of Uganda. These workers established the proportion of the day spent in various activities, grazing, rumination and so on under free-grazing and paddocked conditions. They emphasize the difference in behaviour shown by these animals as compared with other similar studies on cattle and they discuss the individual and herd aspects of behaviour. Rollinson (*in litt.*) sums up the work on the diurnal rhythms of cattle by saying that domestic animals are always under the control of their owners and so the results of experiments or observation of animals allowed to graze freely may not be representative of their behaviour under the control of African pastoralists. Studies of cattle behaviour with particular relation to *Glossina* attack appear to be lacking, despite their obvious significance.

C. BIOLOGY OF MAN

The habits of the people becoming infected with trypanosomiasis are frequently discussed in the literature. Apted *et al.* (1963) discuss the incidence of sleeping sickness in various parts of Africa in relation to the occupation of those infected and conclude that honey-gatherers, cultivators and fishermen appear to be at special risk in one area, travellers and firewood collectors in another. Glover (1961) describes the migrations of the Fulani people of Northern Nigeria which migrations are related to the needs of their cattle. The wet-season grazing grounds for their cattle are in general *Glossina*-free but in the dry season, when water and grass fail, the Fulani are compelled to migrate, either locally into *Glossina*-infected valleys or more distantly to the south. The cattle are then brought into contact with *Glossina morsitans* either on their journey or in their southern grazing grounds.

Very much more detailed information was available to Robertson for his consideration of the epidemiology of *T. rhodesiense* sleeping sickness in Busoga, Uganda, in the work of Fallers (see Robertson, 1963) on the social anthropology of the Soga. The system of land tenure was such as to influence a very high exposure of the settler population to *Glossina* attack.

Information of this sort is of great interest and importance but comparisons of the various potential mechanisms by which man might be infected will depend on more detailed studies of human behaviour in relation to *Glossina* attack which will allow of quantitative assessments.

V. The Trypanosome in the Arthropodan Vector

A. *Glossina*

1. *Development in the Gut*

Wijers (1958) discusses previous work on the factors determining the development of infection in *Glossina* after an infective feed and he cites examples, from the *T. brucei* subgroup, in which high temperatures during the pupal stage were correlated with higher infection rates in the flies reared from these pupae. Fairbairn and Watson (1955) concluded that the temperatures to which the pupa and adult of *G. palpalis* were subjected were important in relation to their infectibility with *T. vivax*.

Wijers' (1958) own work was concerned with the effect of the age of the fly at the time of its taking its infective meal and its liability to become infected. He arranged for *G. palpalis* to take their first blood meal from a host infected with *T. gambiense* and studied the infection rates occurring in flies fed in this way on the 1st, 2nd, and subsequent, days after eclosion. He found, respectively, infection rates of 7·6, 1·1 and 0%. Wijers did not allow any substitute meal to the flies which were not allowed to feed on the infected host on the 1st and 2nd days and so his result might have been related to some starvation effect. However, van Hoof *et al.* (1937) did allow a substitute meal and their results were similar. Wijers considers that the effect is likely to be related to the development of the peritrophic membrane.

2. *Development in the Haemocoele*

Some experiments on the development of *T. brucei* subgroup trypanosomes in the haemocoele of *Glossina* after artificial parenteral inoculation have been reported (Webber, in EATRO, 1961). In nearly all flies inoculated with between 70 and 230 × 10³ organisms, further development took place in the haemocoele. Preserved as well as fresh material initiated infections. Some mice fed upon by flies which had been inoculated intra-haemocoelically with *T. rhodesiense* became infected and so did mice inoculated with a suspension made from these flies. It remains to be established whether infective forms develop in the haemocoele or whether the appearance of infective forms is associated with gut injury and subsequent development in its lumen. However, the behaviour of trypanosomes in the haemocoele is of interest as multiplication may be intense and developmental forms, such as crithidia, occur.

3. *Isolation of Trypanosomes from Wild* Glossina

Knowledge of the incidence of metacyclic infections in *Glossina* in the wild is important for epidemiological purposes but is very laborious to acquire by feeding the flies on animals or by dissection. In an attempt to facilitate this work, Lumsden *et al.* (in EATRO, 1961) triturated wild flies in a buffered saline solution, which was known to preserve infectivity of *T. brucei* subgroup blood forms for several hours, and inoculated the resultant suspensions into mice. *T. congolense* and *T. brucei* subgroup isolations were obtained by this method. The question, however, arises, as to whether these could have been derived from blood forms recently ingested by the flies as well as from metacyclic infections. Cunningham and Harley (in EATRO, 1961) showed that the infectivity of blood forms ingested by the fly persists less than 24 h so that this possibility can be simply eliminated by keeping the flies for that period before processing them.

VI. The Trypanosome in the Mammalian Host

A. THE ESTABLISHMENT OF THE INFECTION

1. *Early Development*

The work of Gordon *et al.* (1956) indicated that the saliva of *Glossina* at the time of biting (and therefore the metacyclic forms of *T. brucei* subgroup trypanosomes) was likely to enter the capillary circulation as well as the tissue spaces. In further studies, these workers (Willett and Gordon, 1957; Gordon and Willett, 1958) have considered this result in relation to the establishment of *T. brucei* subgroup infections in man, monkeys, guinea-pigs, rabbits and rats. The main point at issue was whether or not metacyclic trypanosomes inoculated by the bite of *Glossina* went through a special cycle of development leading to the appearance of blood forms in the peripheral blood of the host at the end of the prepatent period. In the rabbit, but not in the monkey, guinea-pig or rat, there is a local multiplication of trypanosomes at the site of inoculation, the trypanosome chancre, whether the inoculation is of metacyclic trypanosomes by *Glossina* bite or of blood forms by intradermal injection. Gordon and his colleagues concluded that the processes of migration and development of *T. brucei* subgroup trypanosomes in the mammalian host during the prepatent period were fundamentally the same whether metacyclic or blood forms are inoculated and whether into an animal which shows a local reaction, or into one that does not. This conclusion was based mainly on their finding that the peripheral blood of rabbits infected by *Glossina* bite was, usually, infective to rats at a very early stage, and that the length of the prepatent period was related to the size of the infecting inoculum. They pointed out that in parasites with special cycles of development, such as *Plasmodium*, the incubation period is little influenced by the size of the inoculum of the agent. It must be observed, however, that (a) early infectivity of the blood of the host might be contributed by unchanged metacyclics; (b) a relation between the size of inoculum and the length of incubation period might still obtain in a special cycle in which the factor of multiplication at each division was only 2 instead of a large number as in the *Plasmodium*, and (c) there are several examples, e.g. two rabbits described by Willett and Gordon (1957) and a man described by Fairbairn and Godfrey (1957), in which the repeated subinoculation of large quantities of blood to rats failed to demonstrate the presence of trypanosomes in the peripheral blood of the host until nearly the time of appearance of the trypanosome chancre. It seems likely, in general, that there are two possible routes of development of metacyclic trypanosomes, either locally, or in the lymphatic and blood streams, depending on the site of deposition of the metacyclic forms of the infecting *Glossina*. The local multiplication in the trypanosome chancre may be intense (Willett and Gordon, 1957; Robertson, in EATRO, 1956–57) and so the local lesion seems likely to be of some significance, particularly as its development usually bears a nearly constant relationship to the main blood invasion (Willett, 1956b).

2. *Infectivity by Route of Inoculation*

Lumsden *et al.* (in EATRO, 1961) studied the infectivity of a trypanosome stabilate according to the route of its inoculation into mice, whether by the intraperitoneal, intrathoracic, intramuscular, subcutaneous or intracerebral routes. No significant difference according to route of inoculation was demonstrated. Simmons and Knight, however, refining the titration technique by using threefold dilutions and ten test mice at each dilution, showed that the same stabilate was about three times more infective if inoculated by the intraperitoneal than by the intramuscular or subcutaneous routes (Simmons and Knight, in EATRO, 1962–63).

Willett (1956b) found that the threshold infective dose of *T. rhodesiense* for man in terms of numbers of organisms was several tens of thousands; nine men who received subcutaneous inocula of more than antilog 4·9 blood-form trypanosomes all became parasitaemic while none of six men who received antilog 4·3 or fewer became so. This result, surprising as it was at the time, is now seen to be consistent with the profound variations in infectivity of trypanosomes which occur during the course of the infection in rats (see below) and the demonstrated lesser efficiency of the subcutaneous as compared with the intraperitoneal route.

B. THE ESTABLISHED INFECTION

1. *Changes in Trypanosome Potentiality through the Course of the Infection*

Desowitz (1956b) noted variations in the respiratory rate of rat-adapted *T. vivax* through the course of the infection, the oxygen consumption being highest during the increase in parasitaemia, less at peak parasitaemia and least during the decrease in the parasitaemia. Desowitz (1963) related these differences to differences in the "quality" of the trypanosomes instancing cases of variation in the facility with which inocula will "take" in laboratory animals. He suspected that such differences are due to the influence of antibody formed by the host. In quantitative studies, Cunningham *et al.* (in EATRO, 1962–63) found that the relationship between the concentration of trypanosomes in, and the infectivity of, the blood of laboratory rodents was not constant through the course of a *T. brucei* subgroup infection. Until shortly before peak parasitaemia, which was reached on the 4th day after inoculation, numbers and infectivity ran close together, indicating that a high proportion of the organisms was infective. Infectivity fell off in relation to numbers before peak parasitaemia and shortly after that time might be more than 3 log units less than numbers, indicating less than 1 trypanosome in 1000 infective to mice. This result was shown, by measurement of the neutralizing activity of the sera of the animals 10 days after inoculation, against the original inoculum and also against trypanosomes isolated on the 2nd day of the infection, to be related to antibody production (Cunningham and van Hoeve, in EATRO, 1962–63).

2. *Polymorphism*

Wijers (1960) has made a special study of the alterations in morphology of *T. brucei, T. gambiense* and *T. rhodesiense* in the course of the infection in rats and monkeys. After reviewing the opinions of previous workers, he was undecided between the two opposing views, that the trypanosome population is composed of two or three different types defined mainly on length (long, intermediate, and short), and the opposing view that there is a continuous transition from one type to the next. For his own work he uses a trimorphic classification and reverts to the early drawings of Lady Bruce as his standards. The requirements of studies for further resolution of this question have been discussed above (p. 6).

Wijers concludes that the peak proportion of long forms occurs during the time of rise in parasitaemic level, of short forms during a decrease in parasitaemia and that the intermediate form is a transition stage through which individual trypanosomes pass in changing from one of the extreme forms to the other. He considers it most possible that the periodicity of the parasitaemia is decided by antibody production influencing the production of short, stumpy from long, slender forms, each new relapse being caused by variants antigenically different from those of the preceding infection.

Wijers and Willett (1960) reviewed the conflicting evidence on the relation between the polymorphism of *T. brucei* subgroup organisms in the blood of their mammal host and the likelihood of *Glossina* becoming infected by feeding on the host. They point out that the greater susceptibility of *Glossina* to infection at its first, as compared to any subsequent blood meal (Wijers, 1958) may account for some of the inconsistencies in previous work. They attempted to avoid this inconsistency in their own studies by using only newly emerged *G. palpalis* which they fed on *Erythrocebus patas* (Red Hussar monkey) infected with *T. gambiense*. They demonstrated a correlation of probability of occurrence by chance of 0·04 between the numbers of short forms in the peripheral blood of the host and a conversion of the infection rate in *Glossina*. They studied also the change taking place in *T. brucei* subgroup organisms in *Glossina morsitans* in the 24 h following a blood meal on infected rats and observed that in general short forms survived and developed while long forms degenerated. Wijers and Willett concluded, therefore, that the short forms are those infective to *Glossina*. Their numerical results impress, however, also with their variability; for instance 7 (11%) of 64 flies were infected by feeding on an animal in which the number of short forms varied between 68 and 562 per mm³ while only 1 (2·3%) of 43 flies was infected on an animal in which the numbers of short forms were usually much higher than this range. It appears that the number of short forms in the peripheral infection is not the only factor of importance.

C. SUSCEPTIBILITY OF MAMMAL HOSTS

Data on the experimental infection, with one strain of *T. rhodesiense* and two of *T. brucei*, of wild animals derived from tsetse-free areas, at Tinde and Shinyanga, Tanganyika, over a period of 18 years, has been summarized by Ashcroft *et al.* (1959). The course of the infections with *T. brucei* and *T. rhodesiense* did not differ. Some animals, notably *Gazella* and *Rhynchotragus* (dikdik), typically succumbed to the trypanosome infection; others, e.g. *Phacochoerus* (warthog), *Potamochoerus* (bushpig), *Sylvicapra* (duiker), *Redunca* (reedbuck), *Aepyceros* (impala), *Taurotragus* (eland), and *Tragelaphus* (bushbuck), typically survived. In most of the latter group of animals evidence was obtained that parasites may persist in the blood in populations too scanty for detection by microscopy but sufficient to infect subinoculated animals or *Glossina*, for long periods, up to at least 20 months.

Desowitz has made a great contribution towards the clarification of thought about the relations existing between trypanosomes and their hosts in his review of knowledge on the subject of the adaptation of trypanosomes to abnormal hosts (1963). It will be necessary here simply to note the main points of his detailed review.

His work with Watson (1951) showed that rats could be infected with *T. vivax*, to which they are usually refractory, if the inoculum was of heavily infected sheep blood. Attempts at continuous passage in rats, however, failed until sheep serum was given as a supplementary inoculation 24 h after the trypanosome inoculation. After thirty-seven passages the strain could be propagated in rats without the concurrent administration of sheep serum (Desowitz and Watson, 1953). Desowitz (1963) summarizes the information regarding the action of serum as a supplementary factor: only the serum portion of the blood is active; only serum derived from hosts normally susceptible to *T. vivax* is active; the active component is serum protein, the fraction obtained by full saturation with ammonium sulphate, redissolved, was as effective as whole serum; activity was not related to any particular electrophoretic serum fraction. Similar results were obtained by Lincicome (1958) with *T. lewisi*, which could be induced to propagate in the heterologous mouse host by the concurrent administration of as little as 2 mg of rat serum protein. The serum of rats starved for 2 weeks, however, lost the ability to support the heterologous infection and starvation of the mouse host enhanced its susceptibility to infection. Desowitz quotes many interesting examples of the effect of dietary deficiencies or supplements on the development of trypanosomes in the host. A high cod-liver oil diet suppresses *T. congolense* infection in mice but this effect is reversed by vitamin E. Various vitamin deficiencies are associated with enhanced parasitaemias (Desowitz, 1963). Serial passage, splenectomy, or reticulo-endothelial blockade and the injection of various biological or chemical substances such as cortisone or sodium salicylate may enhance the infection in some hosts. The situation is one in which, although a large number of interesting and suggestive observations have been made, the mechanisms by which these effects are caused are still largely hypothetical (Desowitz, 1963).

Desowitz (1963) also surveyed the changes in trypanosome behaviour associated with adaptation to an abnormal host. They are, mainly, loss of ability to be cyclically transmitted, alteration of virulence for the normal host, morphological alterations such as loss of polymorphism in *T. brucei* subgroup organisms, physiological alterations including alterations in drug sensitivity, and immunological alterations. These changes are of great interest and significance but critical consideration of many of the changes taking place is difficult because of the intense variability of the materials under study. Repeated study of these effects, related to stabilate material, should be of advantage.

D. DISTRIBUTION IN MAMMAL HOSTS

Reviews of the accumulated information on the incidence of trypanosomiasis in African wild animals have been made by Ashcroft (1959b) and Lumsden (1962). The former writer combined that information with other data on the behaviour of wild animals in experimental infections and on host selection by *Glossina*. He concluded that some animals, such as *Phacochoerus* (warthog), might be less important and others, such as *Strepsiceros* (kudu), *Giraffa*, or *Redunca* (reedbuck), might be more important, as reservoirs of trypanosomes than might be thought from their importance as hosts of *Glossina*. Lumsden (1962) studied the distribution of trypanosome species in relation to the taxonomy of the animals concerned; he found that high incidence of parasitaemia occurred only in three groups—the Giraffidae and the subfamilies Reduncinae and Tragelaphinae of the Bovidae in which 34–37% of the animals examined were parasitaemic. No other group exceeded 16% and most were much below this. Also he noticed that the comparative representation of trypanosome species differed widely among the three groups most frequently infected; in *Giraffa*, *T. vivax* and *T. congolense* occurred commonly, *T. brucei* only rarely; in the Reduncinae all three species occurred commonly but *T. vivax* predominated; in the Tragelaphinae, *T. congolense* was by far the most frequent and the two others were comparatively rare.

The incidence of any given species found, however, is affected by the methods of investigation used. Godfrey and Killick-Kendrick (1962) examined 145 dromedaries in Northern Nigeria for *T. evansi*; 12% were found infected by the examination of thick blood films, 28% by inoculation of blood into rats. These authors (1961) and Godfrey *et al.* (1962) working with cattle concluded that thick blood films were most efficient for revealing infections of *T. vivax* and *T. congolense*, inoculation of blood into rats for the recognition of *T. dimorphon* and *T. brucei* subgroup organisms; the last mentioned parasites were not recognized except by inoculation.

Besides being of uncertain significance the derivation of important information by these methods may also be laborious. In an attempt to identify the wild animal host of *T. rhodesiense* Ashcroft (1958) collected seventy-four wild animals, mainly artiodactyls, in Tanganyika in areas in which the disease was endemic and inoculated their blood into rats. Only one *T. brucei* subgroup strain was isolated, from *Alcelaphus* (hartebeest), but two human beings into whom the strain was inoculated did not become infected. Heisch *et al.* (1958) isolated one *T. brucei* subgroup strain from thirteen *Sylvicapra* (duiker) and two from ten *Tragelaphus* (bushbuck); one of the latter was demonstrated to be infective to man and so is to be accepted as *T. rhodesiense*.

These findings are in general of great interest but it is clear that the purely parasitological approach is inadequate as a quantitative tool in epidemiological studies. It is not necessarily to be expected that incidence of parasitaemia should be closely related to frequency of being infected. Discrepancies between parasitaemic incidence and probable frequency of being bitten by *Glossina* have been pointed out by Weitz (1963c). Clearly, incidence of parasitaemia may be affected also by the characteristic reaction of a given host species to infection. Whether parasitaemia in an animal species is a reliable guide to the propensity of that species to infect *Glossina* is equally uncertain. Microscopically recognizable parasitaemia is not a prerequisite for the infection of *Glossina* and wide differences may exist in the proportion of flies becoming infected by feeding on different animals with apparently similar parasitaemias (examples in Lumsden, 1962).

E. IMMUNOLOGY

The many studies on the immunology of trypanosomiasis fall into two fairly distinct groups. Firstly there are the studies extending from early in the century till quite recently, by workers who were preoccupied with the development of diagnostic methods or with the possibility of immunizing hosts against infection as a measure of control. These studies were of great general interest but they are typically difficult to interpret and assess because of the extreme antigenic variability of the organisms studied. Workers in Africa worked mainly with local isolates of diverse characteristics maintained by continuous passage in laboratory animals or in domestic stock. Workers outside Africa perforce interested themselves mainly in laboratory strains often maintained for many years by continuous syringe passage in laboratory animals. High passage laboratory material tends to be altered fundamentally, showing changes in morphology and in susceptibility to drugs, and loss of infectivity to the arthropod vector. Possibly the existence of so many uncontrollable factors contributed to the delay in developing quantitative methods in the field of trypanosomiasis as compared with other fields of microbiology.

Secondly, more recently, there are studies which owe their development to two main advances, the development of simple methods of preserving viable organisms by deep freezing and the accession of new powerful tools of immunological analysis—chromatography, gel-diffusion, immuno-electrophoresis and immunofluorescence. The present summary will be concerned more especially with this recent work (Weitz, 1960a, b, 1962, 1963a–c; Gray,

1960, 1961, 1962; Brown, 1963; Seed, 1963; Cunningham and Vickerman, 1962; Soltys, 1957a,b).

1. *Nomenclature*

Some of the difficulties of interpretation in the field arise from nomenclature. It is to be remembered, first, that sometimes the materials confidently discussed under specific names may be of less definite status. For instance, the distinction between "*Trypanosoma brucei*" and "*T. rhodesiense*" rests, still, only on the ability of the latter, but not of the former, to infect man. In this section the use of *T. rhodesiense* or *T. brucei* will be confined to materials of known behaviour in this respect, otherwise *T. brucei* subgroup will be used as a description.

2. *Materials*

a. *Antigens.* *T. brucei* subgroup organisms have attracted the most study. Much attention has been paid recently, particularly by Gray (1960, 1961, 1962), to *T. vivax* adapted to rats by the concurrent inoculation of sheep serum. Because of its intractability as a laboratory tool little or no attention has been paid to *T. congolense* despite its paramount economic importance. Most work has been on long-established laboratory strains, very little on cyclically transmitted organisms. The materials studied, though representative of antigenic and other differences, bear often little more than a chance relationship to each other, though sometimes relapse strains are induced intentionally by exposure of material to homologous antiserum. Many of the materials used may be heterogeneous in their constitution; little work has been done on clones.

The antigens existing in the blood forms and in their ambient fluid as represented by the serum of the infected animal have been most closely studied. Some comparisons have been made with culture forms but, surprisingly, although the ambient fluid of the blood form, as the serum of the infected animal, has been shown to contain trypanosome antigens, no attention appears to have been devoted, similarly, to the ambient fluid of trypanosome cultures.

In some studies the living organisms have been used, either in the plasma of their recent host or washed by differential centrifugation and resuspended in other fluids. In others, the organisms have been separated and washed by differential centrifugation and homogenates prepared by disintegration in the Hughes press (Weitz, 1960b), the Mickel disintegrator (Gray, 1960), by ultrasonication (Brown, 1963) with or without centrifugation to remove particulate material, or simply by lyophilization and reconstitution with grinding (Seed, 1963). Washing is a procedure not free from possibility of damage to the organisms; low pH, as with Alsever's solution, a frequently used diluent, may result in catastrophic falls in trypanosome infectivity (Lumsden *et al.*, 1965). The ambient fluids of the organisms, as the serum of the infected host, may be stored frozen or in the lyophilized condition.

There are three main ways in which antigenic material may be preserved unchanged for long periods:

(a) By preservation of the material −80° C frozen;

(b) By lyophilization;

(c) By rapid passage—every 2 days—in small laboratory animals.

Experiments designed to assess the effect of the exposure of living trypanosomes to antigen or to antibody either *in vivo* or *in vitro* depend ultimately on knowledge of the infective potentiality of the trypanosome material employed. This may vary widely depending on such factors as the pH of the suspending medium (Lumsden *et al.*, 1965) or on the stage of the infection in the experimental animal at which the material is harvested (Cunningham *et al.*, in EATRO, 1962–63). It is clearly advantageous that −80° C-frozen material of previously measured potentiality should be standard use in these situations.

b. Antisera. Gray (1961) has used the serum of cattle naturally infected with *T. vivax* to good advantage in analysing the antigenic constitution of various trypanosome strains. More usually, however, antisera are prepared by the inoculation of dead antigenic material into rats or rabbits usually with Freund adjuvant (Seed, 1963; Brown, 1963) or potash alum (Weitz, 1960b, 1963b). Antisera to living materials have been prepared in rabbits by inoculating them with infective organisms and bleeding them 14 days after inoculation (Cunningham and Vickerman, 1962). This interval is probably on the long side to give antisera specifically related only to the inoculated material; it is probably better for this purpose to inoculate animals with a large infecting dose and prevent antigenic variation by early treatment (e.g. Cunningham and Grainge, in EATRO, 1961). These workers report that agglutinating antibodies homologous to the inoculum are detectable by day 4 in rats and that peak agglutinating titres are reached between 6 and 10 days after inoculation. Such antibodies remain detectable for at least 6–8 weeks in rats, rabbits and cattle.

Antisera to the ambient fluid of the organisms, e.g. infected rat serum (IRS), are prepared by the inoculation of convenient laboratory animals. Antisera may be preserved −20° C frozen or lyophilized.

c. Methods of study. A multiplicity of different immunological tests are available and few have been neglected. Weitz (1963a) has criticized the use of agglutination, neutralization and respiratory inhibition reactions as difficult of interpretation, being manifestations of complex antigen-antibody systems liable to be modified by shifts in the nature of the antigen in the course of an infection. He has suggested that the use of trypanosome extracts made at given stages of the infection allows more precise study of the antigens involved. This is true to an extent but extraction could conceivably abolish some antigens and the preservation of trypanosomes by −80° C-freezing (Cunningham *et al.*, 1963) offers a simple way of arresting antigenic change in whole organisms and so of allowing these methods also to contribute to the building up of concepts of trypanosome antigens.

It is convenient at this point to list the methods used. The various antigens will be discussed below in greater detail; it will be convenient to refer henceforth to Table II which sets out a "working hypothesis" of trypanosomal antigens.

Agglutination. Soltys (1957b) used live trypanosomes from the blood of infected mice for this reaction but it is now more convenient to use $-80°$ C-frozen stabilate material (Cunningham and Grainge, in EATRO, 1961). The antigens concerned with the reaction are type specific, and occur on the trypanosome surface and in the ambient fluid of blood forms.

TABLE II

Working Hypothesis of Trypanosomal Antigens

	Internal antigens	External or released antigens
Occurrence	Inside the trypanosome body, only liberated on disruption of the organism, e.g. in trypanosome homogenate (BTH)	On the surface of the trypanosome and released into plasma of parasitaemic animals, e.g. in infected rat serum (IRS). Washed organisms, disrupted, release more of these antigens, indicating that the antigens are produced inside the organisms, and pass to the surface and are continually released
Specificity and biological activity	Common; found in all "strains" including culture trypanosomes; antibodies not absorbed by IRS. No biological properties known	Specific to individual material; serum of rodents inoculated with IRS contains agglutinins for homotypic organisms and precipitins for homotypic released antigen; animals inoculated with IRS resist homotypic but not heterotypic challenge; antibodies absorbed by homotypic IRS only; species, perhaps type, specific by immunofluorescence
Chemical constitution	Unknown	Protein; 1S and 4S proteins, mainly the latter
Further sub-division	None	Divisible to two groups: PR (protective) antigens which elicit antibody in animals protective against challenge; AG (agar gel diffusion) antigens detectable by agar diffusion, of uncertain biological significance. The two groups are separable by fractionation with $(NH_4)_2SO_4$; type specific AG antigens differ in heat sensitivity and in their elution patterns from calcium phosphate gel

Respiratory inhibition. The recognition of the effect of antibody on the respiration rate of trypanosomes is due to Desowitz (1956a). Respiratory inhibition tests are, however, not very sensitive; Thurston (1958) found that the oxygen uptake of trypanosome suspensions was unaffected by antiserum concentrations which caused agglutination or lysis. She found them also less sensitive than neutralization tests. The methods has, however, interest in that it appears to differ in specificity from other tests (Desowitz, 1961).

Trypanosome survival or multiplication. The effects of either antigen or antibody may be studied. Weitz (1960b) adduced evidence that sera containing "released" trypanosomal antigens preserved the infectivity of trypanosomes *in vitro* more effectively than did normal sera. As regards antibody, the neutralizing activity of sera may be quantitatively estimated by the infectivity titration method of Lumsden *et al.* (1963) and this approach has been followed by Cunningham and van Hoeve (in EATRO, 1962–63). The results obtained by neutralization tests appear to be type specific (Soltys, 1957a) and to parallel those derived from agglutination tests; so the neutralization tests are likely also to be concerned with surface antigens. It is to be noted with regard to neutralization tests that they perhaps offer a tool applicable to studies on *T. congolense* which has not yet been obtained in suspensions which can be used for agglutination procedures.

Challenge. Challenge of experimental animals may follow either passive or active immunization.

Growth inhibition. These tests, applied to trypanosomes in culture, are essentially similar to the challenge of animals after passive immunization.

Immunofluorescence. This offers a convenient method for the assessment of the specificity of different antigens (Weitz, 1963b).

Enzyme assay. The effect of antibody on enzyme activity has been studied by Seed (1963).

Agar-gel double diffusion.

Fractionation of antigens by chemical, chromatographic or electrophoretic means.

Immuno-electrophoresis.

3. *The Antigens*

Thillet and Chandler (1957) by inoculation and challenge experiments in rats showed that the fluid from 24-hour-old suspensions of *Trypanosoma lewisi*, postulated to contain the metabolic products of the organisms, was a much more effective immunizing agent than the triturated bodies of the related organisms. Rats inoculated with trypanosome bodies experienced modified infections as compared to uninoculated controls, but rats inoculated with the fluid of the suspensions never became parasitaemic at all. Also, in *in vitro* experiments, the serum of rats inoculated with the fluid of the suspension agglutinated trypanosomes at titres of up to 1 in 200 as did the serum of rats that had recovered from an infection, while the serum of control rats and of rats inoculated with trypanosome bodies produced slight agglutination only, or none at all. Absorption experiments confirmed the greater antigenic potency of the fluid of the suspension as compared with the trypanosome bodies. Thillet and Chandler equated the antibody to metabolic products with ablastin, an antibody (Taliaferro, 1924) responsible for halting trypanosome reproduction, and suggest that it is responsible also for immobilization and agglutination effects, in combination with the metabolic products adhering to the surface of the trypanosome.

The recognition of similar antigen derived from *T. brucei* subgroup organisms in the blood of infected laboratory animals is due to Weitz (1960a, b). Using blood trypanosome homogenates (BTH) and infected rat serum (IRS) as antigens and unabsorbed and absorbed antisera he established the following facts:

(a) IRS contained a soluble non-toxic antigen peculiar to the infected state. He called this antigen, "exoantigen".

(b) This antigen was derived from the trypanosomes and not from some component of rat serum. The amount of rat serum proteins contaminating the inoculum was insufficient to stimulate antibody production to them.

(c) The antibody induced by the injection of IRS was the same as that induced by living and multiplying trypanosomes. Continuous lines were obtained in agar-gel diffusion systems and IRS inhibited agglutination of living trypanosomes by antisera to living trypanosomes and to IRS.

(d) The soluble "exoantigen", by immuno-electrophoresis, is closely associated with a slow moving component of rat serum behind the γ-globulin component.

(e) IRS had certain biological activities which were attributable to the presence of the antigen: (i) It was protective to trypanosomes *in vitro*. Washed trypanosomes rapidly lost their infectivity; infectivity could be preserved to some extent by NRS, significantly more so by IRS. (ii) Inoculation of IRS into animals protected them against infection with live homologous trypanosomes.

(f) Washed trypanosomes, disintegrated (BTH), release further quantities of "exoantigen" and also other, "bound", antigens not otherwise recognized.

Thus in discussing the immunology of trypanosomiasis we have to consider not only the antigens of the trypanosome bodies but also that significant actions may be occasioned by antigens released by the trypanosomes into the ambient medium.

4. *The Common Antigens*

Gray (1960) working with homogenates of washed trypanosomes (*T. vivax, T. gambiense, T. brucei*) and bovine antisera in gel-diffusion systems showed the existence of precipitating antigens common to several different trypanosome species. Seed (1963) found antigens common to more than one material of *T. rhodesiense* only in the homogenates of the organisms. Weitz (1963b) showed that *T. brucei* and *T. vivax* organisms did not stain differentially when treated with fluorescein-labelled antibodies to the "bound" antigens which are not released except on disintegration of the organisms (Weitz, 1960b). It has been accepted, therefore, in the meantime that the common antigens are internal, occluded in normal circumstances and only manifested by breakdown of the trypanosome body. That this may not be entirely true is shown, however, by the fact that certain bovine sera show continuous lines of precipitation when matched against the serum of rats infected with several different trypanosome species (Gray, 1961). However, this may possibly be due to some breakdown of trypanosome bodies in the process of preparing the serum samples.

Antisera to blood or culture from trypanosome homogenates agglutinated only their homologous organisms despite the presence in them of antibodies to the common antigens. Similarly, these antisera, administered in culture or *in vivo*, inhibited growth or protected the animal only against their homologous materials (Seed, 1963). Thus it appears that the common antigens are not involved in determining the various serotypes of a trypanosome species as evidenced by agglutination or protection phenomena and that they are not exposed on the trypanosome surface.

No biological properties have yet been attributed to the internal or common antigens. There are probably many antigens common to types or species of trypanosomes which are not detected by agar diffusion techniques be-because they exist in the trypanosome in only small quantity. For example, an enzyme, hexokinase, obtained from one trypanosome strain was found to be neutralized by the antiserum to the heterologous strain and also by an antiserum to culture trypanosomes. Thus the enzyme appears to have a common antigenic structure in these three materials, but it is not one of the antigens found as precipitin lines in agar diffusion plates; nor is it eluted from calcium phosphate gel under the conditions under which elute the common antigens detected in agar plates (Seed, 1963).

In a study of closely related materials of *T. rhodesiense* by precipitation in agar-gel, Seed (1963) found at least two antigens common to blood and culture forms, and which occurred also in *T. brucei* and *T. equiperdum*. Curiously, however, another *T. rhodesiense* material lacked one of these antigens and in an example of *T. gambiense* the amounts of these antigens were much reduced. Thus the pattern of common antigens may not follow the present taxonomic arrangement of trypanosome species.

5. *The Specific Antigens*

By the inoculation of trypanosomal antigenic material animals can be protected against challenge only by that material, not against material of other trypanosome species or other types of the same species.

Similarly some of the precipitation reactions taking place in agar gel systems are type specific (Seed, 1963). This worker demonstrated by fractionation of antigens by precipitation with ammonium sulphate that the antigens responsible for eliciting antibodies protective against challenge inoculation (PR antigens) were not the same as those precipitating with homologous antisera in agar gel systems (AG antigens).

The AG antigens occurred mainly in the 65–80% $(NH_4)_2SO_4$ fractions in the purification procedures applied to infected animal serum. This fraction, however, failed significantly to protect mice against homologous trypanosome challenge. On the other hand, it was possible to protect mice by immunization with the 0–65% $(NH_4)_2SO_4$ fractions which contained no detectable AG antigens.

a. The antigens precipitating in agar-gel diffusion systems (AG antigens). Precipitating antigens were first demonstrated in trypanosome infections by Gray (1960). He used as antigenic material the supernates after the centrifugation of homogenates of washed trypanosomes (*T. vivax*, *T. brucei* and

T. gambiense) and as antisera the sera of cattle which had been infected cyclically by *Glossina morsitans* with *T. vivax* and usually also *T. congolense*. He was impressed with the variety in the patterns of precipitation elicited with the sera of individual animals by a single antigenic material. He also showed that precipitating antibodies developed in the rabbit, horse and duiker following trypanosome infections and that they occurred also in man in *T. gambiense* sleeping sickness.

Extending this work, Gray (1961) studied the immunological relationships of several trypanosome species by the use of sera of two cattle infected with *T. vivax* and which contained precipitating antibody against that organism. He studied the antigens present in homogenates of trypanosomes and in the sera of animals infected with two strains of *T. vivax* (one rat-adapted and maintained by syringe passage and another maintained by cyclical transmission in sheep) and with syringe-passaged strains of *T. gambiense* and *T. brucei*. When *T. vivax* infected rat serum was matched against the cattle sera, five lines of precipitation developed in each case but only three of these were common to the two antisera.

The sera of goats, sheep and cattle cyclically infected with *T. vivax* were matched against the same cattle antisera. Reactions showing one to three lines of precipitation were obtained with most of the goat sera but not with either sheep or cattle sera. The occurrence of reactions was correlated to some extent with parasitaemic level; most of the goats showed high parasitaemias, the other animals did not.

When he matched *T. vivax* homogenates (BTH) and *T. vivax* infected rat serum (IRS) against the cattle antisera, Gray found, respectively, three and six lines of precipitation of which only one or two were common. Thus four of the *T. vivax* antigens apparently did not occur inside the trypanosome body.

Seed (1963) has demonstrated the reactions of the specific and common precipitating antigens with closely related *T. rhodesiense* materials and un-absorbed and absorbed sera. Essentially BTH has both common (C) antigen and its own type specific (AG) antigen while IRS contains only its type specific (AG) antigen.

b. The protective antigens. In mice immunized with IRS derived from different trypanosome types and challenged with homologous or heterologous types, the protection is type specific (Seed, 1963). Significant increases in the average survival time after challenge were restricted to homologous challenge: the increase in survival time varied very widely for reasons unknown, perhaps because the strains were not pure.

Similarly, in passive protection tests rabbit anti-BTH serum protected mice against homologous challenge only. Normal rabbit serum and rabbit anti-culture trypanosome (CT) serum failed to protect. As PR antigen is absorbed to calcium phosphate gel and is precipitated by $(NH_4)_2SO_4$ it is suggested that it also is protein in nature.

6. Chemical Characteristics and Location of Trypanosome Antigens

Brown and Williamson (1962a, b, 1964) and Williamson and Brown (1964) have studied the antigens present in disintegrates of *T. brucei* subgroup organisms. The possibility that polysaccharide or lipid antigens were involved was excluded and the predominant association of antigenicity with the proteins established. Two main groups of apparently unconjugated light-weight proteins were recognized as the main precipitinogens, respectively the "1S" and "4S" proteins. The 4S antigens were destroyed by various treatments—heat, pepsin digestion, sodium metaperiodate, acetylating mixture—which the 1S antigens resisted. Variant specific reactions such as agglutination, lysis and precipitation appeared to be associated mainly with the 4S proteins.

By centrifugal fractionation in aqueous sucrose media the homogenates were separated into nuclear, "mitochondrial" (mainly kinetoplasts and flagella), and microsomal fractions, and cell sap, the final supernate. The cell sap contained the highest concentration of antigens. That the bulk of the trypanosomal membranous material occurs in the nuclear, "mitochondrial" and microsomal fractions, which are weakest antigenically, suggested that "fixed" external cell antigens are unlikely to be prominent in the *T. brucei* subgroup. Brown and Williamson considered that the high antigenicity of the cell sap was unlikely to be accounted for by the solution of antigens from cell membrane fragments and that the "exoantigen" postulated by Weitz may represent cytoplasmic antigen released by lysis or "reverse pinocytosis" from the intact cell. However, the immediate agglutination of whole trypanosomes suggests that the reacting antigen is available at the cell surface.

7. *Antigenic Lability*

The antigenic lability of trypanosomes has been recognized for a long time. The numbers of distinct antigenic variants which may occur is apparently large but is probably not unlimited; numbers of twenty or more have been recorded (Brown, 1963). There is apparently a tendency for trypanosomes to revert to a comparatively constant "parent" form on cyclical passage through *Glossina* and this parent form will usually initiate the next vertebrate infection (Broom and Brown, 1940; Gray, 1963).

It should be noted that the material which is used experimentally may be expected to be often of mixed antigenic constitution. Isolations made at weekly or other intervals, or after subcurative drug treatment or in other ways, may show one antigenic type predominant but it is unlikely to be pure. Some of the difficulties of interpretation of results may arise from this consideration; that these variations in antigenicity are, however, not simply the result of selection of variants from a heterogeneous population is shown by the fact that serotypic variants occur in the same way in a population derived from a single individual trypanosome (Gray, quoted by Weitz, 1963c; Willett, 1961).

Antigenic variation leading to specifically different types is not confined to one type of antigen. Seed (1963) has demonstrated trypanosome types differing specifically not only in the PR antigens which have demonstrated biological function in that their inoculation protects animals against challenge with the homologous organisms but also in their AG antigens distinguishable in agar-gel diffusion experiments but which have no known biological function. It has been considered (Weitz, 1963c) that the changes in antigenicity were likely to be too subtle for recognition by chemical means, but Seed (1963) has found differences in resistance to heating and in the pattern of elution from calcium phosphate gels between the AG antigens of two closely related materials.

The appearance of different antigenic types is related to the immune response of the host. Gray (1962) passed a trypanosome infection at weekly intervals in rabbits and accorded the original material and the variant material of each successive passage different designations, respectively, 0, 1, 2, 3, etc. He studied the agglutination titre of the sera of the animal against the variants at weekly intervals after inoculation. Table III gives the reciprocals

TABLE III

Serum Agglutination Titres of Rabbits successively Infected in Passages of T. brucei *Subgroup Material (from data of Gray, 1962)*

Rabbits	0	1	2	3	4	5
Variants and reciprocals of agglutination titres	0:10240 →	1:20480 →	1:20480 →	3:10240 →	4:2560 →	5:5120
	3:1280	4:640	2:5120	5:320	5:40 ⌐	3:10
	5:160	5:40	0:nil	1:80	1:10	0:10
	1:20 ⌐	0:nil	3:nil	2:40 ⌐	0:nil	1:nil
	2:nil	2:nil	4:nil	0:nil	2:nil	2:nil
	4:nil	3:nil	5:nil	4:nil ⌐	3:nil	4:nil

Serum agglutination titres of the six rabbits (0–5) to each of the six variant materials (0–5, respectively) used for the passages, in each case 1 week after inoculation, are shown. Arrows indicate the variant likely to have been transferred at each passage.

of the agglutination titres of the animals, 1 week after inoculation, against each of the variants. If high serum agglutination titres 1 week after inoculation may be taken as contra-indicative of the variant likely to exist in the blood at that time (and therefore to be transferred to a recipient animal), and indicative of the variant received from the donor animal 1 week before, then it appears that, with one exception, the variant transferred is one to which the donor host has reacted little or not at all.

Gray (1962) has shown a similar effect by the passive protection of rabbits by inoculating them with antiserum pools in which antibodies to particular variants were little represented and following that inoculation with another of washed trypanosomes. Subsequent study of the antibody titre of the animals to the various variants showed that the variants which were represented by specific antibodies in the protecting inoculation tended to be suppressed and another selected. Probably another manifestation of the same mechanism is the demonstration of altering infectivity of trypanosomes through the course of an infection by Cunningham *et al.* (in EATRO, 1962–63).

In the field, although a greater wealth of antigenic variation might be expected, some selection appears to take place. A study of ten recent *T. brucei* subgroup isolates from East Africa, derived from man, and from wild and domestic animals, has been made by Cunningham and Vickerman (1962) by means of the agglutination test. Many antigens were found to be common to several isolates; all the cross reactions occurring could be explained by postulating only six different specific antigens. Nevertheless antigenic variation does take place in large animals as in laboratory animals; Cunningham (in EATRO, 1961) has made isolations at frequent intervals from experimental cattle and distinguished a succession of specifically different types by the agglutination test.

8. *The Antibodies*

Desowitz (1960) found the alterations in serum protein pattern in *Gazella*, *Redunca* (reedbuck) and *Sylvicapra* (duiker) relatively uniform after challenge with *T. vivax* and *T. brucei* subgroup organisms, despite wide differences in the severity of the illness caused by the infection. In all cases there was an increase in the levels of both the β_2-globulins and the γ-globulins after challenge. He was impressed by the rise in the β_2-globulins which contrasted with his previous experience with ovines and bovines and in which subjects only the γ-globulin was affected by the infection.

Mattern (1962) has drawn attention to the fact that the sera of *T. gambiense* sleeping sickness patients contain about sixteen times as much IgM immunoglobulin as control normal sera. This elevation was found in all but two of 138 cases examined. The IgM immunoglobulins reached a peak about the 15th day of the infection and returned to normal in a few months in cases in which there was no involvement of the central nervous system. Increase in IgM immunoglobulins occurs in other diseases of man and so its elevation cannot be taken as pathognomonic of trypanosomiasis, but its absence can be regarded as virtually excluding that diagnosis.

VII. THE TRYPANOSOME, THE ARTHROPODAN VECTOR AND THE MAMMALIAN HOST

A. IN THE LABORATORY

1. *The Tinde Experiment*

Willett (1962a) summarizes the context of the Tinde experiment. Essentially the experiment was designed to examine the stability of the biological character of ability to infect man, which by definition distinguishes *T. rhodesiense* from *T. brucei*. A strain of *T. rhodesiense* retained the character of infectivity for man over 23 years of cyclical transmission by *G. morsitans* through sheep and also in other passage lines through antelopes and monkeys (Ashcroft, 1959a). It has been established, then, for one strain of *T. rhodesiense*, that the character of infectivity for man is a stable one; this is probably more generally true. The converse experiment, to determine if infectivity for man can ever be acquired by cyclically transmitted *T. brucei* strains, has not yet been so intensively performed. In view of recent knowledge of the adaptation of trypanosomes to abnormal hosts (Desowitz, 1963) this would seem indicated.

2. Study Methods

The detection of antibodies in the blood of animals infected with trypanosomes by means of an agglutination technique has been described above. An extension of this technique is that of detecting the presence of antibodies in the blood meals of haematophagous insects. *G. morsitans* were fed on a rat with a serum agglutination titre of $10^{-4\cdot9}$ against *T. brucei* subgroup organisms and it was found that antibodies could be detected in the blood meals of the flies up to 96 h after feeding, and that no diminution of titre took place in blood meal samples dried on filter paper and stored in a desiccator for 25 days at about 25° C. The method was shown to be effective also with several species of mosquito, with tabanids and with *Stomoxys* spp. (Cunningham *et al.*, 1962).

Using five *T. brucei* subgroup materials selected at random the same technique was applied to the blood meals of twenty-five wild *G. brevipalpis*. Only two of the blood meals failed to react with any of the antigens and some reacted with all five. When the antigenic constitution of trypanosomes is better understood, it seems that the technique may offer important epidemiological applications (Harley and Cunningham, in EATRO, 1961).

B. IN THE FIELD

It is likely, from an ecological point of view, that each trypanosome species fills an individual niche and so ideally each should be considered and studied as a separate ecological problem. It will be realized, however, from the earlier part of this review that this ideal, individual, approach is often impeded by the lack of means for the identification of particular trypanosome species or types in the field. It will be convenient, then, first to discuss work of general applicability and then later to proceed to the consideration of individual trypanosome species; in fact, it will be possible to add significantly in this section to what has already been recorded earlier, only in relation to the man-infecting species.

Ford and Leggate (1961) relate the infection rate found in *Glossina* spp. of the *morsitans* group to the "*Glossina* equator", 7° south latitude, approximately the middle of the north-south distribution of the genus. Except for some localities in Zululand, a positive correlation was found to exist between infection rates and distance from the *Glossina* equator. This correlation was associated with increasing mean annual temperature and it was suggested that the mean temperature at which *Glossina* exist, and possibly the range of temperature occurring between seasons, accounts for the general level of the infection rate, with local variations depending on differences in the mammal reservoirs. Leggate (1962) examined the seasonal changes in infection rates in *G. morsitans* and *G. pallidipes* in the lower Zambesi region. He discusses many factors likely to be influential—temperature, mean age of the fly population, duration of hunger cycle and so on—and concluded that the distribution of mammal hosts was likely to be most important. Infection rates in *Glossina* in riverine sites were highest in the dry season when wild bovids were concentrated there.

1. *Trypanosoma congolense*

Soltys (1954) reported a field experiment on the mechanical transmission of *T. congolense*. Cattle kept in the same herd as infected cattle occasionally became infected. The species of insect responsible was not identified.

2. *T. brucei Subgroup*

The complexities of the controversies about the status and interrelationships of the *T. brucei* subgroup organisms have been discussed by Ashcroft (1959c) and Willett (1956a, 1962a). These controversies have concerned the significance of the sensitivities of trypanosomes to human serum, the effect of nutritional deficiency on human susceptibility, the role of wild animals as reservoirs of man-infecting strains, the factors likely to select, and so to allow to survive in the field, particular species or types, the stability of the named species, the fluctuation of strain virulence on passage, and other matters. Willett's (1956a) discussion of the occurrence of sleeping sickness outbreaks is excellently illustrative of the difficulties in the way of coming to firm conclusions on circumstantial epidemiological grounds. He shows how the information available regarding the 1940–41 *T. rhodesiense* sleeping sickness outbreak in Busoga District, Uganda, is susceptible of two different interpretations, either that the disease was introduced by immigrant labour, or was derived from indigenous cycles of transmission in the wildlife of the region. Willett examined the historical reports of a number of epidemics to see, in each case, if:

(a) *T. rhodesiense* was brought into the area from elsewhere;

(b) *T. gambiense* was previously present in the area and could have developed a more virulent form;

(c) a mutation of *T. brucei* into *T. rhodesiense* could have taken place.

To these possibilities of the genesis of *T. rhodesiense* epidemics the present author would add another: that typical *T. rhodesiense* might exist continuously in cycles of transmission in the wildlife of the area and only impinge on man when some unusual happening takes place such as his invasion of habitat not usually penetrated by him. Discussions of these points are intensely interesting but inconclusive. It seems that much further progress in understanding of the mechanisms of maintenance of these trypanosomes is dependent on development of better methods for the field recognition of particular trypanosome types than we possess at the moment.

a. Trypanosoma gambiense. It is generally accepted that epidemics of this disease, clinically insidious in onset, may be accounted for by cycles of transmission involving only man and *Glossina*. For example, Morris (1959, 1960a–c) discussed *T. gambiense* outbreaks in East Africa on this basis, and Scott (1960) cited examples of epidemics, the origins of which appear clearly to be associated with population movements.

The development of human outbreaks is related especially to conditions in which a small population of *Glossina* concentrate their biting attack on man. Nash (1958) referred to this as "personal" man-fly contact in contrast to "impersonal" man-fly contact in which man may be bitten frequently but by many different members of a shifting population, presumably, therefore, feeding less constantly on man. He recorded some interesting results bearing on this hypothesis derived from the capture, marking, release and recapture of *G. palpalis* at water holes in a dry region of northern Nigeria and in the forest belt of south-western Nigeria. The percentage of flies recaptured 18 days or longer after marking was taken as indicative of the proportion of flies likely to become infected with *Trypanosoma gambiense* and to pass on that infection to another person at the same water hole. In the forest region the percentages were 0·81 and 0·55%, in the dry and wet seasons respectively. In the drier area, they were 7–9 times as high, 7·52 and 3·86% respectively, in the dry and wet seasons. Thus the chance in the dry season of a fly remaining by a water hole long enough to become infective is much greater in the north than in the south and so correspondingly was the chance of that fly passing on infection to another human. In general this interpretation fits the picture of the incidence of sleeping sickness in West Africa; very high incidences are confined to areas with a prolonged dry season and when the disease occurs in forest country it is usually confined to the drier mixed deciduous forest.

The temperature conditions prevailing may also be influential. Willett (1962a) suggests that *G. palpalis* and *G. tachinoides* will be most efficient as vectors towards the northern limits of their distribution, i.e. in the parts of their distributions where the conditions are nearing the upper temperature limits for the species. He points out that this hypothesis is consistent with the findings that *G. tachinoides* is not of importance as a vector in Ghana but it is in Northern Nigeria near the northern limit of its distribution.

With regard to the possibility of the existence of wild animal hosts of *T. gambiense*, Scott (1960) has pointed out that when the overall incidence is low, infection occurs predominantly among males, when it is higher or in times of epidemics the incidence in females equals or surpasses that in males. This result would be consistent with the existence of a sylvan cycle of transmission, taking place in areas remote from habitation, and therefore involving only males, and an intra-human cycle, operating in inhabited areas, and involving both sexes. Perhaps suids may be important as wild animal hosts of *T. gambiense*; Willett (1961) reported that the black pigs kept by the Tiv tribe of Nigeria infected with *T. gambiense*, infected *Glossina* fed upon them for periods of at least 41 days.

b. Trypanosoma rhodesiense. Typically, *T. rhodesiense* causes acute febrile illness. It cannot, however, be assumed that this is always the case and that either treatment or death will necessarily rapidly remove the recipient from the epidemiological picture. Ross and Blair (1956) cite examples from Southern Rhodesia of persons, in apparently normal states of health, found parasitaemic after periods of up to 29 months outside *Glossina*-infested areas. It is of interest to note that these persons usually showed, not scanty, but intense parasitaemias. Apted *et al.* (1963) believe that the clinical severity of the disease varies with locality, being least severe at the southern end of its distribution, in the Rhodesias and in Bechuanaland, most severe towards its northern limits, in Uganda and Kenya; Ormerod (1963) correlates this difference with differences in the form and numbers of granules in the cytoplasm of trypanosome strains from these two areas. Exceptions to this rule, however, exist as Robertson (1963) has found that a proportion of *T. rhodesiense* cases in south-east Uganda have an insidious onset, presenting first as cases of sub-acute or chronic encephalitis.

Historical descriptions of *T. rhodesiense* sleeping sickness in Africa often begin with the first recognition of the parasite in man in the Zambesi basin in 1909 and relate the subsequent distribution of the disease to human movements (e.g. Fairbairn, 1948; Ormerod, 1961). Willett (1962a) considers that *T. rhodesiense* is simply a virulent type of *T. gambiense* which has been able to continue its geographic spread outside the distribution of *G. palpalis* by becoming adapted to survival in wild animals and to being transmitted by *Glossina* of the *morsitans* group. The distinction between the two types of sleeping sickness often seems difficult. Willett (1962a) quotes Lester's observation that two of thirteen strains isolated in Nigeria were of *T. rhodesiense* type. Buxton (1955) has pointed out that the lack of records of sleeping sickness by early travellers can be held to indicate that epidemics were not prevalent but cannot be considered to exclude that the disease was endemic and even widely distributed. He suggested that the epidemic in the Lake Victoria basin in the years following 1901 might have been caused by *T. rhodesiense*. It is perhaps significant in this context that the area of persistence of the *T. rhodesiense* disease in modern Uganda is that in which the epidemic began at the beginning of the century.

The most detailed recent studies of the epidemiology of *T. rhodesiense* sleeping sickness are those related to the southern part of Busoga District, Uganda (Robertson, 1963; and in EATRO, 1960, 1961) which forms part of the northern coastline of Lake Victoria. The Busoga coastline is tortuous, having been formed by the drowning of an ancient river system, and is fronted by an archipelago of many small islands, carrying woodland or forest; much of the area, because of the presence of sleeping sickness, has been closed to human settlement. More recently two main groups of people have been invading the area, fishermen who work the waters off the mainland and island coasts, and agriculturalists whose settlements invade the woodland bordering the lake from the landward side. Robertson (1963) recognized the need to consider the epidemiology of the disease in relation to the habits and activities of the people becoming infected and so divided his study into two sections, one related to fishermen and the other to agriculturalists.

The fishermen of Lake Victoria habitually set their nets in the late afternoon or evening and take them in the following morning. Conditions demand that they remain in the close vicinity of their nets to protect them from maurauders and so they camp in many places along the lake coast and thereby come into contact with the *Glossina* of the shore wherever they are fishing. The incidence of the disease among fishermen is greater among those using the eastern half of the Busoga shore than among those using the western half. This difference may be due to some difference in fishing habits—the two groups are largely of different tribal affiliation—or to some difference in the risk of infection between the two areas. Variations in the seasonal incidence of sleeping sickness among fishermen appear to be determined primarily by seasonal changes in fishing activity rather than by seasonal variations in the risk of infection. The period of lowest incidence of sleeping sickness, from June to October, coincides with a period of reduced fish production for commerce. This reduction of fishing activity coincides with a time during which the lake waters are thermally unstratified, and therefore generally oxygenated, so allowing *Tilapia*, the main fish exploited commercially, to move away from the coast, making them more difficult to catch. At other times of the year, particularly in April and May, the lake waters are thermally stratified, the deeper waters are depleted of oxygen and the fish are concentrated in coastal waters and are more readily caught, and so fishing activity, and sleeping sickness incidence, are at high levels.

Before considering the incidence of the disease among cultivators it is necessary to describe the character of the settlement developing in Busoga. The pattern of settlement developed depends greatly on the prevailing system of land tenure and allocation. In Busoga, the power to allocate land to settlers is vested in hereditary chiefs who do so for a fee and who, as they are otherwise unpaid, vie with each other to attract settlers to their several spheres of interest. Concentrated occupation of the land tends, therefore, not to occur and a type of settlement develops in which small cleared and cultivated areas are scattered widely, intermixed intimately with untouched woodland, so exposing the inhabitants to attack by *Glossina*. Among settled cultivators, mainly away from the lake coast, sleeping sickness cases are most numerous in May and June, during and following the main rains, and women and children are involved along with the men. It appears, therefore, that these people are infected at or near their places of residence; what species of *Glossina* is mainly concerned in infecting them is still, however, not clear.

Three *Glossina* species occur in south Busoga, *G. palpalis fuscipes*, *G. pallidipes* and *G. brevipalpis*. *G. brevipalpis* seldom or never feeds on man and so is unlikely to be concerned in infecting him with *T. rhodesiense* (Southon, in EATRO, 1961). As regards the other two species in the early work it was considered likely that *G. pallidipes* was the main species infecting man and *G. palpalis fuscipes* was of minor importance, for two main reasons: isolations of *T. rhodesiense* had been made from *G. pallidipes* but not from 3 706 *G. palpalis fuscipes* collected in the area and allowed to feed on rats; *G. pallidipes* was known to bite mainly below the knee, where trypanosome chancres tended to occur also (67% of 40 cases), *G. palpalis fuscipes* mainly the upper body (Robertson and Baker, 1958). The isolation of *Trypanosoma rhodesiense* from wild *G. palpalis fuscipes* at Lugala, Busoga (Southon and Robertson, 1961), however, fundamentally altered basic concepts of the epidemiology of the disease in the area. From 14 500 *G. palpalis fuscipes*, twenty-one strains of *T. brucei* subgroup were isolated by allowing the flies to feed in batches on laboratory rodents. All the strains were morphologically typical, readily infected laboratory rodents, and were little affected by tryparsamide. These twenty-one strains were inoculated in four lots, at separate locations, subcutaneously into a man, who became parasitaemic on day 7 after inoculation. Local reactions were observed at three of the four sites of inoculation. This result was interpreted as indicating that at least one, probably three, and perhaps more of the "strains" contained *T. rhodesiense*.

Further, although *G. palpalis* is mainly coastal in its distribution it also extends in some places far inland; it was found as commonly as *G. pallidipes* in an area, Mayirinya, near Nankoma, Busoga, more than 6 miles from the lake where a particularly marked rise in sleeping sickness took place in May and June 1961 (Harley, in EATRO, 1961). In general the impression has been obtained that the risk of infection during interepidemic periods is greatest near the lake coast; although an analysis of the available data on this point did not give a statistically significant result it was not inconsistent with this belief (Robertson, 1963). The present situation in Busoga would be consistent with a maintenance cycle of transmission of *T. rhodesiense* among wild animals by *G. palpalis fuscipes*, mainly coastal in its occurrence, and involving man only when he comes into contact with it by following some special occupation, such as fishing or hunting, with dissemination of the disease more widely inland under certain conditions, then involving *G. pallidipes* as well and leading to the infection of the inland agricultural populations.

In a study of the hosts of the three species of *Glossina* in the same area, it was found that *G. brevipalpis* was the least catholic, 80% of the meals being from only two hosts, *Hippopotamus* and *Potamochoerus* (bushpig). *G. pallidipes* showed a wider range of hosts, including man, but 90% of the meals were from bovids and suids. *G. palpalis fuscipes* showed the most general feeding pattern; 28% of the meals were from reptiles, 23% from men and 38% from bovids, mainly *Tragelaphus* (bushbuck). These results point to the potential importance of *G. palpalis fuscipes* for transmitting *T. rhodesiense* infection from wild animals to man and from man to man and accord with the high rate of *T. brucei* subgroup infections found in the species in the same area previously (Southon and Robertson, 1961; Southon, in EATRO, 1961).

As regards the identity of the wild animal host of *T. rhodesiense* in the area practically nothing is known. Apted *et al.* (1963) consider *Tragelaphus* (bushbuck) as the wild artiodactyl likely to be the most important host of *T. rhodesiense*. The foregoing data on the hosts of *G. palpalis* in Busoga would support this conviction. *T. rhodesiense* has been isolated from *Tragelaphus* (Heisch *et al.*, 1958). The bushbuck is of especial interest because it lives in close association with man, invading cultivated land to feed (Rosevear, 1953), and perhaps in consequence is one of the few African Artiodactyla at present increasing its numbers (van den Berghe, personal communication).

A point of fundamental interest in the epidemiology of *T. rhodesiense* is the localization of the disease within the distribution of the *Glossina* spp. considered to be its main vectors. Buxton (1955) states that there is evidence that the vector of *T. rhodesiense* is normally one of the "game tsetse" and says that, of these, *G. morsitans* is the most widely distributed; he states that "there are many areas where cases of Rhodesian sleeping sickness occur in the presence of this insect, but of no other *Glossina*". *G. morsitans*, however, is characteristically a widely distributed insect and explanation of the localization of *T. rhodesiense* infection within the wider distribution of *G. morsitans* is lacking. Apted (1962) quotes Taute's observation that the disease was confined to the vicinity of water holes and resting places of the people. Such localization might conceivably be explained by the existence of circumscribed small populations of some other *Glossina* species, undetected by more general sampling, or by the local prevalence of some other factor, such as a particular species of mammal host or some special ecological relationship. The first possibility was considered in relation to a recent *T. rhodesiense* outbreak in South Nyanza, Kenya, but *G. pallidipes* was the only species found (Southon, in EATRO, 1962–63). Isolation of trypanosomes showed a very high incidence of *T. brucei* subgroup organisms in *G. pallidipes* in the area, suggesting that local ecological conditions were particularly suitable for the maintenance of these organisms. But the important constituents of that situation are still unknown.

Recent studies of a *T. rhodesiense* outbreak in Central Nyanza, Kenya, indicated that one thicket area, Uhaya, was of particular importance in the local epidemiology of *T. rhodesiense* sleeping sickness. Three species of *Glossina*, *G. palpalis fuscipes*, *G. pallidipes* and *G. brevipalpis*, were found there and all the trypanosome isolations made from flies, including one of *T. rhodesiense*, were associated with it, despite the trial of considerable samples from other areas. The findings indicated that *T. rhodesiense* was being maintained continuously in the region, with the Uhaya thicket being a significant maintenance factor and *G. pallidipes* the main vector concerned (Lumsden *et al.*, in EATRO, 1961).

VIII. CONCLUSION

A summary of so broad a subject as trypanosomiasis research must be superficial but it is hoped that most of the recent significant additions to knowledge and improved methods have been noted. The application of ecological methods and concepts to the study of trypanosomiasis is much more difficult than it is in some other fields. In particular, the tool provided by tests for the detection in the sera of vertebrate hosts of antibodies indicative of past infection is not yet applicable in the field of trypanosomiasis as it is in that of arboviruses. Numerous trypanosome species, strains and antigenic types are under simultaneous transmission in the field and serum antibodies cannot yet be clearly and categorically referred to pathogens of main interest (Lumsden, 1964b). Primarily there is need for more tools for deriving quantitative information about field situations. The present review has indicated some significant advances in the development of better methods of study. Its conclusion can probably serve most usefully by trying to indicate where research attention in the future would be most likely to improve basic understanding of the mechanisms of survival and transmission of trypanosomes.

The trypanosome. The extended use of stabilate material should greatly improve comparisons between the results of different workers. So far most stabilates used have been of blood forms. Stabilates set up from clones and from metacyclic trypanosomes would have special advantages and there is great need for taxonomic studies of a selection of stabilates established as *T. brucei sensu stricto* by repeated demonstration of their failure to infect man. Infectivity measurement now offers a tool for the quantitative study of the prime feature of trypanosomes, their potentiality to establish themselves and multiply in particular situations. Systematic study of the factors determining the establishment and potentiality of trypanosomes in culture would be advantageous.

The arthropod. The study of *Glossina* has found more devoted adherents than most other aspects of trypanosomiasis and we possess very detailed ecological information, particularly in respect of the economically important species. Nevertheless, further improvement in sampling methods is required, especially for the study of the dynamics of low density populations. Advance in knowledge of the plant ecology of *Glossina* habitats and of the physiology and ecology of *Glossina* should be of application. More detailed knowledge of *Glossina* host relationships, particularly of the mechanisms of discrimination between host species, is desirable.

The vertebrate. Considering that we are concerned with parasites severely affecting man and his domestic stock it is remarkable that so little specific information exists about the habits of man and his stock in relation to these infections. Of equal interest, but more difficult to acquire, is detailed knowledge of the ecology of the wild animal hosts of *Glossina*. Quantitative information on the populations of possible animal hosts existing in infected areas would be especially useful.

The trypanosome in the arthropod. Study of the physiology of the development of trypanosome infections in *Glossina* is likely to facilitate the preparation of metacyclic stabilate materials, to contribute to an understanding of the factors deciding the acquisition of infectivity to the mammalian host by culture forms, and to be significant in epidemiological studies.

The trypanosome in the mammal. The occurrence of a trypanosome chancre at the site of infection in man and in the rabbit, but not in some other animals, is of great interest. A study of this phenomenon might shed light on mechanisms of host resistance to infection. The factors determining natural host susceptibility and resistance are not well understood. For assessment of the comparative importance of different wild animal species as reservoirs of trypanosomes further purely microscopical approaches appear to be futile; perhaps conclusions in this sphere will be most easily reached by the xeno-diagnostic use of standard *Glossina* material. Attempts to acquire comparative information on the importance of wild animal species as hosts of *T. rhodesiense* will need to be carried out in close conjunction with ecological studies of wild mammals and of *Glossina* in order to narrow down the search to a few species. Throughout this section knowledge of the immunological reactions of the host to the infection is pertinent. Although much progress has been made in this area of research, we still lack methods which can be used for epidemiological studies in the field, and we do not understand the mechanisms by which a trypanosome-host relationship is adjusted so that pathogenic effects do not ensue. Immunology is probably the field of research most likely to influence fundamentally the present trypanosomiasis situation in Africa.

The trypanosome, the arthropod and the mammal. The studies described illustrate the difficulties in the way of a comprehensive understanding of the mechanisms by which trypanosomes survive and of the routes by which man and cattle are infected. Much more than in other fields the tools available in trypanosomiasis fail to give quantitative information without which epidemiological interpretations must remain largely conjectural. The main tools still to be evolved have been indicated. The most profitable general improvement of epidemiological understanding will probably emerge from a comprehensive study which brings all disciplines of possible importance to bear on one selected representative locality.

The present review has indicated the breadth of the range of scientific disciplines involved in arriving at an understanding of the mechanisms by which African pathogenic trypanosomes are maintained and transmitted in the field. The research laboratories of Africa, Europe and America all have their distinctive contributions to make towards a synthesis of essential knowledge. Such combination of effort can take place today with a facility impossible only a few years ago, and from the exploitation of this new possibility important advances may be expected in the immediate future.

Acknowledgements

I am indebted to Dr. D. H. L. Rollinson for information on the biology of cattle in relation to trypanosomiasis. My wife, Pamela Kathleen Lumsden, gave me undismayed support throughout the work and was, besides, an essential link in the communication of the final document.

The publishers are thanked for permission to make use of this contribution, while still in the press, as a working basis for deliberations of the World Health Organization Expert Committee on Immunology and Parasitic Diseases which met at Ibadan, Nigeria, from 8 to 15 December 1964.

References

Allen, G. M. (1939). A check-list of African mammals. *Bull. Mus. comp. Zool. Harv.* **83**, 1–763.

Andrewartha, H. G. and Birch, L. C. (1954). "The Distribution and Abundance of Animals." University of Chicago Press.

Apted, F. I. C. (1962). Sleeping sickness in Tanganyika, past, present and future. *Trans. R. Soc. trop. Med. Hyg.* **56**, 15–23.

Apted, F. I. C., Ormerod, W. E., Smyly, D. P., Stronach, B. W. and Szlamp, E. L. (1963). A comparative study of the epidemiology of endemic Rhodesian sleeping sickness in different parts of Africa. *J. trop. Med. Hyg.* **66**, 1–16.

Ashcroft, M. T. (1958). An attempt to isolate *Trypanosoma rhodesiense* from wild animals. *Trans. R. Soc. trop. Med. Hyg.* **52**, 276–282.

D

Ashcroft, M. T. (1959a). The Tinde experiment: a further study of the long-term cyclical transmission of Trypanosoma rhodesiense. Ann. trop. Med. Parasit. 53, 137–146.

Ashcroft, M. T. (1959b). The importance of African wild animals as reservoirs of trypanosomiasis. E. Afr. med. J. 36, 289–297.

Ashcroft, M. T. (1959c). A critical review of the epidemiology of human trypanosomiasis in Africa. Trop. Dis. Bull. 56, 1073–1093.

Ashcroft, M. T., Burtt, E. and Fairbairn, H. (1959). The experimental infection of some African wild animals with Trypanosoma rhodesiense, T. brucei and T. congolense. Ann. trop. Med. Parasit. 53, 147–161.

Azavedo, J. F. de (1964). The maintenance in the laboratory of a colony of Glossina morsitans (Diptera) since 1959. Proc. XII int. Congr. Ent. (In press).

Becker, E. R., Taylor, J. and Fuhrmeister, C. (1947). The effect of pantothenate deficiency on Trypanosoma lewisi infection in the rat. Iowa St. J. Sci. 21, 351–361.

Broom, J. C. and Brown, H. C. (1940). Studies in trypanosomiasis. IV. Notes on the serological characters of Trypanosoma brucei after cyclical development in Glossina morsitans. Trans. R. Soc. trop. Med. Hyg. 34, 53–64.

Brown, K. N. (1963). The antigenic character of the "Brucei" trypanosomes. In "Immunity to Protozoa" (P. C. C. Garnham, A. E. Pierce and I. Roitt, eds.). Blackwell Scientific Publications, Oxford.

Brown, K. N. and Williamson, J. (1962a). Attempts to characterize the antigens of Trypanosoma rhodesiense. Trans. R. Soc. trop. Med. Hyg. 56, 12.

Brown, K. N. and Williamson, J. (1962b). Antigens of Brucei trypanosomes. Nature, Lond. 194, 1253–1255.

Brown, K. N. and Williamson, J. (1964). The chemical composition of trypanosomes. IV. Location of antigens in subcellular fractions of Trypanosoma rhodesiense. Exp. Parasit. 15, 69–86.

Bursell, E. (1957). The effect of humidity on the activity of tsetse flies. J. exp. Biol. 34, 42–51.

Bursell, E. (1958). The water balance of tsetse pupae. Philos. Trans. B, 241, 179–210.

Bursell, E. (1959). The water balance of tsetse flies. Trans. R. ent. Soc. Lond. 111, 205–235.

Bursell, E. (1960a). The measurement of size in tsetse flies (Glossina). Bull. ent. Res. 51, 33–37.

Bursell, E. (1960b). The effect of temperature on the consumption of fat during pupal development in Glossina. Bull. ent. Res. 51, 583–598.

Bursell, E. (1961). The behaviour of tsetse flies (Glossina swynnertoni Austen) in relation to problems of sampling. Proc. R. ent. Soc. Lond. A, 36, 9–20.

Buxton, P. A. (1955). "The Natural History of Tsetse Flies." London School of Hygiene and Tropical Medicine, Memoir No. 10. H. K. Lewis, London.

Caldwell, F. E. and Gyorgy, P. (1947). The influence of biotin deficiency on the course of the infection with Trypanosoma lewisi in the albino rat. J. infect. Dis. 81, 197–208.

Cunningham, M. P. and Harley, J. M. B. (1962). Preservation of living metacyclic forms of the Trypanosoma brucei subgroup. Nature, Lond. 194, 1186.

Cunningham, M. P. and Lumsden, W. H. R. (1964). The standardization of trypanosome material by preservation at low temperatures. Proc. VII int. Congr. trop. Med. Malaria 2, 213-214.

Cunningham, M. P. and Vickerman, K. (1962). Antigenic analysis in the Trypanosoma brucei group, using the agglutination reaction. Trans. R. Soc. trop. Med. Hyg. 56, 48–59.

Cunningham, M. P., Harley, J. M. B., Southon, H. A. W. and Lumsden, W. H. R. (1962). Detection of antibodies in blood meals of hematophagous Diptera. *Science* **138**, 32–33.

Cunningham, M. P., Lumsden, W. H. R. and Webber, W. A. F. (1963). The preservation of viable trypanosomes in lymph tubes at a low temperature. *Exp. Parasit.* **14**, 280–284.

Davey, D. G. (1957). Chemotherapy of animal trypanosomiasis with particular reference to the trypanosomal diseases of domestic animals in Africa. *Vet. Rev. Annot.* **3**, 15–36.

Desowitz, R. S. (1956a). Effect of antibody on the respiratory rate of *Trypanosoma vivax*. *Nature, Lond.* **177**, 132–133.

Desowitz, R. S. (1956b). Observations on the metabolism of *Trypanosoma vivax*. *Expt. Parasit.* **5**, 250–259.

Desowitz, R. S. (1960). Studies on immunity and host-parasite relationships. II. The immune response of antelope to trypanosome challenge. *Ann. trop. Med. Parasit.* **54**, 281–292.

Desowitz, R. S. (1961). Antigenic relationships between polymorphic and monomorphic strains of the *brucei* group trypanosomes. *J. Immunol.* **86**, 69–72.

Desowitz, R. S. (1963). Adaptation of trypanosomes to abnormal hosts. *Ann. N.Y. Acad. Sci.* **113**, 74–87.

Desowitz, R. S. and Watson, H. J. C. (1951). Studies on *Trypanosoma vivax*. I. Susceptibility of white rats to infection. *Ann. trop. Med. Parasit.* **45**, 207–219.

Desowitz, R. S. and Watson, H. J. C. (1953). Studies on *Trypanosoma vivax*. IV. The maintenance of a strain in white rats without sheep-serum supplement. *Ann. trop. Med. Parasit.* **47**, 62–67.

EATRO (1956–57, 1958, 1959, 1960, 1961). Reports (by W. H. R. Lumsden) of the East African Trypanosomiasis Research Organization for these periods, respectively. Government Printer, Nairobi.

EATRO (1962–63). Report (by J. M. B. Harley) of the East African Trypanosomiasis Research Organization for the period. English Press, Nairobi.

Fairbairn, H. (1948). Sleeping sickness in Tanganyika Territory, 1922-46. *Trop. Dis. Bull.* **45**, 1–17.

Fairbairn, H. and Godfrey, D. G. (1957). The local reaction in man at the site of infection with *Trypanosoma rhodesiense*. *Ann. trop. Med. Parasit.* **51**, 464–470.

Fairbairn, H. and Watson, H. J. C. (1955). The transmission of *Trypanosoma vivax* by *Glossina palpalis*. *Ann. trop. Med. Parasit.* **49**, 250–259.

Ford, J. (1962a). Microclimates of tsetse fly resting sites in the Zambesi Valley, Southern Rhodesia. *IX int. Sci. Comm. Tryp. Res.*, 165–170.

Ford, J. (1962b). Game conservation and farming in relation to cattle and bovine trypanosomiasis. *IX int. Sci. Comm. Tryp. Res.*, 119–124.

Ford, J. and Leggate, B. M. (1961). The geographical and climatic distribution of trypanosome infection rates in *G. morsitans* group of tsetse flies. *Trans. R. soc. trop. Med. Hyg.* **55**, 383–397.

Ford, J., Glasgow, J. P., Johns, D. L. and Welch, J. R. (1959). Transect fly-rounds in field studies of *Glossina*. *Bull. ent. Res.* **50**, 275–285.

Foster, R. (1958). Some observations on the breeding of *Glossina morsitans* in the laboratory. *VII int. Sci. Comm. Tryp. Res.*, 351–355.

Glasgow, J. P. (1961a). The feeding habits of *Glossina swynnertoni* Austen. *J. Anim. Ecol.* **30**, 77–85.

Glasgow, J. P. (1961b). Seasonal variations in size and colour and daily changes in the distribution of *Glossina pallidipes* Aust. in the South Busoga Forest, Uganda. *Bull. ent. Res.* **52**, 647–666.

Glasgow, J. P. (1963). "The Distribution and Abundance of Tsetse." Pergamon Press, Oxford.

Glasgow, J. P. and Bursell, E. (1961). Seasonal variation in the fat content and size of *Glossina swynnertoni* Austen. *Bull. ent. Res.* **51**, 705–713.

Glasgow, J. P. and Welch, J. R. (1962). Long term fluctuations in numbers of the tsetse fly *Glossina swynnertoni* Austen. *Bull. ent. Res.* **53**, 129–137.

Glasgow, J. P., Isherwood, F., Lee-Jones, F. and Weitz, B. (1958). Factors affecting the staple food of tsetse flies. *J. Anim. Ecol.* **27**, 59–69.

Glover, P. E. (1961). "The Tsetse Problem in Northern Nigeria." Patwa News Agency, Nairobi.

Godfrey, D. G. (1958). Influence of dietary cod liver oil upon *Trypanosoma congolense*, *T. cruzi*, *T. vivax* and *T. brucei*. *Exp. Parasit.* **7**, 255–268.

Godfrey, D. G. (1960). Types of *Trypanosoma congolense*. I. Morphological differences. *Ann. trop. Med. Parasit.* **54**, 428–438.

Godfrey, D. G. (1961). Types of *Trypanosoma congolense*. II. Differences in the courses of infection. *Ann. trop. Med. Parasit.* **55**, 154–166.

Godfrey, D. G. and Killick-Kendrick, R. (1961). Bovine trypanosomiasis in Nigeria. I. The inoculation of blood into rats as a method of survey in the Donga Valley, Benue Province. *Ann. trop. Med. Parasit.* **55**, 287–297.

Godfrey, D. G. and Killick-Kendrick, R. (1962). *Trypanosoma evansi* of camels in Nigeria: a high incidence demonstrated by the inoculation of blood into rats. *Ann. trop. Med. Parasit.* **56**, 14–19.

Godfrey, D. G., Killick-Kendrick, R. and Leach, T. M. (1962). Recent findings on the incidence of bovine trypanosomiasis in Nigeria. *IX int. Sci. Comm. Tryp. Res.*, 111–117.

Gordon, R. M. and Lumsden, W. H. R. (1940). A study of the mouth parts of mosquitoes when taking up blood from living tissue; together with some observations on the ingestion of microfilariae. *Ann. trop. Med. Parasit.* **33**, 259–278.

Gordon, R. M. and Willett, K. C. (1958). Studies on the deposition, migration and development to the blood forms of trypanosomes belonging to the *Trypanosoma brucei* group. III. The development of *Trypanosoma rhodesiense* from the metacyclic forms, as observed in mammalian tissue and in culture. *Ann. trop. Med. Parasit.* **52**, 346–365.

Gordon, R. M., Crewe, W. and Willett, K. C. (1956). Studies on the deposition, migration, and development of trypanosomes belonging to the *Trypanosoma brucei* group. I. An account of the process of feeding adopted by the tsetse fly when obtaining a blood-meal from the mammalian host, with special reference to the ejection of saliva and the relationship of the feeding process to the deposition of the metacyclic trypanosomes. *Ann. trop. Med. Parasit.* **50**, 426–437.

Grant, P. T. and Sargent, J. R. (1960). Properties of L-α-glycerophosphate oxidase and its role in the respiration of *Trypanosoma rhodesiense*. *Biochem. J.* **76**, 229–237.

Grant, P. T. and Sargent, J. R. (1961). L-α-Glycerophosphate dehydrogenase, a component of an oxidase system in *Trypanosoma rhodesiense*. *Biochem. J.* **81**, 206–214.

Grant, P. T., Sargent, J. R. and Ryley, J. F. (1961). Respiratory systems in the Trypanosomidae. *Biochem. J.* **81**, 200–206.

Gray, A. R. (1960). Precipitating antibody in trypanosomiasis of cattle and other animals. *Nature, Lond.* **186**, 1058–1059.

Gray, A. R. (1961). Soluble antigens of *Trypanosoma vivax* and of other trypanosomes. *Immunology* **4**, 253–261.

Gray, A. R. (1962). The influence of antibody on serological variation in *Trypanosoma brucei*. *Ann. trop. Med. Parasit.* **56**, 4–13.

Gray, A. R. (1963). Antigenic variation in a fly-transmitted strain of *Trypanosoma brucei*. *XI int. Sci. Comm. Tryp. Res.*, 361–368.

Haddow, A. J. and Mahaffy, A. F. (1949). Mosquitoes of Bwamba County, Uganda. Intensive catching on tree platforms with further observations of *Aedes* (*Stegomyia*) *africanus* Theobald. *Bull. ent. Res.* **40**, 169.

Harker, K. W., Taylor, J. I. and Rollinson, D. H. L. (1954). Studies on the habits of Zebu cattle. I. Preliminary observations on grazing habits. *J. Agric. Sci.* **44**, 193–198.

Harker, K. W., Taylor, J. I. and Rollinson, D. H. L. (1956). Studies on the habits of Zebu cattle. V. Night paddocking and its effect on the animal. *J. Agric. Sci.* **47**, 44–49.

Harker, K. W., Rollinson, D. H. L., Taylor, J. I., Gourlay, R. N. and Nunn, W. R. (1961). Studies on the habits of Zebu cattle. VI. The results on different pastures. *J. Agric. Sci.* **56**, 137–141.

Heisch, R. B., McMahon, J. P. and Manson-Bahr, P. E. C. (1958). The isolation of *Trypanosoma rhodesiense* from a bushbuck. *Brit. med. J.* **2**, 1203–1204.

Hoare, C. A. (1956a). Morphological and taxonomic studies on the mammalian trypanosomes. VIII. Revision of *Trypanosoma evansi*. *Parasitology* **46**, 130–172.

Hoare, C. A. (1956b). Revision de la classification des trypanosomes pathogènes Africains. *VI int. Sci. Comm. Tryp. Res.*, 67–80.

Hoare, C. A. (1957). The classification of the trypanosomes of veterinary and medical importance. *Vet. Rev. Annot.* **3**, 1–13.

Hoare, C. A. (1959). Morphological and taxonomic studies on the mammalian trypanosomes. IX. Revision of *Trypanosoma dimorphon*. *Parasitology* **49**, 210–231.

Hoare, C. A. (1964). Morphological and taxonomic studies in mammalian trypanosomes. X. Revision of the systematics. *J. Protozool.* **11**, 200–207.

Isherwood, F. (1957). The resting sites of *Glossina swynnertoni* Aust. in the wet season. *Bull. ent. Res.* **48**, 601–606.

Jewell, G. R. (1956). Marking of tsetse flies for their detection at night. *Nature, Lond.* **178**, 750.

Jewell, G. R. (1958). Detection of tsetse fly at night. *Nature, Lond.* **181**, 1354.

Kenya (1957). Annual Report of the Zoological and Tsetse Section, Department of Veterinary Services. Nairobi.

Knight, R. H. and Southon, H. A. W. (1963). A simple method for marking haematophagous insects during the act of feeding. *Bull. ent. Res.* **54**, 379–382.

Lamprey, H. F., Glasgow, J. P., Lee-Jones, F. and Weitz, B. (1962). A simultaneous census of the potential and actual food sources of the tsetse fly *Glossina swynnertoni* Austen. *J. Anim. Ecol.* **31**, 151–156.

Langridge, W. P. (1960). Scent attractants for tsetse flies. *VIII int. Sci. Comm. Tryp. Res.*, 235–241.

Langridge, W. P., Kernaghan, R. J. and Glover, P. E. (1963). A review of recent knowledge of the ecology of the main vectors of trypanosomiasis. *Bull. Wld Hlth Org.* **28**, 671–701.

Leggate, B. M. (1962). Trypanosome infections in *Glossina morsitans* West. and *G. pallidipes* Aust., under natural conditions. *IX int. Sci. Comm. Tryp. Res.*, 213–227.

Lehmann, D. L. (1960). Some culture differences between *Trypanosoma rhodesiense* and *T. brucei* in autoclaved diphasic media. *Ann. trop. Med. Parasit.* **54**, 419–427.

Lehmann, D. L. (1961). Attempts at the selective cultivation of *Trypanosoma rhodesiense*, *T. brucei* and *T. congolense*. *Ann. trop. Med. Parasit.* **55**, 440–446.

Lehmann, D. L. (1962). Differential effects of osmotic pressure and of suramin upon cultures of *Trypanosoma congolense* and *T. rhodesiense*. *Ann. trop. Med. Parasit.* **56**, 1–3.

Lincicome, D. R. (1958). Growth of *Trypanosoma lewisi* in the heterologous mouse host. *Exp. Parasit.* **7**, 1–13.

Lincicome, D. R. (1959). Observations on changes in *Trypanosoma lewisi* after growth in calorically-restricted and normal mice. *Ann. trop. Med. Parasit.* **53**, 274–287.

Lovemore, D. F. (1958). *Glossina pallidipes* Austen in Southern Rhodesia's northern tsetse belt. *VII int. Sci. Comm. Tryp. Res.*, 235–236.

Lumsden, W. H. R. (1951). The night resting habits of monkeys in a small area on the edge of the Semliki Forest, Uganda. A study in relation to the epidemiology of sylvan yellow fever. *J. Anim. Ecol.* **20**, 11–30.

Lumsden, W. H. R. (1962). Trypanosomiasis in African wildlife. *Proc. I int. Conf. Wildlife Disease*, 66–88.

Lumsden, W. H. R. (1963). Quantitative methods with trypanosomes and their application, with special reference to diagnosis. *Bull. Wld Hlth Org.* **28**, 745–752.

Lumsden, W. H. R. (1964a). Changing patterns of trypanosomiasis research in East Africa. *Trans. R. Soc. trop. Med. Hyg.* **58**, 97–135.

Lumsden, W. H. R. (1964b). The feeding behaviour of haematophagous Diptera in relation to the transmission of trypanosomes and viruses. *Proc. XII int. Congr. Ent.* (In press.)

Lumsden, W. H. R. and Hardy, G. J. C. (1965). Nomenclature of living parasite material. *Nature, Lond.* **205**, 1032.

Lumsden, W. H. R., Cunningham, M. P., Webber, W. A. F., van Hoeve, K. and Walker, P. J. (1963). A method for the measurement of the infectivity of trypanosome suspensions. *Exp. Parasit.* **14**, 269–279.

Lumsden, W. H. R., Cunningham, M. P., Webber, W. A. F., van Hoeve, K., Knight, R. H. and Simmons, V. (1965). Some effects of hydrogen ion concentration on trypanosome numbers and infectivity. *Exp. Parasit.* **16**, 8–17.

McDonald, W. A. (1960). Insecticidal spraying against *Glossina palpalis* in Nigeria, based on a study of its nocturnal resting sites with ultra-violet light. *VIII int. Sci. Comm. Tryp. Res.*, 243–245.

Mattern, P. (1962). L'hyper-β_2-macroglobulinemie et l'hyper-β_2-macroglobulino-rachie, temoins constants de la perturbation proteinique humorale au cours de la trypanosomiase humaine. *IX int. Sci. Comm. Tryp. Res.*, 377.

Morris, K. R. S. (1959). Studies in the epidemiology of sleeping sickness in East Africa. I. A sleeping sickness outbreak in Uganda in 1957. *Trans. R. Soc. trop. Med. Hyg.* **53**, 384–393.

Morris, K. R. S. (1960a). Studies on the epidemiology of sleeping sickness in East Africa. II. Sleeping sickness in Kenya. *Trans. R. Soc. trop. Med. Hyg.* **54**, 71–86.

Morris, K. R. S. (1960b). Studies on the epidemiology of sleeping sickness in East Africa. III. The endemic area of Lakes Edward and George in Uganda. *Trans. R. Soc. trop. Med. Hyg.* **54**, 212–224.

Morris, K. R. S. (1960c). Studies on the epidemiology of sleeping sickness in East Africa. V. Sleeping sickness in the Bunyoro District of Uganda. *Trans. R. Soc. trop. Med. Hyg.* **54**, 585–596.

Morris, K. R. S. (1960d). Trapping as a means of studying the game tsetse, *Glossina pallidipes* Aust. *Bull. ent. Res.* **51**, 533.

Nash, T. A. M. (1958). The effect of different types of man-fly contact upon the distribution of *T. gambiense* sleeping sickness in Nigeria. *VII int. Sci. Comm. Tryp. Res.*, 191–196.

Nash, T. A. M. (1963). Progress and problems in the establishment and maintenance of laboratory colonies of tsetse flies. *Bull. Wld Hlth Org.* **28**, 831–836.

Nash, T. A. M., Page, W. A., Jordan, A. M. and Petana, W. (1958). The rearing of *Glossina palpalis* in the laboratory for experimental work. *VII int. Sci. Comm. Tryp. Res.*, 343–350.

Ormerod, W. E. (1961). The epidemic spread of Rhodesian sleeping sickness, 1908–1960. *Trans. R. Soc. trop. Med. Hyg.* **55**, 525–538.

Ormerod, W. E. (1963). A comparative study of the growth and morphology of strains of *Trypanosoma rhodesiense*. *Exp. Parasit.* **13**, 374–385.

Ormerod, W. E., Healey, P. and Armitage, P. (1963). A method of counting trypanosomes allowing simultaneous study of their morphology. *Exp. Parasit.* **13**, 386–394.

Peel, E. and Chardome, M. (1954). *Trypanosoma suis* Ochmann, 1905, trypanosome monomorphe pathogène de mammiferes, evoluant dans les glandes salivaires de *Glossina brevipalpis* Newst. *Ann. Soc. belge Med. trop.* **34**, 277.

Polge, C. and Soltys, M. A. (1957). Preservation of trypanosomes in the frozen state. *Trans. R. Soc. trop. Med. Hyg.* **51**, 519–526.

Power, R. J. B. (1964). The activity pattern of *Glossina longipennis* Corti (Diptera, Muscidae). *Proc. R. ent. Soc. Lond.* **39**, 5–14.

Rennison, B. D. and Smith, I. M. (1961). Studies of the sampling of *Glossina pallidipes* Aust. IV. Some aspects of the use of Morris traps. *Bull. ent. Res.* **52**, 609–619.

Rennison, B. D., Lumsden, W. H. R. and Webb, C. J. (1958). The use of reflecting paints for locating tsetse fly at night. *Nature, Lond.* **181**, 1354–1355.

Robertson, D. H. H. (1963). Human trypanosomiasis in south-east Uganda. A further study of the epidemiology of the disease among fishermen and peasant cultivators. *Bull. Wld Hlth Org.* **28**, 627–643.

Robertson, D. H. H. and Baker, J. R. (1958). Human trypanosomiasis in south-east Uganda. I. A study of the epidemiology and present virulence of the disease. *Trans. R. Soc. trop. Med. Hyg.* **52**, 337–348.

Rollinson, D. H. L., Harker, K. W. and Taylor, J. I. (1955). Studies on the habits of Zebu cattle. III. Water consumption of Zebu cattle. *J. Agric. Sci.* **46**, 123–129.

Rollinson, D. H. L., Harker, K. W., Taylor, J. I. and Leech, F. B. (1956). Studies on the habits of Zebu cattle. IV. Errors associated with recording technique. *J. Agric. Sci.* **47**, 1–5.

Rosevear, D. R. (1953). "Checklist and Atlas of Nigerian Mammals." Government Printer, Lagos.

Ross, G. R. and Blair, D. M. (1956). Cas de "porteurs en bonne santé" de trypanosomiase humaine en Rhodesie du Sud. *VI int. Sci. Comm. Tryp. Res.*, 9–16.

Ryley, J. F. (1961). Comparative studies on the metabolism of the blood-stream and culture forms of *Trypanosoma rhodesiense*. *Ann. trop. Med. Parasit.* **55**, 149–150.

Saunders, D. R. (1962). Age determination for female tsetse flies and the age compositions of samples of *Glossina pallidipes* Aust., *G. palpalis fuscipes* Newst., and *G. brevipalpis* Newst. *Bull. ent. Res.* **53**, 579–595.

Scott, D. (1960). A recent series of outbreaks of human trypanosomiasis in Northern Ghana (1957–59). *VIII int. Sci. Comm. Tryp. Res.*, 45–64.

Seed, J. R. (1963). The characterization of antigens isolated from *Trypanosoma rhodesiense*. *J. Protozool.* **10**, 380–389.

Smith, I. M. and Rennison, B. D. (1961a). Studies of the sampling of *Glossina pallidipes* Aust. I. The numbers caught daily on cattle, in Morris traps and on a fly-round. *Bull. ent. Res.* **52**, 165–182.

Smith, I. M. and Rennison, B. D. (1961b). Studies of the sampling of *Glossina pallidipes* Aust. II. The daily pattern of flies caught on cattle, in Morris traps and on a fly-round. *Bull. ent. Res.* **52**, 183–189.

Smith, I. M. and Rennison, B. D. (1961c). Studies of the sampling of *Glossina pallidipes* Aust. III. The hunger stages of male flies caught on cattle and in Morris traps. *Bull. ent. Res.* **52**, 601–607.

Soltys, M. A. (1954). Transmission of *T. congolense* by other vectors than tsetse flies. *V int. Sci. Comm. Tryp. Res.*, 137–140.

Soltys, M. A. (1957a). Immunity in trypanosomiasis. I. Neutralization reaction. *Parasitology* **47**, 375–389.

Soltys, M. A. (1957b). Immunity in trypanosomiasis. II. Agglutination reaction with African trypanosomes. *Parasitology* **47**, 390–395.

Southon, H. A. W. (1958). Night observations on *G. swynnertoni* Aust. *VI int. Sci. Comm. Tryp. Res.*, 219–221.

Southon, H. A. W. and Robertson, D. H. H. (1961). Isolation of *T. rhodesiense* from wild *Glossina palpalis*. *Nature, Lond.* **189**, 411–412.

Taliaferro, W. H. (1924). A reaction product in infections with *Trypanosoma lewisi* which inhibits the reproduction of the trypanosomes. *J. exp. Med.* **39**, 171–190.

Taylor, J. I., Rollinson, D. H. L. and Harker, K. W. (1955). Studies on the habits of Zebu cattle. II. Individual and group variation within a herd. *J. Agric. Sci.* **45**, 257–267.

Thillet, C. J. and Chandler, A. C. (1957). Immunization against *Trypanosoma lewisi* in rats by injections of metabolic products. *Science* **125**, 346–347.

Thurston, J. P. (1958). The effect of immune sera on the respiration of *Trypanosoma brucei in vitro*. *Parasitology* **48**, 463–467.

Trager, W. (1959). Tsetse fly tissue culture and the development of trypanosomes to the infective stage. *Ann. trop. Med. Parasit.* **53**, 473–491.

Van Hoof, L., Henrard, C. and Peel, E. (1937). Influences modificatrices de la transmissibilité cyclique du *Trypanosoma gambiense* par *Glossina palpalis*. *Ann. Soc. belge Med. trop.* **17**, 249. (Summary in *Trop. Dis. Bull.* **34**, 926.)

Vickerman, K. (1962). The mechanism of cyclical development in trypanosomes of the *Trypanosoma brucei* subgroup: an hypothesis based on ultrastructural observations. *Trans. R. Soc. trop. Med. Hyg.* **56**, 487–495.

Vickerman, K. (1963). Electron microscopy of parasites. *In* "Techniques in Parasitology." Blackwell Scientific Publications, Oxford.

Weinman, D. and McAllister, J. (1947). Prolonged storage of human pathogenic protozoa with conservation of virulence. *Amer. J. Hyg.* **45**, 102–121.

Weitz, B. G. F. (1960a). A soluble protective antigen of *Trypanosoma brucei*. *Nature, Lond.* **185**, 788–789.

Weitz, B. (1960b). The properties of some antigens of *Trypanosoma brucei*. *J. gen. Microbiol.* **23**, 589–600.

Weitz, B. (1962). Immunity in trypanosomiasis. *In* "Drugs, Parasites and Hosts" (L. G. Goodwin and R. H. Nimmo-Smith, eds.). Churchill, London.

Weitz, B. (1963a). The antigenicity of some African trypanosomes. *In* "Immunity to Protozoa" (P. C. C. Garnham, A. E. Pierce and I. Roitt, eds.). Blackwell Scientific Publications, Oxford.

Weitz, B. (1963b). The specificity of trypanosomal antigens by immunofluorescence. *J. gen. Microbiol.* **32**, 145–149.

Weitz, B. (1963c). Immunological relationships between African trypanosomes and their hosts. *Ann. N.Y. Acad. Sci.* **113**, 400–408.

Weitz, B. (1963d). The feeding habits of *Glossina*. *Bull. Wld Hlth Org.* **28**, 711–729.

Weitz, B. and Glasgow, J. P. (1956). The natural hosts of some species of *Glossina* in East Africa. *Trans. R. Soc. trop. Med. Hyg.* **50**, 593–612.

Wijers, D. J. B. (1958). Factors that may influence the infection rate of *Glossina palpalis* with *Trypanosoma gambiense*. I. The age of the fly at the time of the infected feed. *Ann. trop. Med. Parasit.* **52**, 385–390.

Wijers, D. J. B. (1960). "Studies on the Behaviour of Trypanosomes, belonging to the *brucei* Sub-group, in the Mammalian Host." Rototype/Broos, Amsterdam.

Wijers, D. J. B. and Willett, K. C. (1960). Factors that may influence the infection rate of *Glossina palpalis* with *Trypanosoma gambiense*. II. The number and the morphology of the trypanosomes present in the blood of the host at the time of the infected feed. *Ann. trop. Med. Parasit.* **54**, 341–356.

Willett, K. C. (1956a). Les relations specifiques de *Trypanosoma rhodesiense*. *VI int. Sci. Comm. Tryp. Res.*, 35–50.

Willett, K. C. (1956b). An experiment on dosage in human trypanosomiasis. *Ann. trop. Med. Parasit.* **50**, 75–80.

Willett, K. C. (1961). West African Institute for Trypanosomiasis Research. Annual Report, 1961. Harrison & Sons, London.

Willett, K. C. (1962a). Recent advances in the study of tsetse-borne diseases. In "Biological Transmission of Disease Agents" (K. Maramorosch, ed.). Academic Press, New York.

Willett, K. C. (1962b). A note on the risk of advances by tsetse fly and some of the factors involved. *IX int. Sci. Comm. Tryp. Res.*, 153–156.

Willett, K. C. and Gordon, R. M. (1957). Studies on the deposition, migration, and development to the blood forms of trypanosomes belonging to the *Trypanosoma brucei* group. II. An account of the migration of the trypanosomes from the site of their deposition in the rodent host to their appearance in the general circulation, with some observations on their probable routes of migration in the human host. *Ann. trop. Med. Parasit.* **51**, 471–492.

Williamson, J. (1962). Chemotherapy and chemoprophylaxis of African trypanosomiasis. *Exp. Parasit.* **12**, 274–367.

Williamson, J. (1963). The chemical composition of trypanosomes. *Proc. XVI int. Congr. Zool.* **4**, 189–195.

Williamson, J. and Brown, K. N. (1964). The chemical composition of trypanosomes. III. Antigenic constituents of *Brucei* trypanosomes. *Exp. Parasit.* **15**, 44–68.

Williamson, J. and Desowitz, R. S. (1961). The chemical composition of trypanosomes. I. Protein, amino-acid and sugar analysis. *Exp. Parasit.* **11**, 161–175.

Yaeger, R. G. and Miller, O. N. (1960a). Effect of malnutrition on susceptibility of rats to *Trypanosoma cruzi*. I. Thiamine deficiency. *Exp. Parasit.* **9**, 215–222.

Yaeger, R. G. and Miller, O. N. (1960b). Effect of malnutrition on susceptibility of rats to *Trypanosoma cruzi*. II. Riboflavin deficiency. *Exp. Parasit.* **10**, 227–231.

Yaeger, R. G. and Miller, O. N. (1960c). Effect of malnutrition on susceptibility of rats to *Trypanosoma cruzi*. III. Pantothenate deficiency. *Exp. Parasit.* **10**, 232–237.

Yaeger, R. G. and Miller, O. N. (1960d). Effect of malnutrition on susceptibility of rats to *Trypanosoma cruzi*. IV. Pyroxidine deficiency. *Exp. Parasit.* **10**, 238–244.

Yarmolinsky, M. B. and Haba, G. L. (1959). Inhibition by puromycin of amino-acid incorporation into protein. *Proc. nat. Acad. Sci.*, *Wash.* **45**, 1721–1729.

Yvoré, P. (1962). Quelques observations sur l'ecologie de deux glossines du groupe *fusca* en Republique Centrafricaine. *IX int. Sci. Comm. Tryp. Res.*, 197–204.

Relationships between the Species of *Fasciola* and their Molluscan Hosts

Central Veterinary Laboratory, Ministry of Agriculture, Fisheries and Food, New Haw, Weybridge, England

I. The Species of *Fasciola*.. 59
   A. Valid and Doubtful Species... 60
   B. Physiological Races of Flukes...................................... 62
II. The Life History of the Liver Fluke....................................... 63
   A. Development of Eggs 64
   B. Penetration of the Miracidium into the Snail...................... 65
   C. Normal Development in the Snail................................... 68
   D. Larval Development of *F. hepatica*............................... 68
   E. Larval Development of *F. gigantica*.............................. 70
III. The Snail Hosts... 71
IV. Host Specificity... 77
   A. Physiological Races of Flukes and Snails.......................... 77
   B. Variations of Host Specificity under Special Circumstances........ 78
V. Factors Affecting the Development of the Parasite within the Snail........ 79
   A. Temperature and Rate of Development............................... 79
   B. Temperature Variation and the Formation of Daughter Rediae and Cercariae... 81
   C. The Effect on the Parasite of Changes in the Nutrition of the Host. 82
   D. Aestivation of the Host and its Effect on the Parasite 84
VI. Host Resistance... 85
   A. Barriers to Initial Infection..................................... 85
   B. Barriers to Further Development................................... 85
   C. Resistance to Repeated Infection.................................. 86
VII. The Pathogenicity of Infection in Snails............................... 87
   A. Resolution of Tissue Damage and Loss of Infection................. 88
VIII. Factors influencing the Emergence and Survival of Cercariae........... 89
   A. The Survival of Metacercariae..................................... 91
IX. The Epidemiology of Infection with *Fasciola*........................... 94
   References 95

I. The Species of *Fasciola*

Species of *Fasciola* are characterized by broad flat bodies, relatively small, closely approximated suckers, the ventral larger than the oral, and the possession of a conical process at the tip of which the mouth is situated. The internal organs are complicated by branching and in particular the caeca are long and have numerous lateral diverticula with a number of branches. The eggs are large and thin shelled. The mature flukes are found characteristically in the bile-ducts and gall-bladders of herbivorous and omnivorous vertebrates—especially ungulates. At earlier stages of development they may be found (temporarily) in the peritoneal cavity and during the following period of development in the substance of the liver. Under some circumstances they may be found in other parts of the body, especially the lungs.

A. VALID AND DOUBTFUL SPECIES

Two species, *Fasciola hepatica* and *F. gigantica*, are generally recognized, the former being found predominantly in temperate parts of the world, the latter in the tropics. Dawes (1956) describes *F. hepatica* as being 18–51 mm

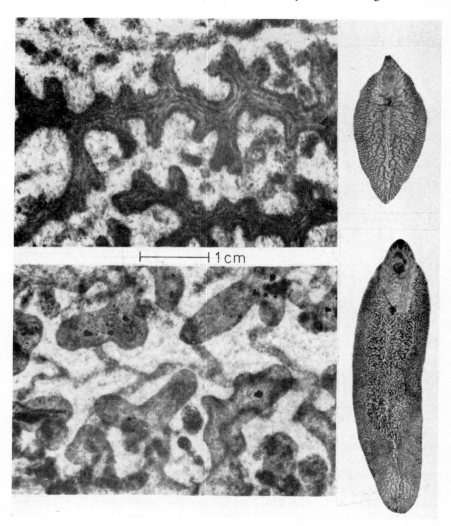

FIG. 1. Adult *Fasciola hepatica* (above) and *Fasciola gigantica* (below) and portions of their caeca.

long with the greatest breadth (near the mid-body) 4–13 mm. *F. gigantica* is decidedly longer—25–75 mm long by 3–12 mm broad (Fig. 1).

There is, in fact, enormous variation in size depending on such factors as the age of the fluke, the species of host in which it is found, the weight of infection (massive infection tends to result in smaller flukes) and, in preserved material, the way in which the fluke has been fixed. Fixation can have a profound effect not only on the absolute size of the fluke but also on the relative sizes of the various parts of the body which are used in identification. Measurement of the fluke in warm isotonic saline immediately after removal from the body is probably the only really satisfactory method.

Certain other morphological characters serve to differentiate the two species of *Fasciola*. In *F. gigantica* the sides of the body are parallel, the shoulders less well developed and the cephalic cone is relatively shorter than in *F. hepatica*. A reliable diagnostic character, moreover, is the degree of branching of the caeca. As figured by Bhalerao (1935), there are many more branches to the caeca of *F. gigantica*, particularly internally (Fig. 1).

There have been several attempts to create new species of *Fasciola* from material originally classified as *F. hepatica* or *F. gigantica*. Thus Sinitsin (1933) suggested the separation of two new species of American liver flukes, *Fasciola californica* and *F. halli*, which he differentiated from *F. hepatica* on the basis of such characters as the distribution of the cuticular spines, the number of generations of sporocysts, the size of the rediae and the diameter of the metacercariae. He suggested also that the eggs of *F. halli* were provided with a subterminal scar whereas those of *F. californica* were not.

In a review of American flukes, Price (1953) referred to Sinitsin's work and indicated that there were in fact morphological differences between liver flukes found in America and that these differences might or might not be significant. Price mentioned that Brahmin cattle had been imported into North America and that these might have been infected with *F. gigantica*. He suggested that hybridization between these flukes and *F. hepatica* might account for the occurrence of flukes of intermediate morphological character. There seems to be no evidence of such an occurrence and Price himself agreed that the different morphological types might be merely variants on a single species.

In 1953 Varma separated the proposed new species *Fasciola indica* from *F. gigantica* Cobbold, 1855 on the basis of apparent differences in morphology between fixed material from Africa and from Asia, and after the examination of small samples of fluke eggs. In accordance with Varma's opinion that the common liver fluke in India is not *F. gigantica*, Thapar and Tandon (1953) proposed that *F. indica* Varma 1953 should replace *F. gigantica*, but they did not contribute any new evidence in favour of the separation. Varma's (1953) work was challenged by Sarwar (1957) who considered that flukes from Asia and from Africa were taxonomically identical. Kendall and Parfitt (1959) mentioned that they were unable to distinguish between flukes which they had obtained from Pakistan and from Africa and the eggs were examined with the same result (Fig. 2).

The results of these observations do not, of course, preclude the possibility that morphological differences may on occasion be found between flukes of *F. gigantica* type from different areas.

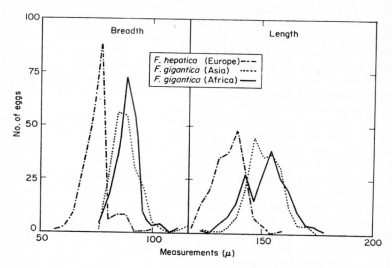

FIG. 2. Graphs showing comparative sizes of eggs of *Fasciola hepatica* in Great Britain and *F. gigantica* in Asia and Africa. (From Kendall and Parfitt, 1959.)

In 1958 Watanabe suggested that in Japan flukes could be divided into those similar to *F. hepatica* and those similar to *F. gigantica* but that an intermediate type existed. Similarly, Ueno and Watanabe (1960) apparently observed a difference in the size of metacercariae from English *F. hepatica* and those from a morphologically similar fluke in Japan. These authors, however, refrained from commenting on the validity of the identification of the Japanese fluke as *F. hepatica*, confining their comments to the differences in host–parasite relationships. Itagaki and Akane (1959), after a comparison of African and Japanese flukes, found considerable variation between individual specimens but no consistent differences between material from Africa on the one hand and from Japan on the other.

It therefore does not appear that there is indisputable evidence of the existence of more than two species of *Fasciola*, and *F. hepatica* and *F. gigantica* are probably the only two valid species. Morphological differences which have been described seem more likely to be attributable to differences in fixation and mounting of the material, normal biological variation within a species or even (*vide* Haiba and Selim, 1960) to the use of material from different hosts.

B. PHYSIOLOGICAL RACES OF FLUKES

Nevertheless, as will be discussed later, there is good evidence for the existence of physiological races of flukes, these being separable on the basis of variations in the susceptibility to infection of different snail hosts. In some instances these differences are so marked that it would seem inevitable that there are associated differences in morphology.

II. The Life History of the Liver Fluke

Species of *Fasciola* have a very wide range of possible definitive hosts (Dawes, 1956) but in practice they are usually maintained by ungulates and, in the case of *F. hepatica*, by rabbits. Sheep are very efficient hosts of *F. hepatica* and the water buffalo is perhaps the best host for *F. gigantica*. Other mammals may serve in special situations. Thus, quite recently, the coypu (*Myocaster coypus*) has been recognized in Britain not only as a new introduction to the feral fauna but also as a host of *F. hepatica* in certain areas where the fluke had previously been considered to be relatively uncommon, probably because the habitats of domestic animals and the intermediate host did not coincide. The coypu may, however, prove to be too susceptible to the pathogenic effects of infection to be a really satisfactory host.

The efficacy of the mammalian host is the resultant of a number of factors of which the grazing habit is one and the susceptibility to infection is another. Small mammals often die but some larger hosts may develop cirrhotic livers and allow very few fertile fluke eggs to escape on to the pasture.

The snails which serve as intermediate hosts of *Fasciola* include some which are essentially amphibious (e.g. *Lymnaea truncatula*) and others which are more aquatic, e.g. *Lymnaea natalensis*. The fact that all occupy watery habitats helps to ensure at least occasional contiguity with the herbivores which are the definitive hosts of the flukes. With *F. hepatica*, the intermediate hosts of which are usually amphibious snails, infection may sometimes occur when an animal drinks at a shallow pool in the habitat, but it is more likely to be effected when the grazing animal eats the succulent herbage at the water's edge or in the moist bottoms of neglected ditches.

With *F. gigantica*, which has an aquatic snail host, Kendall (1953) has described how, in the Manchar Lake area of Sind Province in Pakistan, sheep are normally taken for winter grazing to the Kalat hills where no liver fluke occurs but are returned to the lakeside grazing as the waters recede during the spring. Here fascioliasis is contracted annually as the animals graze on previously inundated herbage on which metacercariae have encysted. If drought occurs in the hills and there is no winter grazing available stock is forced down to the lakeside very early in the year and may be seen to be eating vegetation actually in the water. Under these circumstances very heavy infection is likely to be contracted. This is but one example of the exceedingly important part that water plays in the life cycle of the parasite. Fluke eggs require moist conditions for survival. The miracidia needs free water in which to swim whilst finding a suitable snail; the cercariae similarly need at least a film of water in which to move before encystment and the metacercariae must have protection from desiccation until they are ingested by the final host.

Warmth and conditions of good aeration also are highly important for most developmental stages of the fluke. The outstanding need for moisture will become evident as details of the life history are more closely considered.

A. DEVELOPMENT OF EGGS

Factors influencing the development and hatching of fluke eggs have been studied by several workers although most reports refer to *F. hepatica*. As long ago as 1883 Thomas noted that the eggs of *F. hepatica* did not develop until they had left the host, that hatching occurred in 2–3 weeks when temperatures were most favourable (23–26° C), and that water temperatures in Great Britain in winter were too low for development to occur.

The literature on the bionomics of the eggs of *F. hepatica* has been summarized by Roberts (1950) who added some records of her own, and more recently by Rowcliffe and Ollerenshaw (1960) who carried out an extensive series of observations.

1. *The Effect of Temperature*

Development of the eggs of *F. hepatica* is inhibited at about 9·5° C and above 30° C. If eggs are incubated in the laboratory at 37° C and samples periodically transferred to 25° C, the time taken to hatch varies directly with the time which the eggs have spent at 37° C (Rowcliffe and Ollerenshaw, 1960). The rate of mortality, also, increases the longer the egg remains at 37° C until all die after 24 days at that temperature.

Several workers have noted that eggs cultured under apparently identical conditions do not hatch simultaneously. Thomas (1883), for example, noted a great variation in the speed at which individual eggs developed. Rowcliffe and Ollerenshaw (1960) suggest that the diversity in hatching times and the variability in the rate of mortality may be explained in part, at least, by the fact that eggs had remained for varying periods of time in the body of the mammalian host.

Within a range of temperature of about 10–30° C the rate of development increases with the temperature. Rowcliffe and Ollerenshaw (1960) had difficulty in elucidating the precise value of the critical temperature below which no development at all occurred but concluded that it was about 9·5° C. On this assumption they calculated the total number of day degrees required by the fluke egg for development at temperatures between 10° and 30° C. The data obtained indicate a variation with temperature but suggest that the thermal constant for the optimum temperature range probably lies between 200 and 220—the total number of day degrees required for eggs incubated at 18° and 23° C respectively.

In summary it can be said that the eggs of *F. hepatica* take about 12 days to hatch at 26° C, about 40 days at 15° C and 60 days or more below 12° C. Under field conditions in Britain they are unlikely to hatch in less than 3 weeks (Rowcliffe and Ollerenshaw, 1960). With *F. gigantica*, Alicata (1938) reported that the eggs required 13 days to complete development and to hatch at 78–82° F (26–29° C approx.). Dinnik and Dinnik (1963) found that miracidia hatched in 17 days at a constant temperature of 26° C.

2. *The Effect of Moisture*

By pipetting single drops of water containing a few fluke eggs on to glass slides and placing them in desiccators at varying humidities it was found (Rowcliffe and Ollerenshaw, 1960) that, regardless of temperature, the eggs were killed when the surface film of moisture evaporated. Complete immersion in water was, however, not necessary. Roberts (1950) showed that drying was lethal equally to eggs freshly dissected from flukes and to those which had been incubated at 25° C for 14 days.

3. *Development of Eggs in the Presence of Faeces*

When it first leaves the host the fluke egg is surrounded by faeces and it may remain in this condition for a considerable time. Rowcliffe and Ollerenshaw (1960) investigated the effect on fluke eggs of variation of temperature and of desiccation in the presence of faeces. It was shown that although some development could be noted at high constant temperatures and under favourable moisture conditions in the laboratory this was exceptional. The eggs remained viable in the faeces for up to several months, depending on the time of year, but for normal development to take place they required to be separated from the faeces. On no occasion did any eggs hatch in the presence of faeces.

In concentrated faecal suspensions also, no development took place. Eggs in cultures without faeces showed little variation in mortality at different oxygen tensions but those in aerobic conditions hatched in one-fifth of the time taken by those at a lower oxygen tension.

4. *Hatching of the Eggs*

Separation of the eggs from faeces, the provision of a temperature adequate for development and the continued existence of a surface film of moisture round the egg permit satisfactory miracidial development to maturity.

As suggested by Roberts (1950) it has been common laboratory practice to induce mass hatching of the miracidia of *F. hepatica* by placing eggs which have been incubated to the point of hatching in a strong light. Roberts confirmed that eggs which had been incubated for 14 days in the dark hatched only on exposure to light and not when chilled or stirred vigorously. An attempt was made to see whether any particular wavelength in the spectrum was the essential part of the stimulus. It appeared that hatching did not occur when violet and blue light was excluded but that when the appropriate filters were removed hatching occurred in 1–3 min. It seems that the violet and blue wavelengths of the spectrum are an essential part of the light stimulus.

The actual mechanics of hatching have been reported by Rowan (1956) who investigated the process in considerable detail. He came to the conclusion that exposure to light stimulates the miracidium to release an enzyme that digests the substance binding the operculum to the shell, thus permitting the egg to open. Experiments demonstrated that the escape of the miracidium from the opened egg was due primarily to the hypertonicity of the egg contents and only secondarily to the muscular activity of the miracidium.

B. PENETRATION OF THE MIRACIDIUM INTO THE SNAIL

Dawes (1959, 1960a) investigated the penetration of *F. hepatica* into *L. truncatula* and suggested that although Faust (1955) had given a comparatively accurate description of the process, some other authors had introduced misconceptions. In particular Dawes suggested that the process of penetration is not one of mechanical boring, the initial attempts of the miracidium to attach itself having given this erroneous impression. The initial attachment, which is usually very light, is probably by the suctorial action of the anterior papilla, mucus assisting the adhesion. According to Mattes (1949), anterior and posterior "Klebdrüsen" are concerned with adhesion but Dawes was unable to find evidence of the existence of these glands. Once attachment is established, retraction of the papilla probably creates a saucer-like space between the anterior non-ciliated pit for the reception of secretions from the gut and the unicellular pharyngeal glands. A perforation in the integument of the snail is created by the loosening, cytolysis and abstraction of epithelial cells, the action appearing to be chemical rather than mechanical. Not until marked cytolytic effects have been produced in the epithelium of the snail does the anterior papilla of the miracidium penetrate into this layer (Fig. 3, A, B).

In Dawes' experience complete penetration of the larva into the snail takes only about 30 min from the time of adhesion. During this period the larva is a sac-like object which occasionally contracts and relaxes but which does not rotate. As the larva presses into the cytolysing mass of epithelial cells, some become heaped externally at the margin of the opening. At the same time larval epithelial cells are becoming detached. Cytolysis is particularly evident when attachment is to the mantle which has a shallow epithelium. The papilla now becomes attached to the subepithelial layers of the snail and damage to this tissue soon becomes evident. As the larva draws its anterior end further into the cytolysing host cells it presses aside the damaged epithelium forming the opening, which is thus enlarged. The larva then contracts momentarily inside a kind of sac formed partly of cytolysing cells and partly of its own discarded epithelium, together with some mucus (Fig. 3F). A final swift thrust takes the extending larva into the body of the snail (Fig. 3G). As the larva completes its entry the damaged cells at the rim of the opening are drawn inwardly, partially sealing the opening (Fig. 3H).

Dawes (1959, 1960a) indicated that, although the larva which enters the snail retains eyes, gut and other organs and the germinal cells of a miracidium, it has lost its cilia and is in fact a young sporocyst covered by what was formerly subepithelial tissue.

Dawes (1960b, c) later showed that the penetration of the miracidium of *F. gigantica* into its snail host was a closely analogous procedure. Ingress, as with the miracidium of *F. hepatica*, is achieved by suctorial adhesion, followed by cytolysis of the integument of the snail. The larva which actually enters the snail is a globular young mother sporocyst, not a miracidium. Dawes (1960b) further indicated that the details of the process of penetration vary somewhat according to which part of the snail is selected for entry. Larvae which penetrate the shallow epithelium of the mantle cause much damage to the underlying connective tissue and the epithelium is decidedly undercut. In heavy infections large areas of mantle may, in consequence, be denuded of epithelium. Larvae which penetrate the columnar epithelium of the body or foot cause less extensive damage.

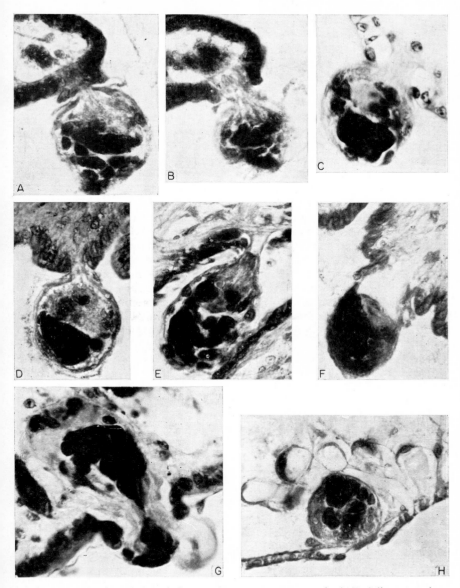

Fig. 3. Penetration of *Fasciola hepatica* into *Lymnaea truncatula*. A, B, Adjacent sections showing attached miracidium and early cytolysis of snail's epithelium; C, extensive damage to mantle epithelium during penetration; D, E, attachment of miracidium to sub-epithelial tissues of snail; F, contracted sporocyst about to enter into snail; G, partially entered sporocyst and compensatory emergence of droplet of liquefied tissue at moment of entry; H, entered mother sporocyst, showing delicate nature of surface, as seen also in G. (From Dawes, 1959.)

C. NORMAL DEVELOPMENT IN THE SNAIL

There is some difference of opinion as to whether the sporocyst can develop successfully in different parts of the body of the snail. With *F. hepatica* initial attachment of the miracidium and the beginnings of penetration can certainly be observed on most if not all the exposed parts of the snail. Roberts (1950) saw a few miracidia swim in through the pulmonary aperture and surmised that they may have invaded the tissues; some became attached to the upper surface of the foot, but with few exceptions they ultimately became re-attached round the base of the tentacles and along the dorsal fold of the mantle. Roberts reported that when each of ten snails was exposed to fifty miracidia the larvae became attached all over the surface of the foot and mantle. Sections cut later indicated that all those that entered the foot degenerated.

There are probably predilection sites for the development of sporocysts within the snail but, from the observed fact that a high proportion of snails exposed to a single miracidium can become infected, it must be assumed that the young sporocyst has the ability either to develop in a variety of sites and/or to seek out predilection sites within the tissues of the host. Thomas (1883) was strongly of the opinion that development ordinarily occurred in the wall of the pulmonary chamber although he did observe a fully developed sporo-cyst in the foot. Cameron (1934) indicated that the commonest sites were the pulmonary chamber and near the oesophagus. Shirai (1925) also mentioned the tissue round the oesophagus. Our observations at Weybridge tend to confirm that most young sporocysts are found in the wall of the mantle cavity lying among the characteristic strap-shaped cells of that organ, where several parasites may often be found close together. The possible movements of the developing mother sporocysts of *F. hepatica* or *F. gigantica* through the tissues of snail hosts constitute a problem which has never been thorough-ly studied and discussed, and it is evident that further investigation is required before firm opinions can be formulated.

D. LARVAL DEVELOPMENT OF *F. hepatica*

In his classic paper of 1883 Thomas gave an account of the subsequent development of *F. hepatica* in *L. truncatula*; an account which has been sub-stantially confirmed by subsequent authors. Thomas describes how the young sporocysts within the snail tend to take on an elliptical shape. The eye-spots of the embryo become detached from one another and lose their crescentic form, but they persist for a considerable time and (in our experience at Weybridge) prove the easiest means of identifying the young parasite within the tissues of the host. At this time the sporocyst is only about 0·07 mm in length and the rudimentary digestive tract remains. The sporocyst commonly retains an elliptical shape until it reaches a length of 0·15 mm after which it tends to become sac-shaped. According to Thomas, the contents of the sporocyst comprise a number of clear rounded cells, some of which are the germinal cells of the embryo or cells derived from them by division. Other cells are formed by a proliferation of the epithelium lining the cavity of the sporocyst. Cells of various sizes with very large nuclei may be seen projecting here and there from the inner surface of the wall of the sporocyst, sometimes in a single layer but otherwise in rounded heaps two or three cells deep. By the time the sporocyst is about 0·2 mm in length there are clear indications of the formation of germinal balls from which rediae will develop.

The sporocyst ultimately reaches a length of about 0·5–0·7 mm. On the outer surface is a structureless cuticle and beneath is the thin layer in which the external circular and internal longitudinal muscle layers are often the only structural elements which can be distinctly observed. Beneath the cuticle there is sometimes a finely granular layer in which the muscle fibres seem to be embedded. The muscle fibres are poorly developed in the sporocyst, as might be deduced from its apparently limited powers of movement. Next to the layer of muscle fibres is an epithelium which lines the cavity of the sporocyst and which forms the greater part of the thickness of the wall. In most places this layer is only one cell thick although it may be thicker, particularly in the less mature sporocyst. The excretory system is lodged in the wall of the sporocyst. Thomas claimed to have seen transverse division of the sporocyst of *F. hepatica* and at Weybridge there has been some evidence that it may occur, although it is difficult to be sure that the apparent segmentation is not traumatic and associated with pressure on the tissues during their isolation and examination.

Normal multiplication is undoubtedly by the production of rediae. The germinal cells which give rise to these are in part already present in the earliest sporocyst but increase as a result of the proliferation of the cells lining the sporocyst (Thomas, 1883). The germinal cells begin to develop into rounded masses or solid morulae. One side of the morula then becomes flattened and the cells appear to become invaginated to form a gastrula. At one end a number of cells separate to form a spherical pharynx leading into the blind digestive tract. A little behind the pharynx, the body shows a slightly raised annular ridge, whilst more posteriorly two short blunt processes are formed. Several rediae, in different stages of development, will often be found in a single sporocyst.

Rediae usually leave the sporocyst when they have reached a length of about 0·26 mm, by rupturing the wall. They then migrate towards the digestive gland (hepato-pancreas) of the snail, usually following the course of the intestine. The rediae increase in size until they measure up to 2·0 mm in length. At about one-quarter of the distance from the posterior end there are two blunt processes which seem to assist locomotion within the tissues of the host. The redial body wall has a structure similar to that in the sporocyst but the muscle fibres are much more strongly developed. The digestive tract is the characteristic structure of the redia and at once differentiates it from the more simple sporocyst. Mouth, muscular pharynx and blind digestive sac constitute the alimentary system. At the side of the redia, a little behind the collar, there is present a birth-opening through which it is believed the cercariae emerge.

Germinal buds occur posteriorly in the redia and mature successively, the most advanced lying anteriorly. Rediae may produce either daughter rediae

E*

or cercariae, apparently under the stimulus of temperature variation (see below).

As the cercaria develops, the rudiment of the tail is at first short and stumpy, whilst at the anterior end cells separate to form an oral sucker in the centre of which the mouth occurs. In the middle of the ventral surface the ventral sucker develops. With increasing growth the cystogenous glands become more apparent and their increasing opacity can be conveniently used as an index of the degree of maturity of the cercaria.

When the cercaria reaches maturity it leaves the redia, presumably by the birth-pore, and remains for a time showing varying degrees of activity within the limiting membrane of the digestive gland of the snail and the adjacent tissue.

Factors affecting the emergence of the cercariae from the snail and their subsequent survival will be considered in Section VIII, p. 89.

E. LARVAL DEVELOPMENT OF *F. gigantica*

The development of *F. gigantica* in its snail hosts has been studied by Alicata (1938) and Dinnik and Dinnik (1956, 1963). Alicata's account concerns development in *Fossaria ollula* (*Lymnaea oahuensis*) in Hawaii at temperatures which ranged from 70° to 80° F (21·5–27° C approx.). Eggs from the gall-bladders of infected cattle were washed and kept in tap water until hatching occurred, the resulting miracidia being allowed to infect laboratory reared snails. Dissection 1 day after experimental infection showed the presence of several early sporocysts, spherical in shape and about 80 μ in diameter. Two days after infection the sporocysts were slightly elongated, about 270 μ long and 410 μ wide, the eye-spots still being apparent. A sporocyst 4 days old was 610 μ long by 190 μ wide and enclosed developing mother rediae each with a well-formed pharynx. Some free rediae were noted as early as 5 days after infection and at 14 days might measure 2 050 μ × 250 μ. The formation of daughter rediae seemed to be characteristic. Snails dissected 31 days after experimental infection contained rediae with well-developed and motile cercariae. These first emerged from snails kept in tap water at 76–80° F 39 days after infection.

In Kenya, Dinnik and Dinnik (1956, 1963) carried out a series of observations on the larval development of *F. gigantica* in *L. natalensis*, including some at a constant temperature of 26° C. Their 1956 paper should be consulted for morphological details of the stages of development of the fluke in the snail. After casting off its ciliated coat and penetrating the snail the miracidium had been transformed into a sporocyst containing up to six germinal balls. Most sporocysts were localized in the tissues surrounding the respiratory cavity, the pre-oesophageal region and in the mantle of the snail (Dinnik and Dinnik, 1956). For the first 2 days in the snail the young sporocyst retained the size, the elongated conical shape and the head papilla of the miracidium from which it had originated. The gut and glands of the miracidium disintegrated during its penetration into the snail and were not seen in the young sporocyst. The eye-spots became detached from one another, lost their definite crescentic shape and their remains, in the form of two granular groups of pigment, were seen floating in the body of the sporocyst.

The largest of the germinal balls in the sporocyst developed into the first redia which ruptured the wall and escaped from the sporocyst. The remaining embryos continued their development to rediae, either in the ruptured body of the sporocyst or lying outside it in the surrounding tissue of the snail and appeared as first generation rediae 6–8 days after initial infection of the snail. Not more than six first-generation rediae (mother rediae) developed from each sporocyst (Dinnik and Dinnik, 1956).

The rediae began to feed on the tissue of the snail as soon as they left the sporocyst and their intestines became filled with tissue debris, yellowish in colour, which had been crushed by the muscular pharynx and swallowed. The rediae started to migrate towards the digestive gland of the snail, feeding on tissue and growing in size (Dinnik and Dinnik, 1956). On the 20th–22nd day daughter rediae developed in the rediae and from the 22nd day onwards these daughter rediae began to leave the mother rediae, to penetrate the digestive gland and feed on the tissue. It was considered that successive generations of rediae developed. After producing daughter rediae and 26 days after infection the mother rediae began to produce cercariae, the first of these escaping from the rediae by way of the birth pore on the 30th – 33rd day, and the snails began emitting cercariae 36–40 days after infection.

III. THE SNAIL HOSTS

Species of *Fasciola* are catholic in their requirements as regards a definitive host and examination of the world literature might suggest that they can be transmitted by almost as wide a range of snails. Thus, in North America Price (1953) recorded *Galba* (*Fossaria*) *bulimoides*, *G. techella*, *Lymnaea traskii*, *Fossaria cubensis*, *F. ferruginea*, *F. modicella* and *Pseudosuccinea columella* as possible hosts. Brumpt (1949) gave a list of no fewer than nineteen species of snails believed to act as field hosts of *F. hepatica* alone, in addition to a further nine species which had proved susceptible under laboratory conditions.

A detailed consideration of the various records of snail hosts throughout the world would be unprofitable. In some instances there is no doubt that the record rests on misidentification, even of the snail genus. It seems certain that the vectors of *Fasciola* are limited to species of *Lymnaea*. The transmission of the fluke seems to depend on a limited number of snail species and usually in each area only one species is involved. Further consideration of the identity of the vectors may be obscured by the remaining doubts about the number of species of *Fasciola* that can be defined, but is rendered extremely difficult primarily by the systematics of the Lymnaeidae.

In the Lymnaeidae the vast number of species, subspecies and varieties which have been described and the gliding transitions between them make identification, at a level useful to the parasitologist, almost impossible. Within the genus *Lymnaea* classification has been mainly on the basis of shell structure—which is notoriously variable according to, for example, the habitat of the snail. In his outstandingly important monograph of 1951 Hubendick gave a critical review of the recent Lymnaeidae taking into account the biological as well as the morphological characters of the species. As well as shell morphology, Hubendick considered the structure of the radula, the genitalia and some other soft structures.

More recently Wright *et al.* (1957) have attempted species differentiation among molluscs using paper chromatography for the analysis of tissues. None of this work, however, seems to be of great assistance at the level of speciation at which host specificity may be evident. After a survey of both species of *Fasciola* and their vectors in Pakistan and a consideration of the world literature, Kendall (1954) used Hubendick's 1951 classification to suggest that throughout the world a re-examination of the systematics of the

FIG. 4. A slender form of *Lymnaea auricularia*, snail host of *Fasciola gigantica* in Pakistan. Aperture of shell high and narrow, spire merging gradually into body whorl. (From Kendall, 1954.)

vectors would indicate that *F. hepatica* is, throughout the greater part of its range, transmitted by *L. truncatula* or by snails not readily distinguishable from it on grounds of morphology or of their ecological requirements. *L. truncatula* itself has a very wide range throughout Europe and north Asia, and in some other places, such as Kenya, where *F. hepatica* occurs the snail host (*Lymnaea mweruensis*) is almost certainly conspecific and may even be a recently introduced *L. truncatula* from Europe. In North America *Lymnaea bulmoides techella* and in Australia *Lymnaea tomentosa* have more evident morphological differences from *L. truncatula* but have many characters in common.

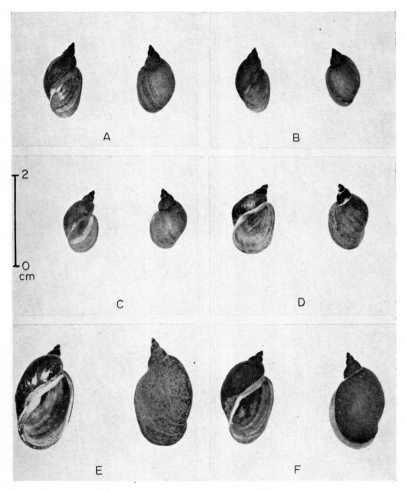

FIG. 5. Species of *Lymnaea* which serve as hosts of *Fasciola gigantica*. A, B, *L. natalensis* from East and West Africa respectively. C–F, species of snails originating from Pakistan. (From Kendall and Parfitt, 1959.)

FIG. 6. Water buffalo in dry season Typha reed bed, habitat of the snail host of *Fasciola gigantica* at Amangar, near Peshawar, Pakistan.

In respect of *F. gigantica*, all snail hosts seem to belong to Hubendick's (1951) superspecies *Lymnaea auricularia*. The fluke is transmitted throughout the Indian subcontinent by the race *rufescens* in several variants. In Malaya the host has been identified as the closely related *rubiginosa*. In Africa the recognized host of *F. gigantica* in both south and west is *L. natalensis* while in East Africa it is transmitted by *L. caillaudi*. *L. caillaudi* is now regarded as a synonym for *L. natalensis* which in turn is not specifically distinguishable from *L. auricularia rufescens* with which it merges in the regions of Oman and Lower Mesopotamia (Hubendick, 1951) (Figs. 4 and 5).

The snail hosts of *F. hepatica* and *F. gigantica* respectively seem to be quite distinct. Snails normally receptive to *F. hepatica* are resistant to *F. gigantica* and vice versa.

A demarcation between the two groups of snails can be made on morphological grounds. The distinction seems to be even more apparent when the ecology of the snails is considered. In Pakistan, for example, the two species of fluke were clearly separated by the ecological demarcation of their respective snail hosts, *F. hepatica* with *L. truncatula*, not occurring below 4 000 ft.

Snail hosts of *F. gigantica* are true aquatics, being restricted in range by the fact that they nearly always live in bodies of water which are permanent throughout the year and which contain abundant vegetation (Figs. 6 and 7,B). Perhaps the most important single factor controlling their distribution is the degree of oxygenation of the water. Clear fresh water seems to be essential and it is usual to find a close association with aquatic water plants such as *Elodea*. Kendall (1954) mentioned that this was particularly evident in the more restricted habitats, such as the smaller "tanks" in East Bengal, where the close association of the species with an abundant aquatic vegetation may have arisen from the snail's need for a high oxygen content in the water. Still or slightly moving water seemed to provide the most favoured habitat for the snail but it was found also in moving water, particularly where the flow was checked by reed beds (Kendall, 1954). A very favoured site was the source of small springs rising from the ground in seepage areas from the great canals in Pakistan, e.g. the Pahawal canal area in the Dera Ismail Khan district of the North-West Frontier Province. The snail was found also in large still-water lakes where the conditions, as pointed out by Boycott (1936), simulate a running-water habitat. The large volume of "free" water promotes cleanliness and dilutes the products of metabolic activity and decay.

L. truncatula, by contrast, in Pakistan occupied habitats similar to those described in Europe (Kendall, 1954). It is an amphibious snail, living on wet mud at the side of shallow water, rarely in water with a pronounced flow, and, unlike *L. auricularia rufescens*, never in deep permanent water. Typically it inhabits "temporary" water (Fig. 7,A), feeds for preference on the algal flora of denuded and recently inundated land and can aestivate, as shown by Kendall (1949b), for as long as a year. There is considerable evidence that short periods of aestivation are part of the normal life cycle. In those areas of the world where the snail host of *F. hepatica* is described as other than *L. truncatula* the ecology seems the same. So, in Australia, *L. tomentosa* has a wide distribution, a capacity for fast reproduction, one generation completes

FIG. 7. A, Muddy gateway, habitat of *Lymnaea truncatula* in Great Britain; B, perennial water in habitat of snail hosts of *Fasciola gigantica* at Amangar.

its development in 1 month and snails survive for almost 1 year in dry mud (Boray, 1963).

In a preface to a study of the susceptibility of some species of *Lymnaea* to infection with *F. gigantica* and *F. hepatica*, Kendall and Parfitt (1959) suggested that, although the view that the flukes were transmitted respectively by the *L. auricularia* complex and by *L. truncatula* and its close allies was broadly correct, it was likely to be an over-simplification. It was necessary to consider whether all the snails which apparently showed such close systematic relationship were in fact uniformly susceptible to infection.

IV. HOST SPECIFICITY

A. PHYSIOLOGICAL RACES OF FLUKES AND SNAILS

The existence of races of schistosomes differentiated on the basis of their vector requirements, has been known for a good many years (Vogel, 1942; Files and Cram, 1949; Files, 1951; DeWitt, 1954; Newton and von Brand, 1955; and others). The incompatibility between snail hosts and parasites of different endemic areas has been explained on the basis of interspecific and intraspecific differences between the hosts in respect of the physiological factors that are responsible for the development of the parasite and on corresponding physiological differences between strains of the parasite. Thus *Australorbis glabratus* from Puerto Rico was found by Files and Cram (1949) to be fully susceptible to Puerto Rican, Venezuelan and a Brazilian/Puerto Rican cross of *Schistosoma mansoni* but only 9% susceptible to an Egyptian strain of the fluke. On the other hand, a snail from Brazil was susceptible to a Brazilian/Puerto Rican cross but not to Venezuelan or Egyptian flukes. In general, although there are some noteworthy exceptions, snails seem to be highly susceptible to infection with schistosomes of their own endemic areas but may be quite refractory to parasites from other areas (Kendall, 1964).

It seemed reasonable to look for simlar relationships between species of *Fasciola* and their vectors from different parts of the world. In 1959 Kendall and Parfitt at Weybridge showed that under controlled conditions adult Lymnaeid snails (*L. natalensis*) from East or West Africa were highly susceptible to infection both with African and Asiatic flukes of *F. gigantica* type, but that the Asiatic snails, while fully susceptible to flukes from their own geographical area, were resistant to infection with the African flukes.

In Japan, both *F. hepatica* and *F. gigantica* have been recognized. Miracidia from eggs sent to Weybridge by Dr. Ueno of Tokyo were used in a series of trial infections with British *L. auricularia* and *L. truncatula*, *L. natalensis* from East and from West Africa and with three known vectors of *F. gigantica* in Pakistan. In no instance did any adult snails become infected, but it was found possible to infect immature African *L. natalensis* and some cercariae emerged. These were later shown to develop in goats into flukes morphologically similar to *F. gigantica*. These observations confirmed the previous indication that the African *L. natalensis* is very receptive to flukes of *F. gigantica* type, but suggested that the Japanese large fluke differs in its vector requirements from *F. gigantica* from both Africa and Pakistan.

There is also evidence in Japan of the existence of a strain of *F. hepatica* differing physiologically from the European. Thus Ueno and Watanabe (1960) found that *Lymnaea ollula* in Japan was parasitized much more readily by miracidia from *F. hepatica*-like flukes collected in Japan than by miracidia from eggs of *F. hepatica* sent from England.

Further observations may indicate an increased range of differences in host susceptibility throughout the world. Certainly the very great variations in morphology which can be observed in the members of Hubendick's super-family *L. auricularia* inevitably suggests the possibility of physiological variation. Even in restricted geographical areas controlled experiment is likely to show minor differences in susceptibility between different strains of snails.

B. VARIATIONS OF HOST SPECIFICITY UNDER SPECIAL CIRCUMSTANCES

Susceptibility to infection may apparently be varied to some extent by the environmental conditions of a snail at the time of exposure to miracidia. This has not been investigated with *Fasciola* and its vectors but DeWitt (1955) showed that raising the temperature had an appreciable effect in increasing the activity of the miracidia of *Schistosoma mansoni*, of assisting their penetration and hence in attaining a higher rate of infection. Five geographical strains of *Australorbis glabratus* were used and there was some evidence of differences of response between the different strains under the different experimental conditions. It would be reasonable to expect an increase in the activity of the miracidia of *Fasciola* also to result in a higher rate of infection, at least initially, and a wider range of hosts might be parasitized. Whether further development would occur in abnormal hosts is another matter.

Another factor which has received considerable attention is the age of the snail at the time of exposure to infection. Various investigators, particularly with the schistosomes, have reported very variable results, and it is pertinent to stress the necessity for distinguishing between susceptibility to infection and its manifestation by the appearance of mature cercariae. Snails of all ages may be susceptible but the maturation of cercariae is dependent on sufficient time and also, as will be shown elsewhere, on sufficient supplies of food. A very young (small) snail without access to sufficient food may be unable to support the normal development of the parasite.

In our work with the two species of *Fasciola* it has seemed that with the preferred host individuals of all ages and sizes are susceptible, but that immature snails of species quite resistant when adult can frequently be infected and the infection may proceed to maturity. This observation is probably an indication of the lack of physiological distinction between young animals of related species. Sandground (1929) suggested that most of the cases in which age resistance to parasites was known to occur applied to slightly abnormal hosts.

Experience with *Fasciola* at Weybridge has taught us that it is essential to use adult snails in order to obtain, in the laboratory, a true assessment of the likely susceptibility of a snail species in the field. Thus there is very little doubt that in Britain *L. truncatula* is the sole host of *F. hepatica*, yet Kendall

(1950) was able in the laboratory to infect five of the six British species of *Lymnaea*. Preliminary observations had shown that, while the miracidia of *F. hepatica* attacked *Lymnaea stagnalis* of all sizes, infection did not persist in the older and larger snails: rediae developed only in the smallest individuals of each group. An experimental infection was therefore arranged in which a large number of freshly hatched *L. stagnalis* was used. Twenty-five of the snails from this group were dissected after intervals of 41–67 days from the date of first infection and of these three were found to contain the rediae of *F. hepatica*. As the observation continued a substantial mortality occurred among the remaining snails, but of seventy-six which were examined 80 days after infection ten were found to be infected and these contained rediae up to 1–5 mm in length with some cercariae which appeared to be mature. Three infected snails were kept alive until cercariae emerged. In all, ninety-nine perfect cercariae emerged from one of the infected snails and one was shown to be infective to a rabbit (Kendall, 1950). It was thus conclusively shown that very young specimens of *L. stagnalis* could be infected with *F. hepatica* and that development could proceed to maturity. Later experiments showed also that of the British species *L. auricularia* alone proved resistant. Full development of the parasite occurred also in *Lymnaea palustris* and *L. glabra* while in *L. pereger* development occurred as far as the production of rediae. Whereas, however, *L. truncatula* could be infected at any age or size, the other species were susceptible only during the first few days after hatching. Only a proportion of these immature snails, moreover, became infected.

The greater susceptibility of immature snails of species other than the preferred host has been observed also in relation to *F. gigantica* by Kendall and Parfitt (1959). Thus snails of a strain of *L. natalensis* from East Africa were exposed to infection with the miracidia of *F. hepatica* when 1–2 days, 8 days and 15 days old and when fully adult. Cercariae developed to maturity in a few of the snails which were exposed at 1–2 days of age, but there was no evidence of infection in any other snails when they were examined 35–112 days after exposure to miracidia.

Similarly when snails known to be vectors of *F. gigantica* in Pakistan were exposed to the miracidia of *F. hepatica* full development with the emergence of cercariae occurred in a group exposed at 1–2 days of age, while there was no evidence of infection in snails exposed when adult.

Further work showed that some abnormal hosts could be infected on rare occasions even when adult and that such infections, though they apparently terminated much sooner than in the normal host, might result in the emergence of mature cercariae. In general young snails were susceptible to infection both to races and even species of fluke to which they were resistant when adult.

V. Factors Affecting the Development of the Parasite within the Snail

A. Temperature and Rate of Development

The effect of temperature on the development of trematodes within their molluscan hosts has been studied quite extensively and, as might be expected,

F

there is a fairly direct relationship between the rate of development of the parasite and the environmental temperature of the host.

With *F. hepatica* in *L. truncatula* about 10° C seems to be the limit below which no appreciable development occurs. Above 10° C the rate of development increases up to about 28° C when it is difficult to maintain the snails in a healthy condition, the minimum period required for completion of the life history within the snail being of the order of 21 days at about 27° C. The maximum period which might be observed at low temperatures can probably be equated with the life of the host but such an investigation has not been recorded.

In Australia Boray (1963) made observations on the development of *F. hepatica* in *L. tomentosa* and recorded the length of time taken at different temperatures from 15° to 35° C. These ranged from 56–86 days at 15° C to 24–28 days at 35° C (a very high temperature for a snail host of *F. hepatica*) and are similar to those quoted by other authors in different parts of the world. With *F. hepatica* in *L. truncatula* at 25° C Roberts (1950) found a sporocyst (0·2 mm long) on the 3rd day in the pre-oesophageal region, rediae (1 mm long) on the 7th day in the pre- and peri-oesophageal regions and cercariae were shed from the 38th day of the infection.

Cameron (1934) observed full development of *F. hepatica* with emergence of cercariae in 50–80 days at 22° C. Shirai (1925) at temperatures of about 16–22° C found that mature cercariae (probably *F. hepatica*) left the snail (*L. pervia*) 45–70 days from the time of infection. Most of these authors gave details of the particular stages of development reached after recorded intervals of time. With *F. hepatica* there is so far no evidence that any particular stages of development are more affected by changes in temperature than are others.

A similar situation is found, in general, with *F. gigantica*. Dinnik and Dinnik (1963) investigated the effect of seasonal variations of temperature on the development of *F. gigantica* in *L. natalensis*. They found, in fact, that under the particular climatic conditions of the Kenya Highlands, the diurnal fluctuations of air temperatures are often much greater than the seasonal variations. One series of observations was made in permanent shade; the other in a place which was in sunlight from 15.00–18.00 h each day.

There was a marked difference (presumably related to the actual temperatures realized in the microclime of the snails but possibly also related to the food supplies of the snails) in the time required for the development of the first stage rediae. In September the development of the first rediae in the snails kept in partial shade took 15–25 days, while in full shade it took 20–31 days. In October this development took 22–27 days in partial shade and 29–36 days in full shade. In November and December 25–31 days, and 28–38 days, were required in the partially and fully shaded aquaria respectively. In the cool season of the year, i.e. in June, July and August, when the temperature of the water in the aquaria dropped to 5° C some mornings and did not rise above 15° C in the afternoon, the conditions were found to be most unfavourable for the development of sporocysts and rediae. The sporocysts either did not grow at all or their growth was delayed and later ceased before they could reach the normal size observed in sporocysts which developed in snails kept in the laboratory at 26° C.

The sporocysts which were able to develop in the snails during the cool season were mostly half the normal size and often abnormal in shape, sometimes being bottle-shaped or stretched into a narrow sausage-like body. In some of these sporocysts the development of germinal balls did not progress at all while in others only one or two germinal balls were present instead of the normal number of four to six. All these sporocysts eventually ceased to move, their bodies became filled with a granular mass and they died. The death rate of the sporocysts in the cool season of the year was always high and in some infected snails all the sporocysts died before they could produce rediae. This effect, i.e. the mortality of the sporocyst, apparently was a direct result of low temperature and is of considerable interest. It has not yet been observed with *F. hepatica*. With *F. gigantica* low temperatures apparently had some effect on rediae also (Dinnik and Dinnik, 1963) and resulted in a small number of malformed parasites. It is suggested that mature rediae within the sporocyst may die because they are unable to leave the sporocyst and commence feeding directly on the tissues of the host.

During the course of this series of experiments it was observed that the shortest time in which *F. gigantica* completed its larval development to a point where cercariae emerged was 69 days. This was during the hottest period of the year when the average morning minimum temperature was 11·5° C and the afternoon maximum was 24·3° C.

B. TEMPERATURE VARIATION AND THE FORMATION OF DAUGHTER REDIAE AND CERCARIAE

Rediae can apparently produce either daughter rediae, cercariae or both. Leuckart (1886), because he had never seen both cercariae and rediae at the same time within a parent redia, considered that there were two distinct kinds of rediae in the life cycle and that their appearance could be related to temperature. Leuckart stated that when a miracidium of *F. hepatica* penetrated a snail host in the autumn the rediae developed from the sporocyst produced only daughter rediae which in turn began to produce cercariae later on in the spring. On the other hand, when a miracidium penetrated a snail in the spring, all the resulting rediae proceeded directly to produce cercariae. Whereas Leuckart believed that only daughter rediae were produced during the winter, Thomas (1883) considered that daughter rediae appeared during the warmth of the summer and that in the cold months cercariae were always produced directly by the rediae developed from the sporocyst. Thomas found rediae that contained both daughter rediae and cercariae and was inclined to think that rediae produced daughter rediae initially but that a fall in temperature induced the formation of cercariae instead.

At Weybridge, during the course of the examination of very large numbers of *L. truncatula* infected with *F. hepatica* and kept under laboratory conditions, there has never been any indication of the production of daughter rediae. Under these conditions rediae proceed directly to the formation of cercariae.

At Weybridge a number of adult *L. truncatula* was accordingly exposed to mass infection with the miracidia of *F. hepatica* and then kept for about 1 month at ordinary laboratory temperatures (mean maximum 20·7° C; mean minimum 11·4° C). The snails were then divided into two groups, one of which was maintained at laboratory temperatures while the other was subjected to periods of cooling by placing the dish containing the snails in the bottom of a refrigerator at 4–5° C for 4½ h daily. About 7 weeks after infection rediae with cercariae with well-developed cystogenous glands were present in the snails which had been kept throughout at laboratory temperatures. At the same time examination of a snail which had been subjected to periods of cold showed the presence of rediae with some immature cercariae but also with daughter rediae. Subsequently, daughter rediae were seen on several occasions when snails from this group were dissected. None was ever seen in the group which had been kept throughout at laboratory temperatures.

It is worth noting, by contrast, that in our experience rediae of *F. gigantica* under ordinary laboratory conditions in England commonly produce daughter rediae.

The situation with regard to *F. gigantica* has been further explored by Dinnik and Dinnik (1956, 1963, 1964). These authors noted (1956) when dissecting snails heavily infected with the larval stages of *F. gigantica* that many rediae contained both daughter rediae and cercariae at the same time. It was considered that after an initial period when only daughter rediae were produced a phase of cercarial production began—about twenty-five cercariae developing. After these two successive phases of redial and cercarial production a new cluster of germinal cells appeared in the mature rediae and gave rise to new germinal balls from which about five daughter rediae and twelve cercariae develop again. Thus there appears to be an alternating development of daughter rediae and cercariae. Dinnik and Dinnik (1956) suggested the possibility that after a long period of larval development some rediae of the later generations did not produce daughter rediae but gave birth to a few cercariae only. At low temperatures this alternation of production of rediae and cercariae was disturbed. It appeared that at temperatures of 16° C or less the rediae produced daughter rediae but not cercariae, whereas cercariae were produced at higher temperatures.

It thus appears that with both species of *Fasciola* first generation rediae are potentially capable of producing either cercariae or further generations of rediae, the former being associated with higher and the latter with lower temperatures. There is an obvious suggestion that the production of daughter rediae is an overwintering device, although it is not easy to suggest a logical explanation of why it should occur.

The question of whether there are, in the life history, two types of rediae—morphologically distinguishable—requires further investigation, but it seems unlikely.

C. THE EFFECT ON THE PARASITE OF CHANGES IN THE NUTRITION OF THE HOST

The great majority of the recorded observations on the development of larval *Fasciola* have made no reference to the nutritional status of the host. It has been traditional to associate a state of malnutrition in a host with a predisposition towards a heavy burden of parasites. Taking one view it is reasonable to suppose that a diet which is not adequate in certain components may effect the immunological competence of the host. On the other hand, and particularly when mechanisms of resistance do not seem to be involved, the fact that a host and a well-adapted parasite are likely to have evolved together for a considerable period of time suggests that the well-being of the one may be dependent on the well-being of the other (Kendall, 1964). In general, factors affecting the rate of development of trematode parasites in their molluscan hosts do not appear to have been studied to any great extent, although observations by such authors as Ross (1930) and Krull (1941) had suggested that factors other than temperature were involved. Both these authors noted that the time necessary for the full development of the cercariae of *F. hepatica* showed considerable variation in individual snails infected at the same time and kept at the same temperatures.

Under laboratory conditions at Weybridge it was noted that there was considerable variation in the number of cercariae which emerged from different groups of snails kept at similar temperatures but in different tanks in the laboratory. It seemed that large numbers of cercariae emerged most often from snails which had grown rapidly during the period after infection and it seemed that the number of cercariae which matured might be related to the amount of food made available to the rediae through the tissues of the snail.

There was evidence in favour of this view (Kendall, 1949a), because Faust (1920), during observations on snails and their trematode parasites, found that the large amount of glycogen, fat and protein normally present in the digestive gland epithelium and intertubular sinuses of uninfected snails disappeared in cases of heavy infection and was apparently transferred to the parasites. If an extensive transference of food from the reserves of the snail to the parasite were to take place without comparable replacement as the result of active feeding by the snail, the development of the parasite would be expected to suffer. In fact, it was possible for Kendall (1949a) to show in laboratory experiments with well-fed and with starved snails that the rate of development of the parasite, as indicated by the number of cercariae which attained full maturity in a given time, was influenced partly by the number of rediae which were present in each snail but more markedly by the amount of food which the snail received. Both these factors are likely to influence the amount of food ultimately available to the individual parasite. There was competition for food within the snail and the rate of development of the parasites was the resultant of their number and the amount of food available.

Kendall and Ollerenshaw (1963) were later able to extend these observations to the field and to show from population studies on *L. truncatula* combined with observations on the incidence of infection with *F. hepatica* that there was no simple relationship between the numbers of snails and the size of the parasite population. The size of the snails and not their numbers seems to be the major factor influencing the numbers of parasites present, and in this instance the size of the snail is important principally as an indication of good nutrition. In a habitat where most of the snails remain small, the population of parasites also is low. In a habitat where more large snails are present, the intensity of infection and the number of metacercariae arriving on the herbage is greater.

It is important to appreciate that snails of all sizes and both well-fed and starved snails are likely to be susceptible to infection. It is the subsequent development of the parasite that is affected by the poor nutrition of the snail.

D. AESTIVATION OF THE HOST AND ITS EFFECT ON THE PARASITE

Although non-operculate, *L. truncatula*, a typical host of *F. hepatica*, lives in shallow well-aerated waters, marshes, water meadows and similar places which are characteristically subject to periods of drought. The snail is amphibious in habit, of an unsettled background, living in the intermediate zone between water and land and from the nature of its habitat subject to extremes of environmental conditions. To meet these it has evolved the ability at one time to grow and multiply with extreme speed and at another to undergo prolonged periods of aestivation when metabolic processes become dormant and feeding ceases. Observations in the laboratory suggested (Kendall, 1949b) that under suitable conditions a percentage of aestivating snails might survive for a year in a dry habitat.

This ability to survive seems to be characteristic of the snail hosts of *F. hepatica*. This was noted by Olsen (1944), who reported on these hosts in southern Texas, and more recently by Boray (1963), who noted that *Lymnaea tomentosa* survived in dry mud for several months in the field and that in the laboratory a few snails survived under mud for 332 days at 18–24°C and r.h. 55–75%.

The capacity to survive drought is not so characteristic of the snail hosts of *F. gigantica*, although Kendall (1954) on one occasion found *L. auricularia rufescens* apparently commencing aestivation in moist debris-covered depressions in the mud of a *Typha* reed-bed which was believed to become dry at intervals (Fig. 6). Under such conditions infection may still occur.

The effect of periods of aestivation on the development of the parasite was investigated by Kendall (1949b), interest having been aroused by evidence of the survival for a period of 3 months of another trematode species in aestivating *L. truncatula*. It was shown experimentally that *F. hepatica* could survive at least 10 months dry weather dormancy on the part of the snail host but that the stage of development of the trematode was less advanced than that in snails which had led an active existence. Aestivation of the snail obviously retarded the development of the parasite to a marked degree, the effect appearing more marked with extension of the dormant period. Further observations with mature infections suggested that the development of cercariae was not only retarded during the aestivation of the snail but that large numbers of mature cercariae disappeared; presumably they died and were absorbed.

Field and laboratory observations show that *L. truncatula* grows to maturity very quickly on the return of moist conditions to a habitat after a period of drought. In the same way, *F. hepatica*, the growth of which has been retarded by aestivation, will undergo extremely rapid development when its host once again becomes active.

In this context the effects on the parasite of aestivation of the host can be regarded as a special case of the effects of malnutrition.

VI. HOST RESISTANCE
A. BARRIERS TO INITIAL INFECTION

Laboratory observations suggest that a wide range of snails may be susceptible to attack by the miracidia of a normally host-specific species of trematode—particularly in the absence of the usual vector—but that a preferred host is actively selected from a mixed collection of snails. The basis for selection seems to be chemotactic (Kendall, 1964). As Faust reported in 1924, once a miracidium of *Schistosoma japonicum* comes within range of the proper snail it swims directly towards it and attacks it at the first point of contact. The chemotactic stimulus probably lies in the mucus secreted by the snail, and Faust observed miracidia attacking a trail of mucus secreted by the host as vigorously as the host itself.

A similar situation can be observed with the miracidia of *F. hepatica*. While they are apparently not attracted by the intact egg of *L. truncatula*, even when fully embryonated, they will vigorously attack embryos which have been exposed by breaking the gelatinous coating of the egg. Pieces of the shell of *L. truncatula* with attached mucus are similarly attacked. Snails will apparently be encountered even in large volumes of water and when found the snail evokes a most striking behaviour pattern in the miracidium.

In the absence of the preferred host attachment to quite unsuitable hosts (e.g. Planorbids) can be seen to occur and the miracidium will commence its penetration. How far it proceeds is often not easy to assess but what evidence there is suggests that penetration is usually completed. Newton (1952) working with *S. mansoni* and *A. glabratus* of different strains noted that miracidia penetrated both susceptible and non-susceptible snails with apparently equal willingness and ease. In this particular instance the barrier to further development seemed to operate quite early. In the unsuitable host parasites were destroyed or removed usually within 24–40 h after penetration and a marked cellular infiltration is associated with the presence of the parasite. Later there was a fibrous tissue reaction which walled it off. Some evidence of tissue reaction to the presence of *F. hepatica* has been observed in *L. stagnalis* 48 h after penetration of the miracidium. The sporocyst (about 56 μ in diameter) was lying in an unpigmented area near the pigmented mantle tissue of the snail.

B. BARRIERS TO FURTHER DEVELOPMENT

With *F. hepatica* it seems that development in relatively unsuitable hosts may be halted at different stages. There may, for example, be no evidence of infection soon after penetration would seem to have occurred; rediae may be formed but proceed no further or full development with the appearance of cercariae may sometimes be observed. In this last instance, however, the number of parasites which develop is likely to be few when compared with those commonly seen in the normal host. Whereas as many as thirty young sporocysts of *F. hepatica* may be found in *L. truncatula*, soon after infection, it is rare to find more than one in *L. palustris*—an abnormal host. Further development is similarly restricted. Thus dissection of specimens of *L. palustris* or *L. glabra* which have been mass-infected with *F. hepatica* suggests that not more than thirty rediae develop as compared with the usual 160 or more found in *L. truncatula* under similar conditions (Kendall, 1964).

It is clear that the unsuitable host often exerts a suppressive effect on the developing parasite. The converse—the deleterious effect of the parasite on its unsuitable host—will be discussed later.

C. RESISTANCE TO REPEATED INFECTION

There is good evidence that exposing snails to large numbers of miracidia results in multiple infection. There is less evidence of whether or not resistance may arise after an interval following infection.

During the course of work on the effect of nutrition on the rate of development of *F. hepatica* Kendall (1949a) exposed a number of specimens of *L. truncatula* to infection each with a single miracidium. Of twenty snails which were found to have become infected, one had forty-one rediae when examined 69 days after exposure to infection; the rest contained smaller numbers. In the same series of experiments a further group of snails was exposed to mass infection with miracidia. On dissection one was found to contain thirty rediae the rest having more than fifty. In a group which had received adequate nutrition the number of rediae ranged from 133 to 334, most containing about 150. Under the conditions of the experiment there was no evidence of the production of daughter rediae, and it was accordingly concluded, first, that a single miracidium normally gave rise to not more than forty rediae and, second, that multiple infection of a snail could occur. It seemed probable that infection with four or five miracidia, within a short space of time, was normal. The suggestion that there may be some sort of a barrier to re-infection originated from field observations that simultaneous infection with more than one species of trematode is relatively uncommon. Thus, concurrent infection with *F. hepatica* and one of the other trematodes parasitizing *L. truncatula* in Britain is exceedingly rare if it occurs at all. In view, however, of the comparatively low incidence of infection with any trematode in a field population of snails, such a situation might be predicted on purely statistical grounds. Experimental evidence of a resistance to heterologous infection is lacking. Some years ago, field observations from Weybridge showed that in one particular area in Britain *L. truncatula* was parasitized fairly heavily either with *F. hepatica* or with *Cercaria cambrensis*, but not both parasites. Snails carrying the latter infection were exposed in the laboratory to infection with the miracidia of *F. hepatica*. Some weeks later the snails were examined but showed no evidence of infection with *Fasciola*. Two facts militated against the validity of the observation as an indication of the existence of a resistance in the usually accepted sense. Firstly, the natural trematode infection was so heavy that young stages of *Fasciola* might easily have been missed. Secondly, competition for food within the snail must have been expected severely to have limited the second infection.

More recently, at Weybridge, groups of *L. truncatula* were exposed to infection with a single miracidium of *Fasciola* either on one occasion only or on two occasions with an interval of 2 weeks between them. The rediae which subsequently developed were counted and the result assessed on the assumption that under the conditions of the experiment each miracidium would have given rise to not more than forty rediae. The technique of infection with a single miracidium is not easy and only a proportion of the snails became infected. In this particular experiment there was, in addition, for reasons probably unconnected with the experimental procedure, rather a heavy mortality among the snails. In consequence, the total number of snails in which the rate of infection could finally be assessed was small. Nevertheless there was some indication that repeated infection had occurred. Among thirteen snails which had been exposed to infection on one occasion only, one contained forty-one rediae, the rest having smaller numbers. Among nine exposed to a double infection there were four snails containing respectively forty-four, sixty-one, seventy-six and seventy-seven rediae.

It seems probable that with *L. truncatula* there is no barrier to re-infection in the early stages of development of the parasite (Kendall, 1964).

VII. THE PATHOGENICITY OF INFECTION IN SNAILS

In many instances of trematode infection in snails there must be considerable demands on the host, for the ultimate mass of parasite material constitutes a considerable proportion of the snail. With the mature infection there may be very little digestive gland left. Various special effects which arise from the destruction of specific tissues have been discussed by Dawes (1956). Brown (1926) suggested that infection with some trematodes, particularly echinostome and stylet cercariae, is more harmful than is infection with others. Agersborg (1924), among others, has described the effect of infection in *Physa*—distortion and disintegration of the tissues of the host—while Faust (1920) has described, among the secondary effects on the hepato-pancreas, the inability of the host to prevent such undigested food and faeces as normally pass down the main digestive tract from entering the lumen of the gland. The poisoning of the tissues involves also the main digestive tube so that the cilia of the intestinal epithelium fail to function. Under these conditions, diatons and algal filaments together with particles of silica frequently get into the ultimate tubules of the hepato-pancreas. Faust (1920), as indicated earlier, described how under normal feeding conditions snails which are not infected give a heavy positive result in tests for glycogen, fats and proteins throughout all of the cells of the epithelium of the tubes. On the other hand, heavily infected tissues give at the most only a very scanty result in tests for foodstuffs in the epithelium, or a fairly heavy test in the intertubular sinuses and a decidedly heavy result in the parasites. This seems clear evidence of a depletion of the reserves of food of the host and there is a consequent assumption of damage. With regard to *Fasciola* and its host this assumption needs qualification in the light of the evidence, discussed in

another section, of the existence of a mechanism which regulates the growth
of the parasite in conformity with the availability of food.

Some authors, e.g. Rees (1931), have in fact considered that in spite of the
damage done to the digestive gland, the vitality of a mollusc does not appear
to be greatly reduced. There is however little published evidence of the effect
of *Fasciola* on its snail hosts.

Our experience at Weybridge has suggested that infected snails kept under
good conditions and not exposed to stress, particularly excessive heat, seem
to suffer only moderately, at least until the infection becomes mature, but
there is undoubtedly considerable and often unexplained variation between
different batches of snails. Faust and Hoffman (1934) indicated that it was the
final stages in trematode development and particularly the emergence of
cercariae which caused most damage. These authors suggested that with
A. glabratus and *S. mansoni* the migration of the first generation sporocysts
through the tissues is accompanied by negligible damage, one reason being
that the number of organisms is at this stage very small. Later, however, the
rapid maturity of the cercariae and their crowding into the distal parts of the
snail leads to great pressure on the *tunica propria*. Rupture follows and if the
rent is very extensive the snail may die. As discussed elsewhere, the emergence of the cercariae of *Fasciola* is accompanied by actual trauma and this is
perhaps one of the reasons why excessive mortality of the host is often
observed at this time.

There seems to be general agreement that adverse conditions have a very
considerable effect on the survival of snails with mature infections. Oliver
et al. (1953) were able to define one factor more exactly by showing that snails
infected with *S. mansoni* were much less able to withstand long periods under
anaerobic conditions than were uninfected snails. At least some of the infected
snails were shown to contain much less polysaccharide than did normal snails,
and since polysaccharide is generally the main source of anaerobic energy
this may be the explanation of the comparative inability of heavily infected
snails to withstand long periods of anaerobic respiration or to survive in
contaminated or partially deoxygenated water.

Flukes developing in snails other than their preferred host may prove to be
considerably more pathogenic. As shown by Kendall (1950), in British species
of *Lymnaea* other than *L. truncatula*, *F. hepatica* appears to have a marked
pathogenic effect, growth is severely retarded, shells are abnormally transparent and lacking in pigmentation, shell whorls are distorted and the snails
themselves appear lethargic, obviously suffering severely from the effects of
the parasite. In the laboratory such snails were kept alive with difficulty,
although when kept separately in small culture dishes and supplied with
ample quantities of readily available food the rate of growth improved.

A. RESOLUTION OF TISSUE DAMAGE AND LOSS OF INFECTION

Rees (1931) indicated that after a period of infection with a trematode is
over the host tissues gradually recover, undergo regeneration and finally
appear in normal condition. Cort (1941), by contrast, suggested that recovery
from an infection would involve extensive repair—the walling off of old

sporocysts and rediae and the regeneration of the tissue. Cort said that in all his examinations of snails infected with larval trematodes there was no case suggesting recovery from an old infection. Standen (1963), however, suggests that some snails infected with schistosomes do tend to lose their infection. Presumably there is likely to be variation between species and perhaps according to the conditions under which the host is maintained. Thus Stirewalt (1954), working with *Schistosoma mansoni* in *Australorbis glabratus*, found that at maintenance temperatures below the optimum snails tended to lose their infection. At temperatures apparently optimal for development they retained their infection until death. The higher percentage of snails losing the infection at low maintenance temperatures was interpreted as indicating suppression of the development of the parasites by conditions markedly unfavourable for normal growth.

The only comparable observation with *Fasciola* is that recently reported by Dinnik and Dinnik (1963) and considered on p. 81. Young sporocysts seemed to be susceptible to low maintenance temperatures, developed abnormally and sometimes died.

In our experience with *F. hepatica* in *L. truncatula* a complete loss of infection has never been demonstrated, although there was some evidence of a partial loss of mature parasites in aestivating snails (Kendall, 1949b). Under ordinary circumstances, because Lymnaeid snails are presumptive annuals and tend to live less than 1 year if kept well fed and warm, they are not likely to outlive the infection. Nevertheless it is at least theoretically possible for the rediae to exhaust their supplies of germ buds, and for the infection to terminate. On one occasion an individual *L. truncatula* which had been kept isolated until 4 000 mature cercariae had emerged was found to contain very few rediae, surely very many less than had been present earlier in its life, and these contained very few or no cercariae and apparently no more germinal balls.

With snails other than the preferred host, however, it seems that loss of infection is much more likely to occur. It was observed in one *L. stagnalis* which had been successfully infected with *F. hepatica*. More than 100 cercariae emerged. The snail was kept in isolation for a total period of 11 months after the date of infection. When finally dissected no evidence of the parasite was seen. Observations on a further small group of the same species of snail suggested that infection was usually retained for a period of about 3 months, when only a very few undeveloped rediae could be found in snails which had previously contained large numbers of mature cercariae.

In snails which had apparently suffered severely, as assessed by rates of growth and shell texture, return to a normal appearance apparently coincided with loss of infection (Kendall, 1950).

VIII. FACTORS INFLUENCING THE EMERGENCE AND SURVIVAL OF CERCARIAE

Different larval stages of a trematode, it is easy to show, may co-exist in a single snail. It follows that all the cercariae do not mature at the same time and as a consequence they are likely to leave the snail over an extended period. Although the emergence of cercariae from any individual snail occupies a considerable period of time it is not a continuous process, groups of parasites leaving the snail at intervals. This periodic emergence of cercariae from their snail hosts and the factors causing emergence have been discussed by numerous workers among whom may be mentioned Walton (1918), Rees (1931, 1948), Swales (1935), Baumann et al. (1948), and Schreiber and Schubert (1949).

Kendall and McCullough (1951) extended these observations in an investigation of the emergence of *F. hepatica* from *L. truncatula* and in the process made some interesting discoveries in relation to the mechanics of the way in which cercariae leave the snail.

With *F. hepatica*, emergence, like other aspects of the life of the parasite, seems to be substantially inhibited at temperatures below 10° C. No act of emergence was observed from snails which were kept for 16 h at a temperature of 7° C although within 1 h large numbers of cercariae left snails when the temperature rose to that of the laboratory (13·9° C). Further experiments suggested that 9° C was the critical temperature below which emergence did not occur. The effect of temperatures higher than 26° C was not observed owing to the difficulty of keeping the infected snails alive under such conditions. There was, however, no evidence that emergence was inhibited at high temperatures (Kendall and McCullough, 1951) and it appeared that cercariae emerged equally at 26° C or at a temperature (10° C) which was only slightly above the critical minimum. Further observations showed that emergence might occur throughout a wide range of intermediate temperatures and under conditions of rising or of falling temperatures.

Light did not appear to be an important factor, emergence occurring equally by day and by night, and there did not appear to be any relationship between the emergence of cercariae from the snails and any particular period of the day or night. The principal factor governing the emergence of the parasites was the immersion of the snail in fresh water. Experience showed that cercariae infecting field snails which had been brought to the laboratory for examination commonly emerged in very large numbers soon after the snails had been placed in clean water in the small glass tubes used for observation. Water acted as a primary stimulus to emergence and in the laboratory it was possible to show that even the small amount of water which accumulated when dry snails were sprayed with an atomiser was sufficient to induce emergence. Under more controlled conditions it was possible to establish that changing the water in which the snails lived was the important factor in inducing emergence. It was clear that the conditions developing in the small volume of water in which a snail was confined tended to restrict emergence. This applied both in the laboratory and, by inference, in the field, because it seemed that even field snails taken from a watery habitat and placed in water in the laboratory shed far more cercariae than could be deduced to be the average leaving the snail. The numbers of cercariae emerging seemed to represent an accumulation which must have matured over a considerable period of time.

Kendall and McCullough (1951) investigated such factors as a change in temperature, depletion of oxygen, an increase in the concentration of carbon dioxide and a change in the hydrogen ion concentration of the water. The methods used to evaluate these changes were not particularly refined, and the precise physical factors inducing emergence have never been defined precisely.

The actual emergence of cercariae was, however, carefully observed and the process described was of extreme interest. It was noted that changing the water in which the snails rested tended not only to induce emergence of cercariae but seemed also to increase the activity of the snails themselves. Consideration of the exact mode of emergence of cercariae from a snail suggests that stimulation of the resting snail may be the principal factor causing emergence. When a snail containing mature parasites is taken from a mud slope or from the shallow water of its habitat large numbers of cercariae may be seen through the shell of the body whorl moving slowly within the cavity surrounding the alimentary tract of the snail. If the snail is placed in a small amount of clean water the cercariae soon show signs of greater activity, which seems to be associated with such movements of the snail as extrusion of head and foot and the stretching and contraction of the mantle wall. After a short time the activity of the cercariae becomes very pronounced and the larvae begin to congregate in the perivisceral space surrounding the distal part of the gut of the snail. Shortly before emergence actually occurs an area next to the anus of the snail becomes tumid and assumes a teat-like appearance. Cercariae can be seen within the perivisceral space surrounding the rectum and moving towards the exterior. As the pneumostome of the snail closes, cercariae begin to be extruded through the teat-like process, Observation of the process strongly suggests that in its later stages emergence of the cercariae is predominantly passive. Each cercaria of a series seems to be extruded with considerable force and is comparatively inactive when newly emerged. After emergence the parasites swim slowly away from the snail and on several occasions individual cercariae have been observed to be sucked into the mantle cavity by an inhalation of water immediately following the emergence. After examining fixed material showing cercariae *in situ* in the act of emerging, Kendall and McCullough (1951) described how they lay in comparatively restricted spaces surrounding the terminal part of the gut, contiguous with the mantle cavity. Pressure set up in the mantle cavity, while the pneumostome is closed, causes pressure on the perivisceral spaces which contain the emerging cercariae and under suitable conditions aids their progress to the exterior. Such an explanation of the mechanism of emergence receives support from the observation that a resting snail when dropped into a vessel of water sometimes emits a cloud of cercariae, apparently as a direct result of a convulsive contraction of the walls of the mantle cavity.

A. THE SURVIVAL OF METACERCARIAE

1. *Humidity and Temperature*

Metacercariae represent a developmental phase with a considerable potentiality for survival and the average life which can be expected under different environmental conditions is of very great importance both in the study of the life history of the parasite and in the epidemiology of fascioliasis. As Leuckart (1886) noted, some degree of moisture is essential for continued survival; the parasites cannot survive complete desiccation. In Australia Ross and McKay (1929) showed that the cysts survived desiccation for 2 days when exposed in air to direct sunlight at 105° F and 98·6° F for about 12 h daily, but they survived for 17 days in shade at room temperatures ranging from 71·6° to 80·6° F. In water, however, they survived for 4 months.

Shirai (1927) similarly found that metacercariae survived for 80 days in frequently changed water at a temperature of 71·3–87·8° F and for 30 days when exposed to sunlight in water at 89·6° F, but in air metacercariae on leaves died in 2–3 h when exposed to direct sunlight. They survived 24 h exposure in shade at room temperature but were dead at 72 h.

Ollerenshaw (personal communication) has found that a relative humidity of 70 or more is necessary for prolonged survival. It is quite clear that moisture is the principal factor controlling the length of life of metacercariae.

From the point of view of the survival of the parasite, or of the epidemiology of disease, the maximum period for which a metacercariae may live, as distinct from the average life of this phase in the life history, is of relatively little importance but deserves some comment. Shaw (1932) found that some metacercariae kept for 11 months in a cold store (26–36° F) with an average temperature "probably above freezing point" were capable of infecting guinea-pigs.

At Weybridge some controlled experiments on the survival of meta-cercariae of *F. hepatica* on herbage have been carried out by Ollerenshaw (personal communication). Snails were induced to shed their cercariae on to grass growing in boxes in which the water level was subsequently maintained about 6 in. below soil level. The viability of the metacercariae was subsequently assessed at intervals by removing the cysts from the herbage, teasing out the metacercariae, and examining them for movement under the microscope, the validity of the method being tested from time to time by feeding "live" or "dead" metacercariae to mice. Several experiments were carried out. One series commenced in autumn and showed the rate of mortality during winter and spring; the other started in summer and showed the rate of mortality during summer and autumn. The results indicated that herbage infected in autumn remained infected for periods of between 270 and 340 days. There appeared to be a low rate of mortality of metacercariae during winter followed by a more rapid decline in survivors in the following spring and summer. By this time the infected herbage constituted the dead matt at the base of the spring growth.

In the series of experiments showing the rate of mortality of metacercariae on herbage during the summer there was an initially high rate, with 50% deaths occurring in about 40 days. By winter about 90% of the metacercariae had died but the remaining 10% remained viable well into the winter. Viable metacercariae were recovered up to 180 days after they had encysted. As already indicated, Ollerenshaw found that a relative humidity of 70 was necessary for prolonged survival. At 20 r.h. and 25–26° C all metacercariae died within 10 days. It was confirmed that the survival of metacercariae is mainly related to humidity but that they live much longer at lower than at higher temperatures.

A number of other authors have reported observations under field or "simulated field" conditions.

Thus Alicata (1938) observed that cysts of *F. gigantica*, attached to "Hono-hono" grass (*Commelina diffusa*) and kept indoors, remained viable after 20 days but not after 30 days. Cysts attached to whole plants and kept in sunny areas were viable after 15 days but not after 42 days. Temperatures during the hours of sunshine were 77–87° F. Showers were common and the cysts were moist during part of the time. In experiments with plants kept under running water some cysts were viable after 122 days.

Observations related to the epidemiology of fascioliasis were carried out by Olsen (1945, 1947) in the Gulf Coast area of Texas. Here it was shown that the snail host (*Stagnicola* (*Lymnaea*) *bulimoides techella*) lived in temporary pools and that cercariae were able to encyst only when standing water was present on the pastures during the winter and early spring. By observation on the times at which infection was contracted by grazing stock Olsen was able to deduce that the metacercariae were able to survive the unfavourable conditions created by the heat and drought of summer. Post-mortem examination showed that both immature and mature flukes were present in cattle during the early summer but that, essentially, only mature parasites remained in the late fall. This suggested that the pastures became free from infective meta-cercariae during the summer. In one year when observations were made the pastures were considered to be entirely or nearly free for at least 3 months prior to the onset of the winter rains.

2. *Effect of Drying and Ensilaging Grass*

Livestock owners are often concerned about the advisability of feeding green, dried or ensilaged fodder to stock and the very practical question of how long metacercariae can remain viable under such conditions may be raised. There is in fact very little published work on the subject. It is obvious, of course, that fresh green fodder can contain large numbers of viable cysts. Marek (quoted by Olsen, 1947) reported that metacercariae that had encysted on grass growing in moist areas and subsequently made into hay during rainy weather survived and were able to infect rabbits after 8 months of storage. Well-made (i.e. well-dried) hay would be likely to retain viable metacercariae for only a much shorter period.

Under experimental conditions Alicata (1938) found that after 3 months the cysts of *F. gigantica* had failed to survive the process of ensilaging under anaerobic conditions.

Wikerhauser and Brglez (1961) found that the metacercariae of *F. hepatica* failed to survive when kept in silage for 35–57 days.

The physical conditions under which silage is made obviously are likely to vary enormously, but it is reasonable to assume that the anaerobic con-ditions and comparatively high temperatures associated with the process are deleterious to the cysts.

3. *Cysts Eaten by Snails*

One further and perhaps minor observation is that metacercariae, under laboratory conditions at least, may be ingested by snails, pass through the digestive tract and remain infective for the definitive host. This has been often observed at Weybridge with the metacercariae of *Fasciola hepatica* and *Lymnaea truncatula*. Metacercariae have been recovered from the snail faeces and shown to be infective to mammals.

Campbell and Todd (1956) reported a similar phenomenon with *Fascioloides magna* metacercariae in *Stagnicola reflexa*. Most of the parasites found in the snail faeces were stated to be in an unencysted and immature state but others were fully encysted. The authors made reference to the work of Kendall and McCullough (1951) on the emergence of the cercariae of *F. hepatica* from its snail host and suggested that, if cercariae of *Fascioloides* were similarly forced, under pressure during the process of emergence along the perivisceral space, it was not altogether surprising that some might penetrate the gut and be expelled with the faeces.

When fully encysted metacercariae are found in snail faeces their presence is no more remarkable than that of any other small foreign body, such as a grain of sand. It would be remarkable if unencysted parasites were able to withstand the digestive processes of the snail for more than a very short period.

IX. The Epidemiology of Infection with *Fasciola*

This review of the host–parasite relationships between snails and flukes has made apparent some major gaps in our knowledge. In particular, practically nothing is known of the physiological basis for host specificity—of what inhibits development of the parasite in one host apparently so closely similar to another in which full and rapid development can be seen. Nevertheless, particularly with *F. hepatica* and its host *L. truncatula*, much information has accumulated and an examination of the seasonal and annual rhythms of the life cycle of the liver fluke, in the light of this new knowledge, has led to importance advances in the control of fascioliasis—this serious disease of livestock.

As suggested by Ollerenshaw and Rowlands (1959) the size of a population of *F. hepatica* in any given area is dependent on a number of environmental factors, some constant and some variable, both seasonally and from year to year. In some areas, e.g. well-drained upland pastures, the fluke could never become established. By contrast, in such an area as Anglesey in north Wales the constant environmental factors favour the parasite. The island is heavily stocked with sheep which graze largely on permanent pasture and, together with cattle and rabbits, are permanently infected with *F. hepatica*. The existence of moisture-retaining clay and extensive areas of badly drained land favours both the snail host and the various developmental stages of the parasite.

Knowledge of the critical temperatures below which development will not proceed and of the accelerating effect of warmth and good food supplies for the snail explains the fact that there is likely to be a mass exodus of cercariae from the snail in September but that a minor overwintering infection will leave the host in early summer. Whether or not large populations of parasites develop in any particular year will depend on environmental factors which are variable, and of these the amount of moisture is by far the most important. From the application of a formula which assesses the degree of moisture in the habitat as a resultant of (a) the differences between rainfall and transpiration and (b) the frequency of rainfall, Ollerenshaw and Rowlands (1959) were able to show a close correlation between the incidence of disease in sheep and the climate and to suggest means of forecasting disease in any particular year.

In certain areas of Britain it is now possible to forecast the likely incidence of disease with a considerable degree of accuracy and in time for emergency control measures to be implemented. The possibility of extending this most useful piece of applied research not only to other parts of Britain but also to other countries, including those where *F. gigantica* is the parasite concerned, depends upon further series of life-history studies and a more precise knowledge of the host–parasite relationship under different ecological conditions.

REFERENCES

Agersborg, H. P. K. (1924). Studies on the effects of parasitism upon the tissues. I. With special reference to certain gastropod molluscs. *Quart. J. micr. Soc.* **68**, 361.

Alicata, J. E. (1938). Observations on the life history of *Fasciola gigantica*, the common liver fluke of cattle in Hawaii and the intermediate host *Fossaria ollula*. *Bull. Hawaii agric. Exp. Sta.*, No. 80.

Bauman, P. M., Bennett, H. J. and Ingalls, J. W. (1948). The molluscan intermediate host and schistosomiasis japonica. Observations on the production and rate of emergence of cercariae of *Schistosoma japonicum* from the molluscan intermediate host *Oncomelania quadrasi*. *Amer. J. trop. Med.* **28**, 567–575.

Bhalerao, G. D. (1935). Helminth parasites of the domesticated animals in India. Imperial Council of Agricultural Research Scientific Monograph No. 6, Delhi.

Boray, J. C. (1963). The ecology of *Fasciola hepatica* with particular reference to its intermediate host in Australia. Proceedings 17th World Veterinary Congress, 1963, Section 6, pp. 709–715.

Boycott, A. E. (1936). The habitats of fresh-water molluscs in Britain. *J. Anim. Ecol.* **5**, 116.

Brown, F. J. (1926). Some British fresh-water larval trematodes with contributions to their life-histories. *Parasitology* **18**, 21.

Brumpt, E. (1949). "Précis de Parasitologie." 6th ed. Masson, Paris.

Cameron, T. W. M. (1934). "Internal Parasites of Domestic Animals," pp. 168–169. Black, London.

Campbell, W. C. and Todd, A. C. (1956). Emission of cercariae and metacercariae in snail faeces. *Trans. Amer. micr. Soc.* **75**, 241–243.

Cobbold, T. S. (1855). Description of a new species of trematode worm (*Fasciola gigantica*). *Edinburgh New Philosophical Journal* **2** (N.S.), 262–267.

Cobbold, T. S. (1864). "Entozoa: An Introduction to the Study of Helminthology." London.

Cort, W. W. (1941). Ecological relations of the larval trematodes of fresh water snails. *In* "A Symposium on Hydrobiolody," p. 115. Madison, U.S.A.

Dawes, B. (1956). "The Trematode." Cambridge University Press.

Dawes, B. (1959). Penetration of the liver-fluke, *Fasciola hepatica* into the snail, *Limnaea truncatula*. *Nature, Lond.* **184**, Suppl. 17, 1334–1335.

Dawes, B. (1960a). A study of the miracidium of *Fasciola hepatica* and an account of the mode of penetration of the sporocyst into *Limnaea truncatula*. *In* "Libro Homenaje al Dr. Eduardo Caballero y Caballero," pp. 95–111. Escuela Nacional de Ciencias Biologicas, Mexico, D.F.

Dawes, B. (1960b). Penetration of *Fasciola gigantica* Cobbold 1856 into snail hosts. *Nature, Lond.* **185**, 51–53.

Dawes, B. (1960c). The penetration of *Fasciola hepatica* into *Limnaea truncatula* and of *F. gigantica* into *L. auricularia*. *Trans. roy. Soc. trop. Med. Hyg.* **54**, 9–10.

DeWitt, W. B. (1954). Susceptibility of snail vectors to geographic strains of *Schistosoma japonicum*. *J. Parasit.* **40**, 453.

DeWitt, W. B. (1955). Influence of temperature on penetration of snail hosts by *Schistosoma mansoni* miracidia. *Exp. Parasit.* **4**, 271.

Dinnik, J. A. and Dinnik, N. N. (1956). Observations on the succession of redial generations of *Fasciola gigantica* Cobbold in a snail host. *Z. Tropenmed. Parasit.* **7**, 397–419.

Dinnik, J. A. and Dinnik, N. N. (1963). Effect of the seasonal variations of temperature on the development of *Fasciola gigantica* in the snail host in the Kenya Highlands. *Bull. epizoot. Dis. Afr.* **11**, 197–207.

Dinnik, J. A. and Dinnik, N. N. (1964). The influence of temperature on the succession of redial and cercarial generations of *Fasciola gigantica* in a snail host. *Parasitology* **54**, 59–65.

Faust, E. C. (1920). Pathological changes in the gastropod liver produced by fluke infection. *Bull. Johns Hopk. Hosp.* **31**, 79–84.

Faust, E. C. (1924). The reactions of the miracidia of *Schistosoma japonicum* and *S. haematobium* in the presence of their intermediate hosts. *J. Parasit.* **10**, 199.

Faust, E. C. (1955). "Animal Agents and Vectors of Human Disease." Philadelphia.

Faust, E. C. and Hoffman, W. A. (1934). Studies on *Schistosoma mansoni* in Puerto Rico. III. Biological studies. *Puerto Rico J. publ. Hlth* **10**, 1.

Files, V. S. (1951). A study of the vector parasite relationship in *Schistosoma mansoni*. *Parasitology* **41**, 264.

Files, V. S. and Cram, E. B. (1949). A study on the comparative susceptibility of snail vectors to strains of *Schistosoma mansoni*. *J. Parasit.* **35**, 555.

Haiba, M. H. and Selim, M. K. (1960). Detailed study on the morphological status of *Fasciola* worms infesting buffaloes, cows and sheep in Egypt. *Z. Parasitenk.* **19**, 525.

Hubendick, B. (1951). Recent Lymnaeidae. *K. Svenska Vetensk. Akad. Handl.* **3**, 1.

Itagaki, H. and Akane, S. (1959). Morphological study on the Japanese liver fluke, compared with the African specimens. *Bull. Azabu vet. Coll.* **6**, 115–123.

Jepps, M. W. (1933). Miracidia of the liver fluke for laboratory work. *Nature, Lond.* **132**, 171.

Kendall, S. B. (1949a). Nutritional factors affecting the rate of development of *Fasciola hepatica* in *Limnaea truncatula*. *J. Helminth.* **23**, 179–190.

Kendall, S. B. (1949b). Bionomics of *Limnaea truncatula* and the Parthenitae of *Fasciola hepatica* under drought conditions. *J. Helminth.* **23**, 57–68.

Kendall, S. B. (1950). Snail hosts of *Fasciola hepatica* in Britain. *J. Helminth.* **24**, 63–74.

Kendall, S. B. (1953). Report to the Government of Pakistan on Fascioliasis. F.A.O. Report No. 83. Food and Agriculture Organization of the United Nations, Rome.

Kendall, S. B. (1954). Fascioliasis in Pakistan. *Ann. trop. Med. Parasit.* **48**, 307–313.

Kendall, S. B. (1964). Some factors influencing the development of trematodes in their molluscan hosts. *In* "Host-parasite Relationships in Invertebrate Hosts" (A. E. R. Taylor, ed.), pp. 51–73. Blackwell, Oxford.

Kendall, S. B. and McCullough, F. S. (1951). The emergence of the cercariae of *Fasciola hepatica* from the snail *Limnaea truncatula*. *J. Helminth*. **25**, 77.

Kendall, S. B. and Ollerenshaw, C. B. (1963). The effect of nutrition on the growth of *Fasciola hepatica* in its snail host. *Proc. Nutr. Soc.* **22**, 41.

Kendall, S. B. and Parfitt, J. W. (1959). Studies on the susceptibility of some species of *Lymnaea* to infection with *Fasciola gigantica* and *F. hepatica*. *Ann. trop. Med. Parasit*. **53**, 220–227.

Krull, W. H. (1941). The number of cercariae of *Fasciola hepatica* developing in snails infected with a single miracidium. *Proc. helm. Soc. Wash.* **8**, 55.

Leuckart, R. (1886). "Die Parasiten des Menschen." Leipzig.

Mattes, O. (1949). Wirtsfindung, Invasionsvorgang und Wirtsspezifitat beim Fasciola-miracidium. *Z. Parasitenk*. **14**, 320–363.

Newton, W. L. (1952). The comparative tissue reaction of two strains of *Australorbis glabratus* to infection with *Schistosoma mansoni*. *J. Parasit*. **38**, 362.

Newton, W. L. and von Brand, T. (1955). Comparative physiological studies on two geographical strains of *Australorbis glabratus*. *Exp. Parasit*. **4**, 244.

Olivier, L., von Brand, T. and Mehlman, B. (1953). The influence of lack of oxygen on *Schistosoma mansoni* cercariae and on infected *Australorbis glabratus*. *Exp. Parasit*. **2**, 258.

Ollerenshaw, C. B. and Rowlands, W. T. (1959). A method of forecasting the incidence of fascioliasis in Anglesey. *Vet. Rec.* **71**, 591–598.

Olsen, O. W. (1944). Bionomics of the Lymnaeid snail *Stagnicola bulimoides techella*, the intermediate host of the liver fluke in Southern Texas. *J. agric. Res.* **69**, 389–493.

Olsen, O. W. (1945). Ecology of the metacercariae of *Fasciola hepatica* in Southern Texas and its relationship to liver fluke control in cattle. *J. Parasit*. **31** (Suppl.), 20.

Olsen, O. W. (1947). Longevity of metacercariae of *Fasciola hepatica* on pastures in the upper coast region of Texas and its relationship to liver fluke control. *J. Parasit*. **33**, 36–42.

Porter, A. (1921). The life-history of the African sheep and cattle fluke, *Fasciola gigantica*. *S. Afr. J. Sci.* **17**, 126–130.

Price, E. W. (1953). The fluke situation in American ruminants. *J. Parasit*. **39**, 119–134.

Rees, G. (1931). Some observations and experiments on the biology of larval trematodes. *Parasitology* **23**, 428–440.

Rees, G. (1948). A study of the effect of light, temperature and salinity on the emergence of *Cercariae purpurae* Lebour from *Nucella papillus* (L). *Parasitology* **38**, 228–242.

Roberts, E. W. (1950). Studies on the life-cycle of *Fasciola hepatica* (Linnaeus) and of its snail host, *Limnaea* (Galba) *truncatula* (Müller) in the field and under controlled conditions in the laboratory. *Ann. trop. Med. Parasit*. **44**, 187–206.

Ross, I. C. (1930). Some observations on the bionomics of *Fasciola hepatica*. *Jap. J. exp. Med.* **8**, 65–69.

Ross, I. C. and McKay, A. C. (1929). The bionomics of *Fasciola hepatica* in New South Wales and of the intermediate host *Limnaea brazieri*. *Bull. Counc. sci. industr. Res. Aust.* **43**, 1–62.

Rowan, W. B. (1956). The mode of hatching of the egg of *Fasciola hepatica*. *Exp Parasit.* **5**, 118–137.

Rowcliffe, S. A. and Ollerenshaw, C. B. (1960). Observations on the bionomics o the egg of *Fasciola hepatica*. *Ann. trop. Med. Parasit.* **54**, 172–181.

Sandground, J. H. (1929). A consideration of the relation of host-specificity o helminths and other metazoan parasites to the phenomena of age resistance an acquired immunity. *Parasitology* **21**, 227.

Sarwar, M. M. (1957). *Fasciola indica* Varma, a synonym of *Fasciola gigantic* Cobbold. *Biologica* **3**, 168–175.

Schreiber, F. G. and Schubert, M. (1949). Experimental infection of the snai *Australorbis glabratus* with the trematode *Schistosoma mansoni* and th production of cercariae. *J. Parasit.* **35**, 91–100.

Shaw, J. N. (1932). Studies of the liver fluke (*Fasciola hepatica*). *J. Amer. vet. Med Ass.* **81**, 76–82.

Shirai, M. (1925). On the intermediate host of *Fasciola hepatica* in Japan. *Sci. Rep Inst. infect. Dis. Tokyo Univ.* **4**, 441–446.

Shirai, M. (1927). The biological observation on the cysts of *Fasciola hepatica* and the route of migration of the young worms in the final host. *Sci. Rep. Inst infect. Dis. Tokyo Univ.* **6**, 511–523.

Sinitsin, D. F. (1933). Studien über die Phylogenie der Trematoden. The life his tories of some American liver flukes. *Z. Parasitenk.* **6**, 170–191, 243–268.

Standen, O. D. (1963). *In* "Experimental Chemotherapy" (R. J. Schnitzer and F. Hawking, eds.), Vol. 1, p. 746. Academic Press, New York and London.

Stirewalt, M. A. (1954). Effect of snail maintenance temperatures on development of *Schistosoma mansoni*. *Exp. Parasit.* **3**, 504.

Swales, W. E. (1935). The life-cycle of *Fascioloides magna* (Bassi, 1875), the large liver-fluke of ruminants in Canada. *Canad. J. Res.* **12**, 177–215.

Thapar, G. S. and Tandon, R. S. (1953). Addendum to the "Life-history of Liver-fluke *Fasciola gigantica* in India." *Indian J. Helminth.* **5**, 121.

Thomas, A. P. (1883). The life-history of the liver fluke (*Fasciola hepatica*). *Quart. J. micr. Sci.* N.S. **23**, 99–133.

Ueno, H. and Watanabe, S. (1960). Ecological studies on the common liver fluke in Japan. I. Comparison of intermediate hosts between the Japanese native liver fluke and *Fasciola hepatica* from England. *Bull. Nat. Inst. Anim. Hlth, Tokyo* **38**, 167–181.

Varma, A. K. (1953). On *Fasciola indica* n. sp. with some observations on *F. hepatica* and *F. gigantica*. *J. Helminth.* **27**, 185.

Vogel, H. (1942). Infektionsversuche an verschiedenen Bilharzia-zwischen-wirten mit einen einzelnen Mirazidiun von *Bilharzia mansoni* und *B. japonica*. *Zbl. Bakt.* **148**, 29.

Walton, C. L. (1918). Liver rot of sheep and the bionomics of *Limnaea truncatula* in the Aberystwyth area. *Parasitology* **10**, 232–266.

Watanabe, S. (1958). *J. Jap. vet. med. Ass.* **11**, 293.

Wikerhauser, T. and Brglez, J. (1961). Viability of *Fasciola hepatica* metacercariae in silage. *Vet. Arhiv.* **31**, 315–318.

Wright, C. A., Harris, R. H. and Claugher, D. (1957). Paper chromatography in taxonomic work. *Nature, Lond.* **180**, 1489.

Paragonimus and Paragonimiasis

MUNEO YOKOGAWA

Department of Parasitology, School of Medicine,
Chiba University, Chiba, Japan

I. Introduction

Within recent years the marked advances of research into *Paragonimus* and paragonimiasis have been shown in the taxonomic, immunodiagnostic and chemotherapeutic fields. With regard to classification of the lung flukes, new species of *Paragonimus* have recently been reported from various countries. In some species the morphological characters of the adult worms and larvae and also the different patterns of the route of migration of the larvae in the final hosts have been clearly indicated by cytochemical and histochemical investigations besides the routine examinations.

The intradermal and complement fixation tests for paragonimiasis have been predominantly improved and widely applied, not only for clinical diagnosis but for the screening of large population masses in the endemic areas of paragonimiasis, because of reliability and simplicity. Bithionol, a new agent against paragonimiasis, has been proved to be the best drug in comparison with the various drugs previously studied. The possibility of control of paragonimiasis can be expected, judging from up-to-date results of mass treatment with bithionol in the endemic areas of Japan. This review will present each topic, including recent advances in this aspect of the subject.

II. SPECIES OF *Paragonimus*

Paragonimus westermani is the only species believed to develop in man. In addition to this one, sixteen species of *Paragonimus* have been reported in various mammals in several countries since the discovery of *Paragonimus rudis* in the lungs of an otter, *Lutra braziliense*, by Diesing (1850) in Brazil (Table I).

TABLE I

Species of Paragonimus

P. rudis (Diesing, 1850)
P. compactus (Cobbold, 1859)
P. westermani (Kerbert, 1878)
P. ringeri (Cobbold, 1880)*
P. pulmonis (Nakahama, 1880)*
P. pulmonalis (Baelz, 1883)*
P. kellicotti (Ward, 1908)
P. edwardsi (Gulati, 1926)*
P. ohirai (Miyazaki, 1939)
P. iloktsuenensis (Chen, 1940)
P. macacae (Sandosham, 1953)*
P. yunnanensis (Ho *et al.*, 1957)
P. skrjabini (Chen, 1959)
P. miyazakii (Kamo *et al.*, 1961)
P. szechuanensis (Chung *et al.*, 1962)
P. fukiensis (T'ang *et al.*, 1962)
P. africana (Vogel, 1963)

*Appears to be identical with *P. westermani.*

Quite a few of these species are considered as synonyms rather than as valid species. Some have been described as new species for the only reason that they have been found in different hosts. The adult worms are so fleshy that it is difficult to work out the details of internal structure, and there is an unusual amount of variation within a species in adult characters and in the sizes and shapes of the eggs. For this reason there is still no general agreement on the relationships of these species of *Paragonimus*, in spite of much careful work over a period of many years. However, recent studies on the morphology of the larval stages and the migration route of the young forms in the final hosts have shown the relationships in some species of *Paragonimus*.

At present the life cycles of four species—*P. westermani, P. kellicotti, P. ohirai* and *P. iloktsuenensis*—are fully known, and therefore there is no doubt about their validity. The validity of *P. compactus* has been doubted both on account of the inadequate original description of Cobbold (1859) and also the apparent inaccuracies in the account of spines by Vevers (1923) for the other species that he described in the paper on *P. compactus*.

Recently, Dissanaike and Paramananthan (1962) found lung flukes in a civet cat (*Vivericula indica mayori*) and a fishing cat (*Felis viverina*) in Ceylon and identified these worms provisionally as *P. compactus*. He pointed out the arrangement of the spines in groups in all regions of this species. However, he stated that it is doubtful whether this characteristic can be employed to distinguish *P. compactus* from *P. westermani*. The metacercariae of *P. compactus* have not been found in Ceylon.

P. rudis can have no standing as a separate species because the original description was not sufficient for identification. Miyazaki (1955) made a morphological study of the cuticular spines and ovaries of specimens from the skunk in Guatemala which Caballero had identified as *P. rudis*. He compared those structures in this material with specimens of *P. kellicotti* from the cat which he had obtained from the U.S.A. From these comparisons he concluded that Caballero's material belonged to *P. kellicotti*.

Ho and Chung (1959) described *P. yunnanensis* in Yunnan province, China, but the description seems to be very meagre except for the extraordinary size of the metacercariae.

Chen (1960) described *P. skrjabini* from *Paguma larvata* in Kwantung province, China. Chung and Tsao (1962) also described *P. szechuanensis* from cats and dogs in Ch'engtu, Szechuan province, China. These two species seem to be identical in the morphological features described by these authors. However, Chung and Tsao stated that, although *P. szechuanensis* more or less resembles *P. skrjabini* in general appearance, it can be distinguished from *P. skrjabini* by its common occurrence in characteristic human pathological and clinical manifestations of subcutaneous nodular paragonimiasis in Szechuan province which are not known with *P. skrjabini* in Kwantung province. Setting aside the question of this difference, it is a very important fact that such lung flukes mainly cause a painful migratory subcutaneous nodule in man in China.

Kamo *et al.* (1961) reported *Paragonimus miyazakii* as a new species, and found a quite different metacercaria from that of *P. westermani* in *Potamon dehaani* in Yamaguchi prefecture, Japan, also obtaining adult worms after feeding the metacercariae to dogs. The structure was compared with specimens of *P. kellicotti* and the conclusion reached that this was a new species. Soon after, Miyazaki reported that the fluke which was found in weasels of Kyushu and identified as *P. kellicotti* by him should be regarded as *P. miyazakii*.

Recently, Vogel (1963) found a lung fluke which he identified as a new species, *Paragonimus africana*, from the lungs of the mongoose and dogs in the Cameroons and Congo, in a survey of paragonimiasis in West Africa. In comparing the morphological features of the adults of this species with those of known species, Vogel stressed the size of the oral and ventral suckers. In *P. africana* the oral sucker is always larger than the ventral sucker, but in any other species at present known the ventral sucker is larger than the oral sucker. In addition to these characteristics, the metacercaria of *P. africana* found in two kinds of crabs, *Sudanatus africanus* and *S. pelii*, is larger than the metacercariae of other species.

Vogel also found flukes from the dog in the Cameroons and *Atilax paludinosus* in Liberia which he regarded as a new species.

III. Species Differentiation

A. CERCARIAE

The body of the cercariae of *Paragonimus* is covered with small spines, the largest of which are 4 μ in length; they are especially dense and quite long from the ventral side of the posterior half of the body to the tail in *P. ohirai* and *P. iloktsuenensis*. The flame cell formula of the cercariae of *P. westermani* and *P. iloktsuenensis* are shown to be $2[(3+3+3+3+3)+(3+3+3+3+3)]$ $=60$ (Yamaguti, 1943). M. Yokogawa *et al.* (1958b) found the flame cell formula of the cercaria of *P. ohirai* to be $2[(1+1+1+1+1)+(1+1+1+1+1)]=20$, while that of the metacercariae was the same as for the cercariae and metacercariae of *P. westermani*, $2[(3+3+3+3+3)+(3+3+3+3+3)]=60$. The first intermediate host of *P. miyazakii* has not been yet determined.

Kobayashi (1921) described in the cercariae of *P. westermani*, in addition to the penetration glands, two irregular rows of gland cells on each side of the body. These glands were also shown by Ameel (1934) for *P. kellicotti* and by Tang (1940) for *P. westermani* and *P. iloktsuenensis*. Kruidenier (1953) described the structure of the glands in detail in the cercaria of *P. kellicotti*. He called them "ventral gland cells" or "mucoid glands" and stated that six pairs of these glands lie parallel to the median axis of the developing cerceria, and that they secrete mucoid substances during the final stages of the development of the cercariae. Kruidenier suggested that these mucoid glands play an important role in the activities of the cercariae after emergence from the intermediate host. Mucoid strands attach them to each other, and make possible their attachment to the substratum by the tip of the tail. Mucoid substance originating in the glands was believed to help cercariae to attach to the surface or appendages of the second intermediate host, and also to have a protective function for swimming cercariae. Yokogawa and Yoshima (1956) examined stained specimens of both mature and immature cercariae of *P. westermani* following the method described by Kruidenier, and also found six pairs of "mucoid glands", but were unable to find in freed cercariae the mucoid strands which had been observed by Kruidenier in the cercariae of *P. kellicotti*.

B. METACERCARIAE

The size and shape of the mature metacercariae freed from the outer

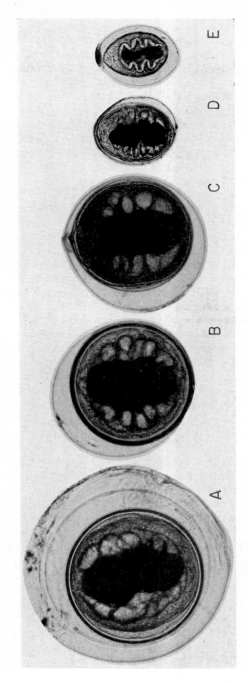

Fig. 1. Metacercariae of *Paragonimus*. A, *P. miyazakii*; B, *P. westermani*; C, *P. kellicotti*; D, *P. ohirai*; E, *P. iloktsuenensis*. All to same scale. (Courtesy of Dr. T. Tomimura and Dr. I. Miyazaki.)

membrane of several species of *Paragonimus* are shown in Fig. 1: *P. miyazaki* 426–515 μ (Kamo *et al.*, 1961), globular, cyst walls consist of thin outer membrane and thick inner membrane; *P. kellicotti*, 381–457 × 381–447 μ (mean 420 × 406 μ) (Ameel, 1934), oval, with thin outer and thick inner membrane; *P. westermani*, 340–450 × 320–440 μ (Yamaguti, 1943), globular, with thin and thick membrane; *P. ohirai*, 264–348 × 300–352 μ, oval, with thin and thick membrane; *P. iloktsuenensis*, 302–230 × 214–200 μ (mean 258 × 216 μ) (Chen, 1940), oval and rarely spherical, cyst wall consists of only one layer. The mature encysted metacercariae of these species, except *P. iloktsuenensis*, are greatly contracted and rarely folded. The most conspicuous features of the mature encysted metacercaria are the large median excretory bladder filled with highly refractive excretory granules and the twisted lateral intestinal caeca.

The cyst wall of the metacercaria of *P. iloktsuenensis* differs from that of any *Paragonimus* species mentioned above. Notably, the simple cyst wall around the metacercaria of *P. iloktsuenensis* is a thin hyaline membrane, like the outer layer of the cyst walls of *P. westermani*, *P. kellicotti* and other species. The mature form of this species inside the cyst is usually stretched. Pigment present in the parenchyma of the metacercariae of *P. westermani*, *P. ohirai* and *P. iloktsuenensis* create a pinkish tint visible to the naked eye.

Komiya and Tomimura (1964) studied the morphology of the metacercaria of *Paragonimus miyazakii*, which is larger in diameter than that of *P. westermani* and has no pink colour such as is frequently seen in that of *P. westermani* isolated from *Eriocheir japonicus*. They also pointed out that in the metacercariae of *P. miyazakii* the vitellaria rudiment was usually better developed than that of *P. westermani*, but this characteristic would not always serve to identify metacercariae of the two species. On the contrary, the existence of several gland cell-like structures lateral to the oesophagus in the metacercaria of *P. miyazakii* serves for identification, that of *P. westermani* having no such cells.

C. ADULT WORM

1. *Cuticular Spines*

It is generally believed that cuticular spines on the body surface cannot serve for species differentiation, because they vary greatly in size, structure and arrangement according to their position, and also in individuals of different age or species of host. It may be impossible to identify the species solely by the cuticular spines. However, in spite of their variability, differences in the cuticular spines, especially their arrangement in groups, definitely distinguish the "*iloktsuenensis-ohirai*" group of the genus *Paragonimus* from the "*westermani-kellicotti*" group in which the spines are singly spaced (Chen, 1940; Miyazaki, 1944; Dissanaike and Paramananthan, 1962).

2. *Ovary*

There have been many discussions on whether the form of the ovary in adult worms can be said to be a characteristic feature of the species. Miyazaki (1943) reported that *P. westermani* and *P. ohirai* were easily distinguished from

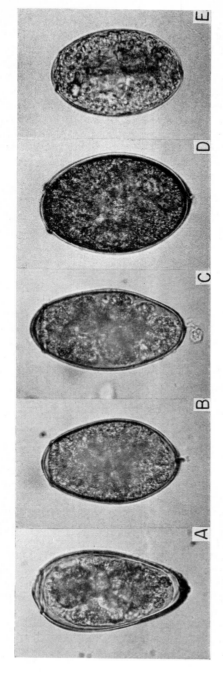

FIG. 2. Eggs of *Paragonimus*. A, *P. westermani*; B, *P. ohirai*; C, *P. iloktsuenensis*; D, *P. kellicotti*; E, *P. miyazakii*. All to same scale. (Courtesy of Dr. T. Tomimura.)

each other in stained specimens. However, Nagayoshi (1942) reported the detailed structure of the ovary of *P. westermani*, making a wax reconstruction model of the organ. He stressed the necessity of making models of the main internal organs and observing them in order to distinguish species in three dimensions.

Miyazaki reported that, although to distinguish *P. westermani* from *P. kellicotti* was impossible by cuticular spines, it was possible by the structure of the ovary. Miyazaki (1961) reported that *Paragonimus* can be divided into four groups according to the shape of the ovary and arrangement of cuticular spines as follows: (1) *westermani*-group, ovary simply branched off into four to six lobes, cuticular spines singly spaced; (2) *compactus*-group, ovary simply branched off into four to six lobes, cuticular spines in groups; (3) *kellicotti-miyazaki* group, ovary profusely branched, cuticular spines singly spaced; (4) *ohirai-iloktsuenensis* group, ovary profusely branched, cuticular spines in groups.

As for the position of the ovary of *P. westermani*, Kubo (1912) reported the ratio of the left and the right to be 11:7; Nagayoshi (1942) 30:30; Tanabe (1950) 6:24 and Yokogawa (1964) 50:50.

3. *Eggs*

The eggs of *P. westermani* are generally irregular in shape, mostly asymmetrical, and the egg shell varies in thickness throughout. The eggs of *P. ohirai* are shaped like hen's eggs and the shell has a uniform thickness, usually having a small knob-like process at the opercular end. The eggs of *P. kellicotti* also have a uniform thickness except for a slight thickening at the anopercular pole, which tapers more sharply than in *P. westermani* giving a somewhat pointed tip. The eggs of *P. westermani* and *P. kellicotti* can easily be distinguished when in batches, but it seems to be quite difficult to distinguish the individual eggs.

The eggs of *P. westermani*, *P. kellicotti*, *P. miyazakii*, *P. ohirai* and *P. iloktsuenensis* are shown in Fig. 2.

IV. LIFE CYCLE

A. *Paragonimus westermani*

1. *First Intermediate Hosts*

The snail intermediate hosts of *P. westermani* all belong to the Thiaridae, which is a widely distributed family of rather large operculate snails. This family contains many genera and several hundred species which live in fresh and brackish water. Until recently, members of this family that serve as intermediate hosts for trematode species have all been assigned to the genus *Melania* (*Semisulcospira*) in the medical and parasitological literature. *Semisulcospira libertina* (*S. bensoni*) is probably the most important intermediate host of *P. westermani*. This species has an insular distribution which extends from Japan and Korea to Okinawa, Formosa and China. In Japan, it has been observed that *S. libertina* is omnivorous and that it feeds on the decayed remains of water plants and animals. *Melania amurensis* (*Hua amurensis*) and several of its varieties were implicated by Kobayashi (1926) as intermediate host of *P. westermani* on Korea. In regard to this species Abbott (1948) states: "The animals of this species have not been examined, and it is provisionally included in *Hua*, although subsequent work may place it in the genus *Semisulcospira*."

Melania obliquegranosa (*Tarebia grarnifera*) was reported as the first intermediate host of *P. westermani* in Formosa by Nakagawa (1917). This species has a wide distribution from the East Indies, Melanesia, Micronesia, throughout the Philippines and northwards to Formosa. *Brotia asperata* has been shown to be an intermediate host of *P. westermani* in the Philippines by Tubangui *et al.* (1950) and Yogore (1956, 1957).

Many researchers in Japan have attempted the experimental infection on *Semisulcospira* sp. with the miracidia of *P. westermani* but none was completely successful in producing fully developed cercariae.

Recently, Komiya *et al.* (1961) reported that they obtained mature cercariae from *Semisulcospira bensoni* experimentally infected with the miracidia of *P. westermani*. According to their description, 315 of the young snails, *Semisulcospira bensoni*, were exposed to a large number of newly hatched miracidia (140–2 940 miracidia per snail) of *P. westermani* for 20 h in a Petri dish with water. After exposure, these snails were bred in an aquaria at 25° C, and three snails per week were dissected. In six out of 315 snails exposed mature cercariae were found as early as 9 weeks after infection. Although many snails were exposed to a large number of miracidia, the infected snails with the cercariae of *P. westermani* were not many. They reported, therefore, that it would be doubtful whether such a method of infection as they used, would really occur in nature.

2. Second Intermediate Hosts

More than eleven species of crayfish and freshwater crabs have been reported as the second intermediate hosts of *P. westermani*. Until the experimental studies of M. Yokogawa (1952a) there appears to have been no report of the natural shedding of the cercariae of *P. westermani* by the snail intermediate host. In his experiments only a very few cercariae escaped, most of which were from one snail for which the temperature was accidentally raised to 37° C. He therefore concluded that under natural conditions the cercariae of *P. westermani* rarely, if ever, escape naturally from the snail hosts. Yokogawa (1952a) reported about 10% of the specimens of *Eriocheir japonicus* that he examined harboured immature and/or degenerated cercariae of *P. westermani* in the intestinal wall and blood vessels of the gills of the crabs. He never found cercariae or immature metacercariae attached to the outside of the gill filaments of the crabs. He interpreted these observations to mean that the cercariae had not invaded the second intermediate host by active penetration. Yokogawa (1953) carried out a series of experiments in which he fed to crabs the digestive glands of infected snails containing mature cercariae. He succeeded in obtaining mature metacercariae of *P. westermani* in those crabs which were fed the cercariae. He concluded from the experiments that the second intermediate hosts of *P. westermani* can be infected by eating snails containing mature cercariae. However, Wu (1935) reported that the crabs can be infected by the penetration of free cercariae. Recently, Noble (1963) reported that the result of his experimental infection of the crabs with the cercariae of *P. westermani* tends to support the view of Yokogawa (1953) that crabs acquire *Paragonimus* infection by eating free cercariae or possibly infected snails. Nicolaus and Panning (1933) reported that *Eriocheir sinensis* in Germany commonly feeds on snails.

3. Definitive Hosts

The most common wild animal hosts of *P. westermani* belong to the cat family (including tigers, lions, leopards, panthers and wild cats), pigs and dogs. In Japan, early records showed that the weasel (*Mustela itatsi itatsi*), the badger (*Nycterentes procyonoides viverimus*) and the marten are the definitive hosts of *P. westermani*. However, in these records the species of *Paragonimus* are lacking in specificity in their definitive host relations. It is sometimes difficult to be sure of the particular species to which host records refer. Later reports in Japan indicate that all the worms recovered from such animals as weasels, badgers, martens and wild boars are identified as *P. ohirai* or *P. miyazakii*.

M. Yokogawa *et al.* (1957a,b) and Shigemi (1957) reported that the badgers, weasels and mink were refractory to infection with *P. westermani*. S. Yokogawa (1919, unpublished) reported that the experimental infections of Formosan monkeys with *P. westermani* was successful, producing serious inflammatory adhesions in the abdominal and thoracic regions.

Sandosham (1950) has reported *Paragonimus macacae* which seemed to be identical with *P. westermani* from a Kra monkey of the Malayan jungle. M. Yokogawa *et al.* (1962–64, unpublished) carried out a series of experimental infections of Japanese monkeys and crab-eating monkeys (*Macaca cynomologi*) of Malaya with the metacercariae of *P. westermani*. They found that it seemed to be more difficult to produce infection in the Japanese monkey than in the crab-eating monkey.

B. Paragonimus kellicotti

1. First Intermediate Host

Pomatiopsis lapidaria is the only known intermediate host of *P. kellicotti* (Ameel, 1932, 1934). Ameel (1934) studied the development of the cercariae of *P. kellicotti* in experimental infection of *Pomatiopsis lapidaria*. It is estimated that a mother sporocyst can produce at least twenty-five first generation rediae and that each of those can produce at least thirty daughter rediae: this would make a conservative estimate of the potential daughter rediae production about 750. Actually in natural infection only a small number of daughter rediae have been found; in twenty-one infections in which the daughter rediae that were producing cercariae were counted the number varied from eleven to sixty-two.

Recently, Basch (1959) reported the results of experimental infection in four related species of amphibious prosobranch snails with *P. kellicotti*, in which adult and laboratory-raised young *Pomatiopsis cincinnatiensis* from a colony on the Raisin River near Clinton, Michigan, adults of *Oncomelania nosophora* from Japan, *O. formosana* from Formosa, *O. quadrasi* from the Philippines and *Pomatiopsis lapidaria* as controls, were exposed to the miracidia of *P. kellicotti*. Of those snails which could be definitely evaluated for the presence of larval *Paragonimus* (at least 1 month after exposure), 6 out of 8 *P. cincinnatiensis* and 2 out of 5 *O. nosophora* were found to be well infected in addition to 8 out of 12 *P. lapidaria*. Normal cercariae were produced in all three species of snails. Six each of other two species of *Oncomelania* were negative.

2. Second Intermediate Hosts

Ameel (1934) reported that several species of crayfish of the genus *Cambarus* serve as second intermediate hosts of *P. kellicotti* in the United States and most of the specimens of *Cambarus propinquus* collected from a small stream near Ann Arbor, Michigan, contained twenty to thirty metacercariae, although forty was not uncommon.

3. Definitive Hosts

Ameel (1934) reported that worms in experimentally infected cats became sexually mature and produced eggs in 5½–6 weeks. Cats, dogs, pigs, mink (*Mustela vison*), and muskrats (*Ondatra zibethica*) are known as the definitive hosts of *P. kellicotti*. Experimental infections with *P. kellicotti* were carried out by Ameel (1934) in white rats, which however, were not considered a normal host because the worms usually disappeared from the worm cysts of the lungs within 2–3 months after infection. Waitz *et al.* (1964) reported that the infection in rats does persist for several months and includes both immature forms in the body cavities and stunted adults in the lungs.

c. *Paragonimus ohirai*

1. First Intermediate Hosts

Ogida (1954) and Ikeda (1957) reported experimental infections demonstrating that *Assiminea japonica* can serve as the intermediate host of *P. ohirai*. However, these authors examined several hundred thousand specimens of *Assiminea japonica* without finding any natural infections of the cercariae of *P. ohirai*.

M. Yokogawa *et al.* (1958b) found the snails naturally infected with the cercariae of *P. ohirai* in Minato and Kisami, Shimoda machi, Shizuoka prefecture, Japan. This snail was identified as *Paludinella devilis* (Gould, 1861), Habe (1942). In August 1957 four snails positive for the cercariae of *P. ohirai* were found out of 6 082 snails examined, and in August 1958 two positive in 862 snails examined.

At the same time examinations were made for natural infections of *P. ohirai* in *Assiminea japonica* and no positives were found in 15 410 snails examined. Successful experimental infections of *P. devilis* with the miracidia of *P. ohirai* were also carried out by Yokogawa *et al.* (1958b), while attempts to infect *Assiminea japonica* experimentally failed.

Kuroda (1958) did not agree with Yokogawa's classification of the intermediate host of *P. ohirai* and considered it to be a new species of the genus *Assiminea* to which he gave the name *Assiminea parasitologica*. Yoshida and Miyamoto (1960) reported another new species, *Assiminea yoshidayukioi*, as the intermediate host of *P. ohirai*.

Kawashima and Miyazaki (1963) reported the successful experimental infection of *Oncomelania nosophora* with *P. ohirai* in which these snails were exposed to a number of newly hatched miracidia (25 miracidia per snail) of *P. ohirai* for 24 h. In all sixty-three snails examined between 123 and 134 days after exposure, the second generation rediae and mature cercariae of *P. ohirai* were found. They stated that miracidia of *P. ohirai* and *O. nosophora* have a great affinity for each other, and this seemed to suggest that *P. ohirai* has a high infectivity for amphibious snails such as *Assiminea parasitologica*, *A. yoshidayukioi*, *Paludinella japonica* and *O. nosophora* rather than aquatic snails.

2. Second Intermediate Hosts

The following five crabs, *Sesarma intermedia*, *S. dehaani*, *Helice tridens tridens*, *Chasmagnathus convexus* and *Sesarma hematocheir* are known as the second intermediate hosts of *P. ohirai*. The metacercariae were loosely attached to the liver and rarely to the muscles. Yoshida and Miyamoto (1960) reported that the infection of the crabs can occur by penetration of free cercariae.

3. Definitive Hosts

Rats, pigs, dogs, weasels, badgers, anakuma and wild boars have been found to serve as natural definitive hosts of *P. ohirai*. Miyazaki (1940) and Mannoji (1952) experimentally infected dogs, cats, rats, mice, rabbits and guinea-pigs with *P. ohirai*. Of these animals the rabbits and guinea-pigs seemed to be unsuitable because the experimental infections were not always successful. In rats the flukes became sexually mature within 30 days, but the adult worms in the worm cysts of the lungs gradually died several months after infection.

D. *Paragonimus iloktsuenensis*

1. First Intermediate Hosts

Assiminea lutea was implicated as the intermediate host of *P. iloktsuenensis* by Chen (1935). Tang (1940) reported that *Katayama tangi* served as the intermediate host of the rodent lung fluke which was considered as *P. iloktsuenensis* in Fukien province, China. In Japan *Assiminea parasitologica* and *A. yoshidayukioi* were implicated as the first intermediate host of *P. iloktsuenensis* by Tomimura *et al.* (1960). Kawashima and Miyazaki (1963) reported the successful result of the experimental infection of *Oncomelania nosophora* with the miracidia of *P. iloktsuenensis*. They stated that *P. iloktsuenensis* is closely related to *P. ohirai* in its affinity to the snail host, also showing greater infectivity to amphibious snails (*Assiminea parasitologica*, *A. yoshidayukioi* and *O. nosophora*) than to aquatic snails.

2. Second Intermediate Hosts

Chen (1935) first found the metacercaria of *P. iloktsuenensis* in *Sesarma dehaani* and *S. sinensis* in China. Mannoji (1952) found the metacercaria of *P. iloktsuenensis* in *Helice tridens tridens*. Tang (1940) reported that *Parathelphusa sinensis* was the second intermediate host of this species. Chiu (1962) found for the first time the metacercaria of *P. iloktsuenensis* in *Potamon* sp. in Formosa.

3. Definitive Hosts

Chen (1940) reported that natural infections of *P. iloktsuenensis* were found only in rats (*Rattus rattus* and *R. norvegicus*). Chen also stated that his experimental infection showed that mice, rats, cats, dogs and wild pigs were suitable hosts for this species, while monkeys, domestic pigs, guinea-pigs and wild cats were unsuitable.

Isshiki (1953) has reported a case of spontaneous infection with *P. iloktsuenensis* in a dog in Japan. *Rattus norvegicus* and *R. coxinga* were confirmed as reservoir hosts of *P. iloktsuenensis* in Formosa by Chiu (1962).

E. OTHER SPECIES OF *Paragonimus*

Chung *et al.* (1963) reported that the little snails, called *mienchu hsiaoluo* in Szechuan province, looking rather like but much smaller than *Oncomelania*, were naturally infected with typical microcercous cercariae of *Paragonimus*, probably of *P. szechuanensis*. This minute snail was identified as *Tricula* sp.

Vogel (1963) reported that adult worms of a new species of *Paragonimus*, for which the name *P. africana* is proposed, were recovered from five mongooses (*Crossarchus abscurus*) and from a dog. Immature worms of the same species were obtained from another mongoose (*Atliax paludinosus*) and a civet cat. Experimentally, flukes of this species could be raised to maturity in cats, dogs and a monkey (*Mandrillus leucophaeus*) by feeding the metacercariae. The metacercariae of this species were found in two species of crabs, *Sudanautes africanus* and *S. pelii*. He reported that a melaniid snail, *Potadomus freethii*, is probably the first intermediate host.

V. BIOLOGY AND PHYSIOLOGY

A. DEVELOPMENT OF THE MIRACIDIUM

The optimum temperature for the development of the eggs of *Paragonimus westermani* has been shown to range from 28° to 32° C.

Ameel (1934) found that the most suitable temperature for the development of the eggs of *P. kellicotti* was 27° C. When kept at this temperature in an incubator, they developed to the miracidial stage in about 2 weeks and began to hatch in about 3 weeks. Chen (1940) found that the eggs of *P. iloktsuenensis* took about the same time for development.

Ito (1949) reported that the eggs taken from the uterus of adult *P. westermani* from the lung of the infected dog developed more rapidly than those taken from the stool. Sano (1959) mentioned that bile acids of the host probably inhibit the development of the eggs.

Beaver *et al.* (1964) reported on the successful development of *Paragonimus* eggs in Harada-Mori's culture, using filter paper. Eggs of *P. kellicotti* in faeces were spread in a thin film on a strip of filter paper, the tip of which was soaked in water from the test tube according to the method of Harada and Mori (1951). They found that the miracidia developed in the eggs within 17–20 days, and eggs with miracidia remained viable in the cultures for 3 months. They also reported that when these eggs were placed in water, a high proportion of the miracidia hatched, especially if subjected to a sudden change of temperature. However, hatching in water was not necessary for infecting snails. They reported that of sixty-seven *Pomatiopsis lapidaria* allowed to feed directly on the leached culture faeces, six became infected and shed cercariae in 60–68 days.

The miracidia of *P. westermani*, being different from those of *Schistosoma japonica* or *Fasciola hepatica*, are retained in the eggs for a long period without hatching and a considerably high proportion of them die in the eggs. Garrison and Leynes (1909) reported that the miracidia of *P. westermani* were retained in the eggs for as long as 160 days after completion of miracidial development. Ameel (1934) and Chen (1940) found the same lag in the hatching of the eggs of *P. kellicotti* and *P. iloktsuenensis*, respectively. Ameel found that hatching could be readily initiated by a sudden lowering of the temperature through the introduction of cold water into the culture. Hatching was also brought about by transfer of such cultures from room temperature or incubation temperature to an ice box at 7° C for 5–10 min. According to Chen, an increase in temperature sometimes induced hatching but this change was not always effectual. He considered that the strong light or the increase in temperature was one of the factors stimulating the hatching, and he also found that a good method of inducing it was to stir up the culture containing the eggs with a pipette. Methods of hatching presently used in addition to the above are to put the eggs into a small bottle with a small amount of water and shake the bottle vigorously, or to project artificial light directly on to the culture.

Sano (1959) reported that natural hatching continued little by little at 20–30° C after the development of the miracidia and it took 5–6 weeks to hatch 70–80% of the eggs.

B. RESISTANCE OF THE METACERCARIAE

Shimono and Yamaoka (1957) and Tsuda (1959) investigated the period spent by the metacercariae of *P. westermani* in water and the life span of the metacercariae in the second intermediate host, *Eriocheir japonicus*, after its death. Most of the metacercariae removed from the body of the hosts in water at high temperature in summer died within 3–5 days, while in winter, when the temperature of water decreased to 4–5° C, they survived for 10–20 days. These authors also reported that the metacercariae in the body of *Eriocheir japonicus* continued to live for 3–4 weeks even after its death, as long as the crab was kept at 2–5° C.

Considering that in summer the metacercariae in warm water are often found to possess an enlarged cyst wall and to excyst naturally, Oshima (1957) measured the osmotic pressure of tissue fluid of *Eriocheir japonicus*, and showed that it was as high as or greater than 2% NaCl solution. He also reported that the reason why the metacercariae in water died earlier lay in the difference of the osmotic pressure and that they certainly survived for 4 months at 5° C in the following preservative solution (which has about the same osmotic pressure as that of crayfish): NaCl, 2·20 g; NaHCO$_3$, 0·02 g; MgCl$_2$, 0·02 g; CaCl$_2$, 0·15 g; and H$_2$O, 100 ml.

Ando (1915) and Nakagawa (1916) studied the resistance of the metacercariae of *P. westermani* to heat, and stated that by boiling *Eriocheir japonicus* for 20 min at 55° C, the metacercariae in the body of the crabs all died. It was also reported that if the crabs were soaked in *shoyu* (Japanese soy-bean sauce), the metacercariae in the muscles of the host died in 24 h, but they survived in vinegar, sugar, *miso* (bean-paste), salt and *sake-kasu* (brewers' grains).

Tsuda (1959) stated that all the metacercariae died when they were frozen for more than 2 days at −10° to −13° C, while, if frozen for a short time and then slowly warmed, the metacercariae had their activity restored. When frozen at −40° C, they were all dead within 30 min. He also reported that the metacercariae of *P. westermani* were very vulnerable to desiccation. If water covering the metacercariae be removed to dry them, the cyst wall is broken within 3–4 min and the worms inside die. Metacercariae soaked in 3% antiformin solution lost the cyst wall within 2 h.

C. EXCYSTMENT OF THE METACERCARIAE

The excystment of the metacercariae of *P. westermani* has been studied by many early researchers in Japan, and the digestive enzymes have been said to play an important part in the process. According to S. Yokogawa (1917), when metacercariae are immersed first in an artificial gastric juice and then in an artificial intestinal juice, excystment soon occurs, but when kept in the artificial gastric juice for a long period the larvae die without being able to excyst.

Recently, Oshima (1956) and Oshima *et al.* (1958) reported that both temperature and pH of the medium were the most important factors to stimulate excystment. When the metacercariae of *P. westermani* were kept in Tyrode's solution at a temperature of 40° C and a pH of 8·0–8·5, more than 80% of them excysted within 4 h; whereas when kept at a pH of less than 7·0 at the same temperature of 40° C, only a few of them excysted. He also reported that when kept at a temperature lower than 34° C even at pH 8·0–8·5, only a few of them excysted. In these experiments no influence on excystment by such digestive enzymes as pepsin (at pH 1·5) and trypsin (at pH 8·0) was found. Oshima also pointed out that cholic acids, such as sodium deoxycholate, sodium taurocholate, and sodium cholate acted as stimuli on the excystment, as well as temperature and pH; for instance, in 0·1% sodium deoxycholate at 40° C, almost 100% of metacercariae had excysted within 30 min. However, all the investigations on excystment of the metacercariae mentioned above have been carried out *in vitro* and no information had been given as to their activity in the body of the final host until M. Yokogawa *et al.* (1958c, 1959) investigated the migration route of *P. westermani* in the final host, using the Evans blue technique. In rats the excysted forms penetrating through the intestinal wall were found within 30 min after giving metacercariae of *P. westermani*; in cats the excysted larvae were found in the intestinal wall within 1 h. On the other hand, in guinea-pigs those excysted forms were not found even after 3 h. The contents of the small intestines in these animals where excystment had occurred usually showed a pH of 5·0–6·0. It is impossible to regard pH and temperature of the medium as the only stimulating factors during excystment.

D. DEVELOPMENT OF THE EXCYSTED FORMS CULTURED *in vitro*

No attempt had been made to culture the excysted forms of *Paragonimus westermani in vitro* before M. Yokogawa *et al.* (1955b, 1958a) succeeded in their attempt. Excysted forms which were kept in a test tube at 37° C for 204 days showed a marked development, growing more than a dozen times larger, and also showing remarkable differentiations of the internal organs, especially the ovary, uterus and testes.

The method used was as follows. The metacercariae of *P. westermani* were separated from *Eriocheir japonicus* and placed in Tyrode's solution, pH 8·0–8·4, in an incubator at 38° C for 8–10 h. The excysted larvae then obtained were cultured in a medium consisting of cat serum diluted two to four times with Tyrode's solution. Penicillin 100 u./ml, streptomycin 100 μg/ml were added to the medium and the pH adjusted to 7·0–7·4. In each small test tube, two to five excysted worms were placed in the medium which was kept at 37° C in an incubator with a rubber stopper. The medium was changed every 3 days. After the 3rd day a small quantity of cat blood cells was added and was ingested by the trematodes. In addition to the above method chick-embryo extract was also used but without bringing about a notable effect. Furthermore, sera of humans, dogs, cows, rabbits and goats were tried as media but no special difference from cat serum was observed.

Also, using the serum of cats infected or uninfected with *P. westermani* a comparison was made of the survival time of the trematodes and their development; but no remarkable difference was observed between them.

Culture was possible for only 2–3 weeks in the Tyrode's solution without additional constituents, and during this period death hardly ever occurred. So the effects of various drugs on the excysted forms were also investigated.

E. EGG PRODUCTION

Regarding the number of eggs laid by an adult *Paragonimus westermani*, it is difficult to make a general statement because their development is influenced by the kinds of host, the site of parasitism or the number of parasites. Very few reports related to the subject have been available.

Oshima (1953) observed the egg-laying habit of *P. westermani* maintained in Tyrode's solution at 37° C and obtained the following results. During the first 24 h, 25 000–20 000 eggs per worm were produced, then the number of eggs decreased suddenly, and after 48–72 h the inside of the uterus of the worm was empty. When S. Yokogawa and Ro (1939) carried out an experimental treatment of infected dogs, they counted eggs per day (E.P.D.) in stools by Wakeshima's egg counting method (1932) before treatment. The result was that the E.P.D. varied widely at this time. In a dog infected with 17 worms E.P.D. was 233 896–463 727 (E.P.D./worm: 16 900–27 300), in another dog with 18 worms 479 541–480 354 (E.P.D./worm: 26 600–26 700) and in a third dog with 26 worms 2 751 000–285 731 (E.P.D./worm: 104 400–11 000), i.e. E.P.D. per worm was between a minimum 11 000 and a maximum of 104 000.

M. Yokogawa (1955a) counted E.P.D. in the stool of a cat (infected with three worms of *P. kellicotti*) daily for 23 days starting 3 months after infection and reported that the average E.P.D. per worm was 11 100 ± 1 400, inferring that if the observations were carried out for longer period the range of fluctuation would be less. In order to ascertain if this were so, Suguro (1959) observed the E.P.D. in stools of nine infected dogs daily for as long as 110–300 days after the beginning of egg-laying, after giving twelve to twenty-five metacercariae of *P. westermani* to each dog. The result was that the mean E.P.D. for every 5 days became quite constant without much fluctuation during the period from 64 days to 151 days after the beginning of egg-laying, the E.P.D. per worm being between 9 530 ± 1 300 and 18 380 ± 4 200. Suguro also pointed out that an evaluation of the effect of treatment would be possible by observing the change in E.P.D. in the stool.

Yumiba (1959, unpublished) counted the E.P.D. in the stool of an in-patient infected with *P. westermani* who had not expectorated for 9 days. He reported that E.P.D. was between a minimum of 58 and a maximum of 2 380.

Yokogawa *et al.* (1962a) observed the E.P.D. for 2–4 days in both the sputum and the stool of thirteen in-patients with paragonimiasis. The number of eggs was much greater in the stool than in sputum, and the total number of E.P.D. in stool and sputum was between a minimum of 120 and a maximum 23 435, and the mean E.P.D. of each case was between a minimum 371 and a maximum 11 700.

F. HISTOCHEMICAL CHARACTERISTICS

Few histochemical studies concerning the metabolism of *Paragonimus westermani* have hitherto been made and there still remain many obscure points. Yamao (1952) reported the distribution of glyceromonophosphatase in the tissue of the adult worms of *P. westermani*. He stated that if we classify the type of phosphatase reactions in cuticle of the flukes into the *"Fasciola hepatica* type" which shows strong acid phosphatase reaction and the *"Eurytrema pancreaticum* type" which shows strong alkaline phosphatase reaction, we would find *P. westermani* to be perfectly of the *"Fasciola hepatica* type", except that *P. westermani* showed the strongest acid phosphatase reaction in the subcuticular layer. He also reported that the digestive organs, reproductive organs, and nervous system showed the *"Fasciola hepatica* type" reactions in the phosphatase test. It was again reported that *P. westermani* differs from other species in that it produces the worm cyst in the lungs of the host, and nucleus-like granules in round cells found in the worm cysts showed strong positive reaction for acid phosphatase, while the coagulum

H

inside the worm cyst generally showed an alkaline phosphatase reaction.

Yoshimura and Yokogawa (1958) observed the distribution of glycogen, nucleic acids and phosphatases which are thought to have the most important roles in the metabolic process of the adult *P. westermani*, and also investigated the functional relations between these substances and the organs of the worms. Glycogen was abundant in the vitelline glands, reticular tissues, subcuticular muscle cells and yolk cells of the eggs in the uterus. A moderate amount of glycogen was also detected in the ovary, epithelia of the intestines, oral sucker, pharynx and oesophagus. Polysaccharides other than glycogen were observed in those organs in which glycogen was detected. Regarding the distribution of nucleic acids, ribonucleic acid (RNA) was shown to a considerable extent in the vitelline glands and the ovary; and moderately in the yolk cells of the eggs in the uterus, subcuticular muscle cells, and testes, and slightly in the epithelial cells of the uterus. RNA detected abundantly in the vitelline glands was proved to be closely correlated with mitochondria and lipids detected by Sudan black B. On the other hand, deoxyribonucleic acid (DNA) was proved to be abundant in the nuclei of the testes, ovary and vitelline glands.

Alkaline phosphomonoesterase, capable of hydrolysing sodium glycerophosphate, was clearly detected in the epithelium of the excretory bladder and its ductules, the epithelia of the uterus, the vitelline glands, the oral sucker, pharynx, oesophagus, cuticle and subcuticular tissues.

Acid glycerophosphatase was strongly positive in the oral sucker and pharynx and weakly positive in the vitelline glands, ovary and cuticle. Yoshimura and Yokogawa (1958) pointed out that glycogen, RNA, DNA, lipids and phosphomonoesterase were abundantly present in reproductive organs such as the vitelline glands, testes, ovary and uterine epithelium, but alkaline and acid phosphatases were present in the excretory system, digestive tract and the cuticle. As stated above, organ specificity was observed in the distribution of glycogen, nucleic acids and phosphatases. It might be considered that the complicated and dynamic metabolic processes between carbohydrates, protein, RNA, DNA, and enzymes dealing with these substances would proceed in the body of *P. westermani*. That is, these chemical substances and enzymes probably contribute to the mechanism of egg formation, resorption of the nutriment and excretion of the end products of metabolism.

Yokogawa and Yoshimura (1957) also made histochemical studies on the adult *Paragonimus ohirai* and reported that the vitelline glands may play an important role in forming the egg shell, and also observed histochemically the process of its formation. In the cells of the vitelline glands much polysaccharide including glycogen could be found, while in the egg no glycogen was found and the basic chemical composition was considered to be protein. Therefore, the vitelline glands seem to have some bearing on the supply of protein substances consisting mainly of RNA for the formation of the egg shell; at the same time in this biochemical process, glycogen, lipid and phosphatases interact smoothly with one another in the complicated mechanism of protein synthesis associated with the phosphorus metabolism of the worm.

Kang *et al.* (1963) also made histochemical studies on the adult worms of *Paragonimus westermani*, and obtained about the same distribution of glycogen, nucleic acid, fatty substances and polyphenoloxidase in the reproductive organs as was mentioned above.

VI. Development in Definitive Hosts

A. MIGRATION IN DEFINITIVE HOSTS

1. *Migration Route of the Young* Paragonimus westermani

Otani (1887) was the first to give an opinion regarding the migration route of *P. westermani* from the mouth to the lungs of man. His histopathological studies on the worm cyst in the lungs suggested the haematogenic route of migration because the worm cysts are formed by expansion of the blood vessels, and some of their inner walls are covered with endothelia. On the other hand, Yamagiwa (1890) believed that the worm cyst was a "softening cyst" resulting from the destruction of lung tissues, and that the fibrous adhesions and nodules in the intestinal walls, mesenteries, capsule of the liver and diaphragm, which are often found at autopsy in patients with paragonimiasis, might indicate the passage of the young forms of *P. westermani* penetrating through these organs into the pleural cavity to enter the lungs.

Katsurada and Fujiki (1899) suggested that juveniles might penetrate the intestinal walls and mesenteries and then directly reach the lungs through the lymph canal, and that in respect of structure the worm cysts in the lungs appear to be formed by expansion of the terminal bronchii.

S. Yokogawa (1915, 1916a, b, 1917, and unpublished) proved by many experiments that the metacercariae excyst in the small intestine, penetrate the intestinal wall and enter the peritoneal cavity; they then penetrate through the diaphragm into the pleural cavity to enter the lungs through their surface.

S. Yokogawa (1916a) also reported that the shortest time was $5\frac{1}{2}$ h for the excysted young forms to reach the peritoneal cavity after the oral administration of metacercariae. M. Yokogawa (1961) and Yokogawa *et al.* (1962c), studied the migration route of juveniles of *P. westermani* in puppies and rats by using Evans blue technique. The penetration sites of young forms of *P. westermani* in the intestinal wall or muscle of the hosts were shown as prominent blue spots when 0·3–0·5% Evans blue solution was injected intravenously 15 min before autopsy (Fig. 3A, B).

Using this technique, they investigated the period which elapsed from the time of ingestion of the metacercariae of *P. westermani* to the time of appearance of excysted young flukes in the peritoneal cavity and the penetration sites in the intestines of the hosts. The results in puppies and rats were strikingly similar: in puppies 30 min after ingestion, nearly one-third of the metacercariae had already appeared in the submucosa or muscle layer of the intestinal wall and sometimes in the peritoneal cavity; in rats within 30 min after ingestion some of them had already appeared in the peritoneal cavity. The above facts prove that the excystment of the metacercariae occurs much more quickly than had been supposed.

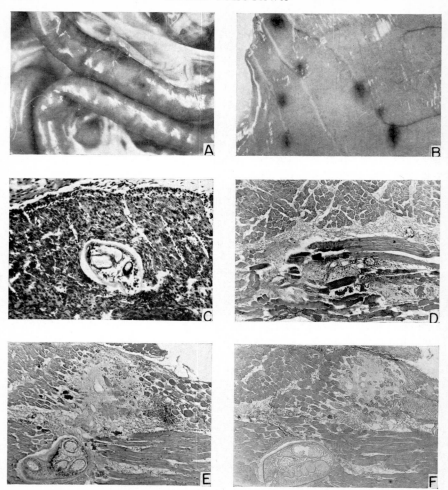

Fig. 3. Migration route of juveniles of *P. westermani* in the final hosts demonstrated by Evans blue technique. A, Evans blue spots in the intestinal wall demonstrated by the larvae 30 min after infection. B, Evans blue spots demonstrated by the larvae in parietal peritoneum of the abdomen of the rats 30 min after infection. C, Transverse section of the penetrating forms through the muscle layer of the intestine of the cat. D, Transverse section of the penetration site of juveniles through the abdominal wall of the rat. E, Advanced changes due to the penetration of juveniles in the abdominal wall of the rat. F, Histochemical alternation of the penetration site of juveniles in the abdominal wall of the rat demonstrated by Tropeolin O.

The sites of penetration of young forms in the intestinal wall covered an 80 cm extent of the small intestine from the beginning of the duodenum, and no young forms were found in the wall of the stomach or the large intestine.

Fan and Khaw (1963) reported that the minimum time of excystment of the metacercariae of *P. westermani* in the small intestine of a young cat could be 24 min and that the stomach may be an occasional site of excystment.

Yokogawa and Yoshimura (1960) investigated the appearance of the deep blue spots after using with Evans blue stain in the penetration sites of juveniles of *P. westermani* in the tissue. Histopathologically, moderate oedema and cellular responses accompanied the lymphoid cells, and mononuclear large cells including histiocytes and neutrophils were seen around the forms penetrating the intramuscular connective tissue or serous membrane (Fig. 3C). Around the penetrating forms in the muscle and intramuscular connective tissues of the abdominal wall the marked degeneration, resolution and oedema associated with the cellular infiltration of neutrophils were observed histopathologically (Fig. 3 D, E). The marked stagnation of the tissue fluid in those areas which would probably be stainable by Evans blue and severe segmentation and fibrin-like degeneration of the muscle and connective tissues were especially characteristic.

Histochemical study of the site in which such pathological changes presented as described above gave clear proof of depolymerization or decomposition. Entire or partial disappearance of polysaccharides including glycogen was observed by the periodic acid–Schiff (PAS) technique and also the marked decrease of basic protein was confirmed in Tropeolin O staining (Fig. 3F).

Tsuji (1961) investigated the influence of vitamin C, vitamin K, testosterone, calcium chloride, hyaluronidase, antihistamine and cortisone on the appearance of the Evans blue spots caused by the passage of *P. westermani* through the host's tissues. In the rats treated with hyaluronidase an increase of the blue colour and enlargement of the size of the blue spots were found, but antihistamine and cortisone injections inhibited their appearance. Judging from the results, Tsuji stated that the appearance of Evans blue spots around the young trematodes in the tissues could be explained by the belief of Lewert and Lee (1954) that Evans blue has the capacity to bind itself to the area of formation of water-soluble carbohydrate-containing protein.

In addition, histopathological changes of the tissues penetrated by the young forms should be also emphasized. Primarily it can be shown that polymerization or decomposition of polysaccharides, glycoproteins and protein substances consisting of both extra- and intracellular components would probably be affected by the collagenase-like activities and proteolytic enzymes originating from the penetrating *P. westermani*; secondly, the mechanical damages of the tissues caused by the trematode itself should not be neglected. It is of interest that hyaluronidase and collagenase activities of adult *P. westermani* were also detected biochemically by Murakoshi (1960, unpublished) at the writer's laboratory.

It was quite interesting to investigate the feeding habits of the juvenile *P. westermani*. Pyknotic nuclei and remnants of the tissue cells and fluid-like substances which were homogeneously stained by the polysaccharide staining (PAS) were found in the intestinal caeca of young *P. westermani* penetrating through the muscle of the host. Similar findings were also reported by Dawes (1963) in his study of the migration of the juvenile forms of *Fasciola hepatica*.

It may be considered that there would be a close relation between the intake of the nutritive substances and biochemical or histochemical alteration as depolymerizations of polysaccharides and glycoprotein during the development of the young of *P. westermani* in the host's tissues. Yokogawa *et al.* (1962c) investigated the migration route of young *P. westermani* in cats and rats by using the Evans blue technique mentioned above. They found a new course of migration of the trematodes in a cat that has never been mentioned previously: the young *P. westermani* migrating into the abdominal cavity after penetration of the intestinal wall immediately enter the inner wall of the abdominal cavity and then, after a certain period of development (5–7 days), reappear in the abdominal cavity. These young forms penetrate the diaphragm and appear in the pleural cavity about 14 days after infection. Yokogawa *et al.* stressed the fact that these juveniles penetrate into the inner wall of the abdominal cavity soon after their appearance in the peritoneal cavity and stay there for about 1 week. They considered that this stay in the abdominal wall of the host has an important meaning during the period of development of the young forms in the final host. Takizawa (1964) showed that *P. westermani* which had penetrated into the abdominal wall of a cat showed a significant increase in size and development.

Yokogawa *et al.* (1962c) also reported the migration route of the juvenile *P. westermani* in rats. The rats were dissected at appointed times and observed by the same procedures as were used in experiments with cats. Of the metacercariae given, 15·5% were already found in the abdominal cavity 30 min after ingestion. Worms which migrated to the abdominal cavity began to penetrate into the abdominal wall 1 h after infection. In the body of rats, however, the majority of worms which penetrated into the abdominal wall did not return to the abdominal cavity during the 180 days of examination and no worms reached maturity. Thus, the route and time of migration of the worms through the body differed greatly in rats and cats.

2. *Migration Route of the Larva of* P. ohirai

Okura (1963) studied a course of infection and migration of the juvenile *P. ohirai* in rats using the Evans blue technique. He reported that the excysted forms of *P. ohirai* appeared in the abdominal cavity of rats within 1 h of infection, and 10–14 days later most of the worms which had migrated to the abdominal cavity penetrated into the liver for 3–4 days, then migrated through the diaphragm to the pleural cavity and lungs. No worms were found which penetrated into the abdominal wall soon after their appearance in the abdominal cavity as seen in *P. westermani*.

3. *Migration Route of the Larvae of* P. miyazakii

Yokogawa *et al.* (1963b) reported the migration route of young *P. miyazakii* in rats. Of the metacercariae given, 30–50% were found in the abdominal cavity 2 h after infection. One-third of the forms began to penetrate the abdominal wall and they re-entered the abdominal cavity after 5–6 days. The other two-thirds of the forms which migrated into the abdominal cavity began to penetrate into the liver for a few days without entering the abdominal wall and migrated through the diaphragm to the pleural cavity and lungs.

It seems noteworthy that the pattern of migration and development of the young trematodes in the definitive hosts differs significantly according to the kinds of host or the species of *Paragonimus*.

B. DEVELOPMENT AND FORMATION OF WORM CYSTS

Growth and development of *Paragonimus westermani* in the definitive host varies according to the kinds of host, their physiological condition and the number of parasites, even when the worms are of the same age.

Ando (1917a, b) examined 1 304 flukes of different ages obtained from the abdominal cavity, the pleural cavity and the lungs of cats and dogs experimentally infected with *P. westermani*, and reported in detail the relation between their size and the period of infection based on examination of 1 114 perfect worms. He observed eggs in the worm cyst wall in the lungs of the host first during a period of 68–69 days after infection, and the sizes of the worms found at this time were 4·1–5·0 mm (length) and 2·3–2·7 mm (breadth); 113 days after the infection they measured an average of 6·07 mm × 2·97 mm; between the 168th and 370th day after infection the size was 8·9–13·5 mm × 5·1–8·0 mm. Thus, the size of the worms gradually increased even after reaching sexual maturity and through all the stages they gave a common relative ratio of length to width of 2:1.

Takizawa (1964) reported that the sizes of *P. westermani* in the worm cyst within the lungs of dogs gradually increased until 720 days after infection, but the sizes of the worms 2 460 days old in the worm cyst of the lungs showed a significant reduction. According to his description the mean sizes of the worms of various ages are as follows: 281 days after infection, $11·23 \pm 0·95 \times 7·21 \pm 0·21$ mm; 720 days old, $15·97 \pm 1·7 \times 10·20 \pm 1·02$ mm; 2 460 days old, $11·30 \pm 2·32 \times 6·91 \pm 0·89$ mm. The sizes of the oral sucker, ventral sucker and cuticular spines showed a gradual increase until 720 days after infection but a decrease in worms 2 460 days old.

These measurements were taken from worms found in cysts in the lungs. Worms found in the body cavity are usually underdeveloped, especially those which wander in the pleural cavity without a cyst and do not attain sexual maturity even after 100 days. The following different cases show that flukes found underneath the skin and in locations other than the lungs and brain are underdeveloped and do not become mature even after several months. It appears that, if *P. westermani* does not reach the lungs, it does not reach maturity. The very interesting point that the lung is the only location for development to sexual maturity leads the writer to believe that adult worms found in the brain or spinal cord are forms which had previously developed in the lungs and which wandered by chance out of the lung into such unusual locations.

Yogore (1956) infected each of ten cats with twenty-five metacercariae of *P. westermani*. In four of the infected cats the worms found in the lungs at necropsy formed 40–88% of the number of metacercariae given, with an average of 71%.

In a large series of experimental infections of dogs and cats with *P. westermani*, using known number of metacercariae, Yokogawa *et al.* (1958c) found that more than 68% of the metacercariae had developed, and that there was no significant difference in the percentage development of the metacercariae in these two hosts. Of the seventeen dogs which were fed 10–20 metacercariae each, 100% were infected and 68·1% of the metacercariae given had developed. Eleven dogs were given 21–50 metacercariae each and all became infected, 74·1% of the 368 metacercariae which were given developing. Of thirteen dogs given 51–100 metacercariae each, all became infected and 68·1% of the 986 metacercariae had developed. Yokogawa et al. (1958c) also carried out an experiment on superimposed infections with P. westermani in dogs. The first dog was fed 25 metacercariae and 3 months later was given 100 more. On autopsy 299 days after the first infection 80 adult worms were recovered, i.e. 64·1% had developed. The second dog was given 30 metacercariae and 50 more 3 months later. At autopsy 235 days after the first infection 50 adult worms or 62·5% of the metacercariae that were fed were found. The third dog was given, respectively, 40, 110 and 50 metacercariae at intervals of 3 months and at autopsy 225 days after the first infection a total of 167 adult worms were found, i.e. 83·5% of the administered metacercariae had developed. All the worms recovered were sexually mature. The surprising thing in these experiments was the high percentage of the administered metacercariae that developed into sexually mature worms. There was thus no evidence that the first infections had invoked a protective immunity against subsequent infections.

Yokogawa et al. (1960c, 1961c) fed each of seven puppies with one metacercaria and each of ten puppies with 3 metacercariae of P. westermani. At autopsy 70–180 days after infection they observed in the first experiment three out of seven puppies having one immature worm each, located in the pleural cavity, and no worm cyst was observed in the lungs. In the second experiment all of the puppies became infected with three worms in each of four puppies, two worms in each of five puppies, and one worm in one puppy. In eight cases one cyst containing two worms was seen; in another case, three worms were found in a cyst; in the other case, that is, in the one puppy having one worm, no cyst formation could be seen, but an immature worm was found free in the pleural cavity. In the case having three worms, two worms living together in the worm cyst were mature while the other one found free outside the worm cyst was immature.

However, in the case of P. ohirai, even when only one worm was found in a rat, it was mature and egg production was observed; although no worm cyst could be found in the lungs, the worm was found in the pleural cavity. This interesting observation shows that in P. ohirai a mate is not needed to produce maturation, while in P. westermani a mate is necessary. However, a mate is necessary in either species for the formation of worm cysts in the lungs. This conclusion is supported by the findings of Omura (1960), who reported that when one to three adult worms of P. westermani or P. ohirai were removed from the lungs of infected animals and transferred into the peritoneal cavity of rats, the worms almost always migrated into the pleural cavity (after 3 weeks in the case of P. westermani and after 2 weeks in P. ohirai). Omura showed that when more than two adult worms were transferred at a time, these worms entered the lungs immediately after migration into the pleural cavity and formed a worm cyst in the lungs in either species, although, when only one adult worm was transferred, the formation of a worm cyst was never observed in either of the two species even after migration into the pleural cavity. It would thus appear that two worms must be present for the formation of the worm cysts. However, in the case of human paragonimiasis it has been established by autopsy and surgical excision of worm cysts of the lung that a worm cyst almost always contains only one worm. The reason for this is still obscure.

Yokogawa and Yoshimura (1960) reported that when an autopsy was made after 6 years 8 months on a dog fed 65 metacercariae of *P. westermani*, ten worm cysts were observed in the lungs, but only one worm cyst contained two worms and six contained only one worm each, while three empty worm cysts were observed to contain only eggs. All these worms were mature and the uterus contained many eggs. When dogs or cats are fed with metacercariae, it is usually observed that the worm cysts found 1–3 years after infection contain two or three worms. Very few cysts show only one worm, the only explanation for which seems to be that at first two worms are present in the cyst but that after a long period the mate is lost. It may also be supposed in the human case that after a long period of infection, one of two which have been living together has died. Yokogawa and Yoshimura (1960) stated that in thirteen out of sixteen patients with paragonimiasis, from whom worm cysts in the lungs were removed by operation, each cyst was found to harbour one adult worm, while in the other three cases the cysts contained eggs but not flukes. The history of these sixteen cases indicated that the period from the onset of the disease was 1–7 years.

Paragonimus westermani infects various kinds of mammalian hosts but the infection rate and the development of worms in their host may differ according to the species of the animals. It has been said that in small experimental animals such as rabbits, rats, mice and guinea-pigs no worms could reach sexual maturity. However, Fan and Khaw (1964) recently reported that in an experimental infection of rats with the metacercariae of *P. westermani* a few sexually mature worms were found in the worm cyst in the lungs. Possibly after passing eggs such flukes might die and then atrophy and disappear.

C. LENGTH OF LIFE IN THE DEFINITIVE HOST

No exact assessment has been made as to the length of life of the adult *Paragonimus westermani* in man, and longevity may vary according to the various conditions existing in the hosts. According to Ando (1924) eggs are still found in the sputum of a patient with paragonimiasis even 20 years after he has left an endemic area of this disease.

Iwasaki (1955) reported a clinical observation on eighty-seven patients with paragonimiasis in Kochi Hospital, Japan, which indicated that they had all suffered from paragonimiasis for a very long time, i.e. twenty-one patients for more than 5 years, three for more than 10 years, one for more than 20 years and one for more than 30 years. However, in these cases the possibility of re-infection cannot be ruled out because this examination was carried out in an endemic area.

The average length of life of the adult *P. westermani* in man seems to be less than 10 years. The duration of life in locations other than the lung may be shorter, but the worm found for the first time in the human eye by Taniguchi (1893) lived for 15 years after the onset of the disease.

Miyazaki (1940) found that *P. ohirai* developed readily in rats and produced eggs about 4 weeks after infection, but about 3 months after infection the parasites began to die. *P. kellicotti* develops more rapidly in its definitive host than *P. westermani*. Ameel (1934) reported that the worms in experimentally infected cats became sexually mature and produced eggs from $5\frac{1}{2}$ to 6 weeks after infection. For *P. iloktsuenenesis*, Chen (1940) found that maturity was reached in experimental rats in less than 1 month; but the parasites began to die in the cysts about 2 months after infection and after 5 or 6 months they were rarely found alive.

Yokogawa *et al.* (1959) reported the results of an experiment in which known numbers of metacercariae of *P. ohirai* were fed to rats. Eighty-seven rats were given 1 metacercaria each and forty-three rats (49·4%) became infected. In these rats no worm cyst formation was found in the lungs and the worms that developed to sexual maturity were found free in the pleural cavity. Seventy-two rats were given 3 metacercariae each; sixty-two rats (86·1%) were infected and 112 adult worms (51·9% of the metacercariae given) were recovered. Whenever more than two worms were found on autopsy, worm cysts were always formed in the lungs. Two groups (13 rats and 16 rats) were given 5 metacercariae each. The first group was examined within 97 days of infection. All thirteen of the rats were infected and thirty-five worms (54·0% of the metacercariae given) were recovered. An autopsy was made on the second group of sixteen rats 103–173 days after infection. All were positive and thirteen adult worms (16·2% of the metacercariae given) were recovered. Degenerated worms which were not counted were found in many of the cysts in these animals.

In another experiment two groups of three and thirteen rats were tested. At first they were given 10 metacercariae each. An autopsy was made on the first group within 60 days of infection. All were positive and fourteen worms (47·0% of the metacercariae given) had developed. The other group of thirteen rats was examined 78–97 days after infection: all rats were infected and forty-seven worms (36·1% of the metacercariae) were found. There were also some degenerate worms. Finally, forty rats were given 20 metacercariae each and were autopsied within 46 days of infection; all were positive and 513 worms (64·1% of the metacercariae given) had developed. From these observations it appears that the duration of life of *P. ohirai* in rats is much influenced by the number of worms developed.

VII. EPIDEMIOLOGY

A. GEOGRAPHICAL DISTRIBUTION

Lung flukes of the genus *Paragonimus* are found in a wide variety of mammalian hosts which feed on crabs or crayfish. *P. westermani* develops normally in man, and therefore it is a potential danger to him wherever it is found. However, paragonimiasis in man is limited in its distribution to places where food habits make infection possible. The most important endemic areas are found in Korea, Japan, Formosa, central China and the Philippines. According to records the few scattered human cases that have been reported from Manchuria and Indo-China are probably due to this species. In animal hosts they appear to be widely distributed in the east Asian and Pacific region from Manchuria and Korea in the north to India and Indonesia in the south (Table II).

TABLE II

Distribution of Paragonimus *Infection*

Africa	Asia	South America
Belgian Congo	Central China	Brazil
British Cameroons	French Indo-China	Peru
French West Africa	Japan	Ecuador
Tripoli	Korea	Venezuela
	Manchuria	
	Formosa	
	Samoan Islands	
	Malayan Peninsula	
	Philippines	
	Indonesia	
	New Guinea	
	Thailand	
	Assam	
	Bengal	
	Malabar	
	Ceylon	
	Nepal	

In Thailand a short note on paragonimiasis has been written by Prommas (1928). Recently Harinasuta *et al.* (1957) and Vajrasthira *et al.* (1959) reported that an endemic area of paragonimiasis was first recognized in Nong Mu district of Saraburi province in central Thailand.

Daengswang (1963) reported that three fully grown Thai leopards from Dusit Zoo, Bangkok, were found infected with *P. westermani* for the first time in Thailand. These animals were brought into Dusit Zoo about 4 years before from a hilly forest of Choom-Porn province which is situated in southern Thailand about 450 km south of Bangkok.

Chung and Tsao (1962) reported human paragonimiasis caused by a new species, *P. szechuanensis*, in China; and Vogel (1963) also suggested that a new species of *Paragonimus* occurred in human beings in West Africa.

While there are other species of *Paragonimus* in animals, viz. *P. ohirai*, *P. iloktsuenensis*, *P. miyazakii* and *P. compactus*, there is no evidence that they can infect man. *P. kellicotti* appears to be almost entirely limited to the western hemisphere. Perhaps the autochtonous cases of human infection in this region, especially from Peru and Ecuador, may be attributed to this species, and the absence of human infection over most of its range merely indicates that favourable food habits do not prevail.

Recently, Iwamura (1964) found the first authentic cases of human para-gonimiasis contracted locally in west Nepal (where he had been working at the United Mission Hospital, Jansen, Palpa, west Nepal, as a Mission Doctor from 1962 to 1964). He found twelve patients with paragonimiasis who showed *Paragonimus* eggs in sputum or faeces among 432 patients treated by him for pulmonary tuberculosis. The paragonimiasis in these patients had been wrongly diagnosed as pulmonary tuberculosis. Freshwater crab, *Potamon Atkinsonianus* (Wood-Mason, 1871) was eaten raw by the natives, but no metacercariae have yet been found from the crab. He carried out an intradermal test on the natives with V.B.S. antigen as described by Yokogawa and found that in some limited areas (Bainshikatta, Chichipani and Malang) three out of sixty-two cases (4·8%), three out of forty cases (7·5%) and five out of fifty-three cases (9·4%) were positive for the test, respectively, but in other places no positive reaction occurred. It may be said, with reservations, that human paragonimiasis is probably endemic in some areas in west Nepal.

B. METHOD OF HUMAN INFECTION

The most important method of human infection with *P. westermani* throughout all the endemic areas is undoubtedly the eating of raw or imper-fectly cooked crabs. Some of the crabs, e.g. *Eriocheir* sp. that serve as the second intermediate host of *P. westermani*, are very important items of food. There is abundant evidence that these hosts are not infrequently eaten raw or partly cooked in China, Korea and some other countries. However, another possible method of human infection is an accidental transfer of the encysted metacercariae to the mouth through the handling of crabs when preparing them for food.

M. Yokogawa (1952b) noted the possibility of this method of infection in the endemic areas of paragonimiasis in Japan. Here the important second intermediate host is *Eriocheir japonicus*. When questioned, people stated that they commonly ate the crabs but that they were always well cooked. The crabs were sometimes boiled, fried or baked, but were usually eaten in soup. To prepare the soup the shells and legs of the crabs are removed while they are still alive and their bodies are crushed and chopped up with a knife on a chopping block. They are strained through a bamboo basket with water. Soybean paste or soybean sauce are added and the crab soup is cooked for 10 or 20 min with vegetables or noodles. This much cooking would certainly kill all the encysted metacercariae. However, Yokogawa found that during the preparation of the crab soup the encysted metacercariae cling to the chopping block, the knife, the bamboo basket in which the crab meat is strained, and to the hands of the cook. They could therefore easily be transferred to other foods or directly to the mouth. Actually in a study of the preparation of the crab soup, two cysts were found on the knife, three on the hands of the cook, twenty-five on the bamboo basket, fourteen on the chopping block, and one on the table. It was a common practice to prepare vegetable pickles and spices on the same chopping block immediately after the preparation of the crab soup. Yokogawa concluded that the infection of paragonimiasis in Japan came mostly from the preparation of crab soup and not from the eating of raw crabs. Considering the quite large number of encysted meta-cercariae in the crabs in the endemic area of Japan, the infection would have undoubtedly been much more serious and the disease more severe if the people ordinarily ate raw crab meat.

Yogore (1957) described a situation in the Philippines where he believed that the people might get the infection when preparing crab for food. The juice of the crab is used in the preparation of a dish called *Kinagang*. In the preparation of *Kinagang* the raw crabs are first chopped into small pieces and then ground in a mortar with a pestle. To collect the juice the ground crab meat is placed in a cloth and the juice squeezed out. The juice is added to the meat of grated coconut, and the mixture is wrapped in leaves and boiled. While there would seem to be no possibility of getting infected from eating *Kinagang*, metacercariae might easily get on to the hands of the cook during the preparation of this dish. They probably also get on the chopping block and the knife and might contaminate food that is usually eaten raw.

In Korea, *Eriocheir sinensis* appears to be the most important source of infection. As a source of animal protein these crabs are a common and im-portant item of food and are frequently eaten raw or partially cooked. The Korean crayfish, *Camboroides similis*, also harbours the metacercariae of *P. westermani*, but are not usually used as food. It was a common practice for people to use their raw juice as medicine for fever and diarrhoea. In certain areas in Japan the juice of the crabs *Eriocheir japonicus* and *Potamon dehani* are occasionally used as an anti-febrile medicine or as an ointment for lucker poisoning or other types of urticaria. In China the stone crab, *Potamon denticulatus*, is often eaten, sometimes after immersion in wine for 12 h or less. Those not covered with wine and still living when they are eaten, are called "drunken" crabs. According to Wu (1938) the habit of eating "drunk-en" crabs as *hors d'oeuvres* is quite wide-spread in Chekiang province. Fan and Khaw (1964) reported on the viability of metacercariae of *P. wester-mani* in *Eriocheir japonicus* treated with alcohol ("drunken" crabs) when fed to cats and dogs. Living crabs were brushed until thoroughly clean in fresh water, and then immersed in Kao-Liang wine (made from sorghum) contain-ing 47% alcohol until they were foaming at the mouth and quite intoxicated—about 3–5 min. They were taken out and kept in a glass jar until used for the experiments after 1, 2, 3, 4 and 5 days respectively. The metacercariae were removed from these "drunken" crabs and fed to nine dogs and three cats. The infection rate of these animals was 100%, indicating that viable infective larvae were present in all the 5-day drunken crabs. They concluded that the native recipe for preparing "drunken" crabs is a dangerous method of spreading paragonimiasis in endemic areas.

VIII. PATHOLOGY

A. PULMONARY PARAGONIMIASIS

Although some knowledge of the pathology of pulmonary paragonimiasis in man has been gained previously by many workers, since Otani (1887) first described the lesions of the lungs and brain produced by invasion of adult worms of *P. westermani*, the findings presented by them were not always identical.

The wide variation in the histopathological findings in the lungs of man with paragonimiasis would probably be due to differences in the number of infecting worms, the duration varying from the onset of this disease to autopsy and the susceptibility of the individuals to the worms. The most recent investigation of pathomorphology and pathogenesis of pulmonary paragonimiasis was carried out by Diaconita and Goldis (1964) on sixteen necropsies of patients with paragonimiasis. The pathomorphic picture of this disease evinced specific as well as non-specific lesions. The specific lesions are represented by abscess cavities and parasitic caverns, improperly called distoma cysts, and foreign-body granulomata due to *Paragonimus* eggs. The cavities of paragonimiasis are produced by bringing about an infarction of the respective portion of the lung tissue, tributary to the arteriole which it obstructed, or through necrosis of a granulomatous or pneumonic mass followed by a process of softening on liquefaction or, in certain cases, following the disintegration of the dead parasite. The granulomatous lesions, in the main, show the features of the foreign-body granuloma, the foreign-body being usually represented by *Paragonimus* eggs with a "chitinous" cuticle. Vascular granulomata, vasculitis lesions and generally eosinocytic alveolitis with the occurrence of pneumonic and bronchopneumonic processes of a perifocal nature show that the initial stage of the disease may point to a toxic aetiology. All these lesions tend towards fibrous transformation and sclerosis, lesional processes including parasite eggs and indicating a chronic state of the disease. In the cases with a very long development, calcification processes may also occur. Diaconita and Goldis thus attempted to classify the morphopathological changes according to the clinical stages of this disease.

However, it seems to be quite difficult to do so, because various morphological changes were sometimes seen in the same lungs of the patients. Yokogawa and Yoshimura (1960) made macroscopical and microscopical examinations of lung lesions which were surgically excised from sixteen patients with paragonimiasis in Japan. Most of these patients were wrongly diagnosed as pulmonary tuberculosis and treated with streptomycin and PAS.* Others were treated in the sanatorium for about 1–6 years until diagnosed correctly as paragonimiasis through finding the worms or eggs of *P. westermani* in lung biopsies. In thirteen out of sixteen cases one adult worm each was found in every worm cyst of the lungs and in the other three cases *Paragonimus* eggs were found but no worm was seen. These authors also reported the locations of the worm cysts in the lungs of these patients as follows: in the upper right lobe (7 cases); in the middle right lobe (4 cases); in the lower right lobe (1 case); in the lower left lobe (1 case), and the remaining 2 cases were not clear. By and large, worm cysts predominated in the right lung.

The pathological findings of these cases can be summarized as follows. Macroscopically the worm cyst was generally distended and greyish-white nodules about the size of a grape or a plum were found. In cross-section, however, they were not round or oval and showed irregular or uneven

* Sodium *p*-aminosalicylate.

cavities. The cyst wall was mostly thick and fibrosclerotic, having a woody consistency. Some of them seemed to have originated in the bronchial cavity. Numerous foci of the nodules, surrounded by old haemorrhages and stagnation of the lung parenchyma, were found in the vicinity of the cysts. Occasionally, marked athelectatic change or so-called hepatization was seen around the cyst. Some of the blood vessels showed sclerotic alteration.

Microscopically the cyst walls were composed of fibrous granulation tissues

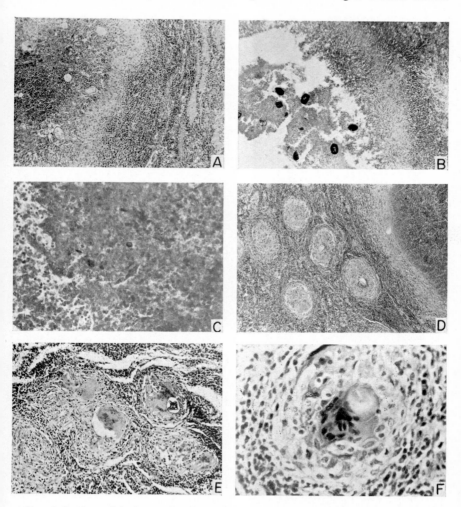

FIG. 4. Sections of the lungs of patients with paragonimiasis (I). Haematoxylin and eosin. A, Worm cyst and its wall thickened with fibrous granulation. B, Cyst cavity with calcified eggs. C, Charcot-Leyden's crystals within the bronchiectatic cavern. D, Egg tubercules in the vicinity of the worm cyst. E, Various types of giant cells in the granulomas. F, Egg shell engulfed by the giant cell.

consisting of fibroblasts, lymphoid cells, mononuclear large cells like histiocytes, plasma cells, and sometimes eosinophils. Numerous *Paragonimus* eggs
were observed side-by-side within the parasitic abscess or cavity and in its
vicinity (Fig. 4A). Calcified eggs were found in some preparations (Fig. 4B).
Charcot-Leyden's crystals or rhomboid bodies in large numbers were found
in the cavities of the worm cysts or bronchiectatic cavities contained within
the necrotic masses (Fig. 4C). Granulomata due to *Paragonimus* eggs were
frequently encountered in the vicinity of the worm cysts, and manifestly the

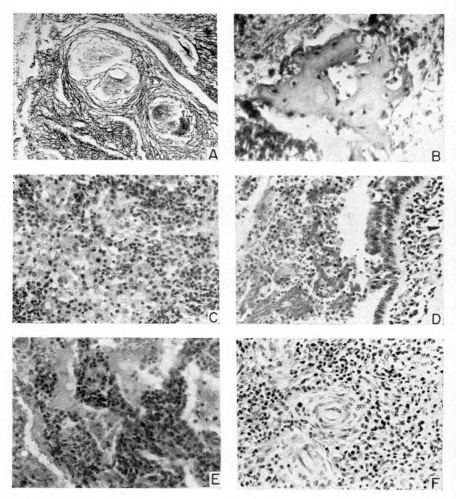

Fig. 5. Sections of the lungs of patients with paragonimiasis (II). Haematoxylin and eosin.
A, Reticular fibres of egg tubercules demonstrated by Gomori's silver impregnation.
B, Focus of ossification. C, Alveolar catarrh around the worm cyst. D, Exudative bronchitis.
E, Interstitial pneumonitis. F, Lung cirrhosis and new formation of capillaries.

egg tubercules consisted of epithelioid cells, lymphoid cells, plasma cells, eosinophils and peripheral fibroblasts (Fig. 4D). In addition to these components, the giant cells of Langhan's and multinuclear foreign-body types appeared around the eggs and some engulfed them (Fig. 4E and F). The reticular fibres demonstrated by Gomori's staining in these tubercles were mostly disintegrated or resolved in the centre (Fig. 5A). The characteristic feature of these granulomata was similar to that encountered in the lungs in tuberculosis. In one case some granulomata with giant cells showed ossifications (Fig. 5B). Haemosiderosis, hyperaemia, marked stagnation and haemorrhages were often observed in pneumonic foci. Two types of pneumonic process were encountered. One of them was bronchopneumonia accompanied by alveolar catarrh and peri- and endo-bronchitis. The macrophages, neutrophils, erythrocytes, lymphoid cells and sometimes eosinophils as well as desquamative alveolar epithelia were seen in the alveolar lumina (Fig. 5C).

Similar responses were also found in bronchi (Fig. 5D). Hyperplasia of peribronchial lymph nodules were constantly observed. Athelectatic changes and vascularization were frequently present in the vicinity of the worm cyst and egg tubercles. According to Yokogawa and Yoshimura (1960), another type of pneumonia was interstitial pneumonitis; proliferation of the fibrous tissues composed of lymphoid cells and plasma cells and histiocytes were found in the septum of alveolar wall (Fig. 5E). These findings exactly coincided with lung cirrhosis (Figs. 5F and 6A). Bronchi characterized by marked hyperplasia of the bronchial epithelia corresponding to squamous metaplasia, and advanced ulcerative lesions were often observed in the chronic stage of pneumonitis. The *Paragonimus* eggs scattered in the lung parenchyma were surrounded by the non-specific reaction of the inflammatory cells. These authors stressed that the vascular lesions were of particular importance, since cellular infiltration of lymphoid cells, plasma cells, histiocytes and fibroblasts were present in the wall of some arterioles and venules. The typical figures of intimal hyperplasia (Fig. 6B), angitis obliterans (Fig. 6C) and periphlebitis were seen in some preparations. Hyalinization of the granuloma which would probably originate from the angitis obliterans and egg tubercles was rarely recognized (Fig. 6D). Yokogawa and Yoshimura stated that they could not pursue the pleural lesions in detail because the materials examined were limited to the foci of the worm cyst and its vicinity. They stated that from the results mentioned above macroscopical and histopathological changes of the lungs caused by the adult worm *P. westermani* in man were characterized by formation of the worm cyst and egg tubercles with various types of giant cells, various processes of pneumonia, and vascular lesions. The characteristics of these pathological findings are similar to those of pulmonary tuberculosis, as described by previous investigators (especially Katsurada and Fujiki, 1899).

Histogenetic pathology of this disease, however, has not been set out in previous works. The appearance of the epithelioid tubercles due to *Paragonimus* eggs, plasma cells and eosinophils, as well as the vascular lesions, could be interpreted as the response of allergic or toxic aetiology in *Paragonimus* infection. In addition, the mechanical damage to the lung tissues by the worm itself cannot be negligible in the formation of the worm cyst and bronchiectatic process of the lungs. Yokogawa and Yoshimura (1960) emphasized the fact that polymorphism of the pathological figures of the lungs of patients with paragonimiasis, e.g. co-existence of both acute reactions and extremely chronic responses in the same case, was always observed. It is considered that these complicated figures could probably be attributed to the lesions caused by the migrating habit of *P. westermani*. With regard to Charcot-Leyden's

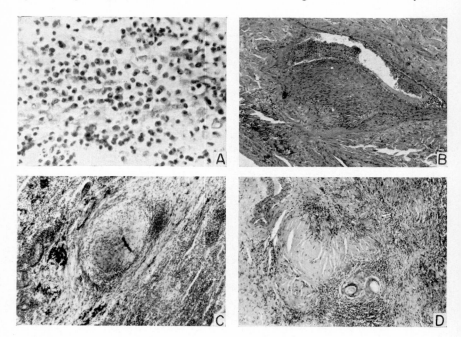

FIG. 6. Sections of the lungs of patients with paragonimiasis (III). Haematoxylin and eosin. A, Marked infiltration of plasma cells in pneumonic focus. B, Intimal hyperplasia of blood vessel. C, Angitis obliterans in the cirrhotic lung. D, Hyalinization of granuloma containing egg shell.

crystals or the rhomboidal bodies pointed out by Diaconita and Goldis (1964), Yokogawa and Yoshimura also found these frequently in the cyst cavities and bronchiectatic caverns. They stated that they do not know whether Charcot-Leyden's crystal is exactly identical to the rhomboidal body mentioned by Diaconita and Goldis or not. It is of interest that these bodies were constantly found in the foci in which a large number of eosinophils were present. The origin and mechanism of the formation of these bodies should be studied.

B. EXTRAPULMONARY PARAGONIMIASIS

A number of reports have been published on injuries produced by worms of *Paragonimus westermani* which wander from the normal path of migration and develop outside the lungs.

Otani (1887) was the first to find tumours of the worm cyst not only in the brain but in the liver, abdominal wall, peritoneal cavity, diaphragm, mesenteries and cervical lymph nodes. Muta (1912) proved in a severe case in a Korean that, in adipose tissues around the kidney or in adrenal gland, many encysted tumours varying in size were found to contain adult *P. westermani* and their eggs. He also observed adult worms and eggs in the encysted tumours of various sizes, some being as big as a bean and others like silk worm cysts, inside the liver adhering to the diaphragm. The lesions having worms in unusual locations occur in the pericardium, pancreas, large omentum, mesenterium, stomach wall, scrotum, epididymis, spinal cord, eye orbit, eyelids, bone marrow, subcutaneous tissue, urinary bladder, ovary and uterus. Recently Hsü *et al.* (1959) reported one case of a woman in Formosa who was diagnosed wrongly as having cancer of the uterus, but after operation *Paragonimus* eggs were found abundantly in the excised lesions and no evidence of cancer was proved.

Chung and Tsao (1962) reported that sixteen patients with paragonimiasis having characteristic pathological and clinical manifestations, such as subcutaneous nodules, were located in Szechuan province, China, and this disease may have been caused by a new species of *Paragonimus*.

From the fact that cases of cerebral or spinal paragonimiasis accounted for about 30–60% (average 45%) of extrapulmonary paragonimiasis, it can be said that the frequency of occurrence of cerebral or spinal paragonimiasis is quite high compared with other extrapulmonary paragonimiasis cases. Hosokawa *et al.* (1957) tried to analyse the histopathological findings of nine patients with cerebral or spinal paragonimiasis and reported that the focus consisted of three layers, the centre of which, the deep layer, contained eggs, giant cells, and Charcot-Leyden's crystals while the middle layer consisted of connective tissues and the outer layer showed infiltrations of plasma cells, lymphocytes and eosinophils. Two kinds of cerebral foci, the node form and cystic form, were combined in some cases. The findings were in agreement with those of Inamoto (1916). In addition, Nonomura (1941), Kaku (1950) and Hosokawa *et al.* (1957) have collected so far 204 cases of extrapulmonary paragonimiasis, of which 105 cases (51%) were of the cerebral and spinal type.

However, among the cases of paragonimiasis of the central nervous system, migration of the adult worms to the spinal cord is very rare, and there have been only a few reports in Japan (e.g. Moriyasu, 1917; Domen and Abe, 1955; Okamoto *et al.*, 1959). Okamoto *et al.* (1959) reported an extraordinary case of a 17-year-old youth with a syndrome of spinal transverse lesions repeated for 5 years; he reported that the migration on *P. westermani* into the spinal cord was confirmed by operation on the vertebral arches.

Akaiwa *et al.* (1931) reported that at autopsy in twenty-five cases of cerebral paragonimiasis, the lesions were located in the left hemisphere in five cases (20%), in the right in thirteen cases (52%) and in both hemispheres in seven cases (28%). In only four cases were adult worms of *P. westermani* actually found.

Jinnai *et al.* (1952) published an account of six cases of cerebral paragonimiasis on which they operated, together with thirty-four cases of cerebral paragonimiasis which they examined, stating that the lesions were located in the right hemisphere of the brain in eight cases, in the left hemisphere in sixteen, and in both hemispheres in nine cases. According to Jinnai *et al.* the data concerning the time between the onset of cerebral paragonimiasis and death was less than 1 year in nine cases and 2–4 years in eight cases.

It has been reported by several workers that cerebral paragonimiasis occurs more frequently in men than in women and that children are more likely to be infected than adults. According to Mitsuno *et al.* (1952), 109 out of 187 reported cases of cerebral paragonimiasis were males, and 100 out of 128 cases were less than 20 years old.

Kim and Walker (1961) also reported that 41 out of 47 patients with cerebral paragonimiasis which they treated by surgical operation were men and 21 of them were under 20 years old, but there were 40 patients who were less than 30 years old.

From the observations made on the lesions, cerebral paragonimiasis seems to be caused by the adult worm itself and not by the embolism of the *Paragonimus* eggs; this has been commonly found in any case of cerebral paragonimiasis at autopsy or in surgically operated cases. It has been said that cerebral paragonimiasis can hardly be regarded as an original focus without any pulmonary symptoms being seen, and it is believed that worms which have migrated into the lesion after the development of the worm cysts in the lungs are the cause.

By experimental infection of animals as well as by autopsy of patients with paragonimiasis, S. Yokogawa (1919, unpublished) proved that the routes of migration of the worms of *P. westermani* into the cerebral cavity run along soft tissues around the neck veins, and that the worms which once enter the brain may return to the lung.

Lei and Yen (1957) and Shih *et al.* (1958) supported Yokogawa's theory. The results of their experiments showed that symptoms of cerebral paragonimiasis mostly occurred about 10 months after the appearance of pulmonary symptoms in patients with cerebral paragonimiasis in Formosa.

Kim and Walker (1961) also examined the times of occurrence of the cerebral and pulmonary symptoms in patients with cerebral paragonimiasis in Korea. He stated that 29 out of 43 cases (67·4%) showed cerebral symptoms several months after the appearance of such pulmonary symptoms as cough and blood in the sputum.

Yumoto and Nagayoshi (1943) found many *Paragonimus* eggs in the heart, cerebrum, cerebellum and kidney of dogs infected with *P. westermani* and proved that these eggs had migrated via the blood stream; indeed such an egg embolus was found in the heart. In the heart of a heavily infected dog, egg embolisms were irregularly distributed along the coronary arteries, and somewhat elevated granular and verruciform products were seen whose surface was rough and villous. Egg embolisms in the cerebrum and cerebellum were distributed almost homogeneously, regardless of the white or grey matter. They were detected in 5–10% of the sites examined and scattered sporadically in single forms. It was also stated that the small arterial branches often showed atrophy and collapse due to egg embolism. Around the eggs degeneration of some nerve cells or destruction of tissue in extremely small areas could be observed. It is conceivable that embolism of *Paragonimus* eggs in a location distant from the lung should also be present in human cases.

IX. SYMPTOMATOLOGY

At an early stage of paragonimiasis almost all cases show pleurisy of varying severity and occasionally pneumothorax. The most remarkable symptom is cough and blood-stained sputum. Besides this, such symptoms as anaemia, eosinophilia and so forth have been pointed out, but they are not particularly characteristic of paragonimiasis.

Iwasaki (1955) investigated 87 patients with paragonimiasis at Kochi Hospital: the main symptoms of those patients were blood-stained sputa in 56 cases (64·4%) and haemoptysis in 13 cases (16·1%). He stated that in spite of their long history of disease, their health was not impaired. This is a characteristic feature of paragonimiasis and, as Iwasaki reported, a number of mild cases of paragonimiasis probably pass without any evident symptoms. It is also said that the findings by auscultation and percussion of the chest are generally light; therefore, when dullness and some moist *râles* are heard on chest examination, it should be appreciated that there is a possibility of pulmonary tuberculosis.

Hirano (1957) carried out various clinical examinations on 69 patients with paragonimiasis diagnosed by the intradermal test in the endemic area for paragonimiasis, and compared the results with those taken from 62 healthy individuals who served as controls. The following symptoms disclosed significantly higher ratios in the "patient" group than in the "healthy" group: (1) feeling of heaviness in the legs, (2) pains in the limbs, (3) coughing, (4) expectoration and (5) bloody sputum. However, clinically, there were no remarkable differences between the two groups except for the decrease in the capacity of the lungs and eosinophilia. Hirano also reported that no significant difference could be found in the number of red cells, whereas in the patients leucocytes tended to increase. Other data (Table III) indicate a slight increase in mean haemoglobin index among patients as compared with controls, a

TABLE III

Clinical Examination of 69 Cases of Paragonimiasis (Hirano, 1957)

	Patients (69)			Controls (62)		
	High	Low	Aver.	High	Low	Aver.
Haemoglobin index (%)	108	75	90	103	73	87·6
γ-Globulin (g/dl)			1·01			0·96
Erythrocyte sedimentation (mm)*	49·0	1·5	N.S.	26·3	1·0	
Eosinophil count (%)**	21			13		

*No significant difference.   **Significant difference.

tendency for serum proteins to increase, no significant difference in erythrocyte sedimentation rates, but a significant increase in eosinophil counts.

Chang *et al.* (1958) reported the results of the clinical examination on patients with paragonimiasis in Korea: 191 out of 200 cases (95·5%) had haemoptoe, 9 of them had haemoptysis, and quite a few complained of breathlessness and difficulty in breathing.

The clinical symptoms of cerebral paragonimiasis are similar to those of Jacksonian epilepsy, cerebral tumour or embolism in the brain, and the most conspicuous symptom is paralysis. Often the disease is accompanied by fits such as apoplexy, but its progress is gradual as in cases of softening of the brain. Hosokawa *et al.* (1957) drew up statistics on 105 cases of cerebral paragonimiasis, stating that the symptoms were sudden headache, vomiting, epileptic seizures, paralysis, and meningitic symptoms often with fever; it is necessary to differentiate the disease from true epilepsy, meningeal haemorrhage, softening of the brain, uraemia and meningitis.

Shih *et al.* (1958) reported that visual disturbances were found in about 50% of patients with cerebral paragonimiasis in Formosa. As for the pyopneumothorax caused by paragonimiasis, reports have hitherto been made by many workers but the time of onset varies from 2 months to 3 years after infection. There are very few reports of spontaneous pneumothorax in human cases of paragonimiasis; Shibata (1951) found 2 out of 178 patients, and Nakayama (1954) and Iwasaki (1955) found one case each. Miyake (1952) indicated that the spontaneous pneumothorax usually found in dogs infected with *P. westermani* could rarely be observed in human paragonimiasis and this was attributed to the thickness of the pleura.

X. Diagnosis

Paragonimiasis in endemic areas can be diagnosed clinically by an occasional light cough and yellowish brown pus-like sputum in which bloody spots or lines can sometimes be seen. However, the diagnosis should always be confirmed by microscopic examinations of the sputum or stool in order to find the eggs of *Paragonimus*. Charcot-Leyden's crystals in sputum assist the diagnosis.

A. LABORATORY DIAGNOSIS

The eggs of *Paragonimus* can be found in blood-stained sputum of patients with paragonimiasis by the direct smear method, but when few eggs appear the centrifuge sedimentation technique with 1–2% sodium hydroxide should be used. In a light infection, however, sputum is not always produced, and in those patients who have a habit of swallowing it, the eggs can be found only by examination of the stool. Komiya and Yokogawa (1953) carried out examinations of both sputum and stool at the same time on 35 patients 189 times. They found *Paragonimus* eggs in 136 (72·0%) of the sputa examined and in 123 (65·1%) of the stools. The cases where *Paragonimus* eggs were found only in stools, but not in sputum, occurred 25 times (13·2%), mainly in children and elderly people. The finding of *Paragonimus* eggs in stools was in unexpectedly high ratio. They recommended that sputum and stool examinations should be made simultaneously and repeated at least three times to confirm negative results for *Paragonimus* eggs. In the stool examinations the AMS III centrifuging technique (Hunter *et al.*, 1948) was used.

Hatano (1960) made a comparative study of stool and sputum specimens examined at the same time on 131 individuals who showed a positive intradermal test for paragonimiasis in an endemic area, Ehime prefecture, Japan. *Paragonimus* eggs were found in sputum of 54 (41·2%) and in stools of 47 individuals (35·8%).

Okada (1959) in the endemic area of paragonimiasis in Shizuoka prefecture, Japan, carried out simultaneous examinations of gastric juice, sputum and stool for each of 60 individuals who showed a positive reaction to the intradermal test. *Paragonimus* eggs were found in 63·3% of gastric juice samples, in 40·0% of stool samples and in 26·6% of sputum samples.

Kitamoto *et al.* (1958) reported that *Paragonimus* eggs can be easily aspirated in the secretion of the affected portion of the bronchi sucked by means of Metra's tube.

B. SERO-IMMUNOLOGICAL DIAGNOSIS

It is, of course, true that an unequivocal diagnosis of this infection depends on the recovery of *Paragonimus* eggs from the sputum or stool, and the intradermal test, complement fixation test and other serological tests described here are all supplementary diagnostic methods. But some of them can be widely applied, as indicated below.

(a) An intradermal test for paragonimiasis is easily carried out, and there are no side effects, so the test is therefore useful as a screening method for *Paragonimus* infections of man in endemic areas.

(b) Clinically, the intradermal test is useful in differentiating paragonimiasis from pulmonary tuberculosis and some other chest disease, or cerebral paragonimiasis from brain tumour, cerebral haemorrhage or other extrapulmonary paragonimiasis. In such cases, if the intradermal test showed negative results, paragonimiasis can almost certainly be ruled out.

(c) An intradermal test continues to show positive reactions for as long as 10–20 years after complete recovery, while the results of the complement fixation test or agglutination test have closer relations with the life and death of the worms. Consequently, when the presence of *Paragonimus* eggs cannot be proved although the intradermal test gives a positive result, the complement fixation test or agglutination test may be used to obtain an important clue for diagnosis.

(d) Complement fixation and agglutination tests turn negative within 3–9 months after complete recovery and this serves as the criterion of cure after chemotherapy in paragonimiasis.

1. *Intradermal (I.D.) Test*

A considerable amount of work has been done especially during the last ten years. The preparation of the antigen, and the technique are standardized and the I.D. test has been widely used for clinical diagnosis and for screening of *Paragonimus* infections in endemic areas.

I

Yokogawa *et al.* (1955a,c), Chung *et al.* (1955a), Sadun *et al.* (1960) and others have reported on the technique of this test and matters concerning the antigen amount of antigen for the test and criteria.

Technique: About 0·01 ml of the antigen is injected intradermally into the forearm; this is enough to raise a weal 2–3 mm in diameter. Any reaction is considered positive in which the diameter of the weal after 15 min exceeds by 5 mm the diameter of the weal raised immediately after injection. The reaction usually appears 3–5 min after the injection, reaches its maximum with 15 min and disappears within 3–6 h. The weal is usually accompanied by redness and in many cases "pseudopodia" are present.

Antigens: Various kinds of extracts of adult and larval *P. westermani* are mentioned by Yokogawa (1956b,c), Yokogawa *et al.* (1955a,c, 1959), Sadun *et al.* (1959), Yamamura (1959), Miyazaki (1959) and others: e.g. metabolic products, secretions and excretions of the adult worms of *P. westermani* (Nunogami, 1931; Yokogawa *et al.*, 1955a.c); saline extract of the adult worms (Tominaga, 1939); saline extract of miracidia (Morishita, 1954); saline extract of sputum of a patient with paragonimiasis (Ishigaki *et al.*, 1954); saline extracts of cercariae and metacercariae (Yokogawa *et al.*, 1955a); Coca's solution extract of the adult worms (Okabe, 1956); veronal buffered saline extract of the adult worms (Yokogawa, 1952a,b); alkaline soluble protein fraction of the adult worms (Sadun *et al.*, 1959; Yokogawa and Oshima, 1959); polypeptide fraction of adult worms (Yamamura, 1959; Miyazaki, 1959; Yokogawa *et al.*, 1960a). Mannoji (1952) reported that a cross reaction was found in a patient with paragonimiasis treated with the antigen prepared from adult worms of *P. ohirai*, and Yokogawa *et al.* (1955a) 'also stated that the antigen from the adult worms of *P. kellicotti* has a cross reaction with that of *P. westermani*.

Yokogawa suggested that the veronal buffered saline extract of adult *P. westermani* (V.B.S. antigen) seems to be more useful than the purified antigen for the I.D. test, considering its ease of production and high yield. Sadun *et al.* (1958) reported that the I.D. test with purified antigens can be used to great advantage in epidemiological investigations for paragonimiasis and for the differential diagnosis of other trematode infections.

The preparation of V.B.S. antigen was described by Yokogawa (1956b,c). Adult *P. westermani* from the lungs of experimentally infected dogs and cats are washed several times in sterile saline and finally in distilled water and placed in small ampoules. After alternate freezing and thawing twenty times with a mixture of dry ice and acetone the worms are dried in a vacuum-freezing desiccator. The lyophilized material is then pulverized in a tissue grinder and 5–10 parts of ether are added to 1 part of this material to exclude the ether soluble substance at 0–4° C. Then extraction with 99 parts of V.B.S. to 1 part of dried material is carried out for 48 h at 4° C. The suspension is then centrifuged at 10 000 r.p.m. for 30 min by refrigeratory centrifugator. This liquid serves as the stock solution for the antigen to be employed in the I.D. tests and in the complement fixation test in dilution of 1:100. When used in the I.D. tests the stock solution is diluted to 1:10 000 with 0·01% merthiolate in normal saline.

When the alkaline-soluble protein fraction is used for the I.D. test, the standardization of antigenicity can be made by the protein content in this antigen. No reports have been made about the standardization of the antigenicity of the V.B.S. antigen.

Tsuji (1963, unpublished) examined the amount of total nitrogen (N) of adult and immature worms of *P. westermani*, respectively. The total nitrogen in the adult worms was 727–792 μg per 10 mg of dried material but in the immature worms within 5–6 weeks after infection there were only 252–275 μg per 10 mg of dried material.

Yokogawa (1964) compared the amount of nitrogen contained in V.B.S antigen from the adult *P. westermani* with other antigens prepared from *Clonorchis sinensis*, *Schistosoma japonicum* and *P. ohirai* by the Micro-Kjeldahl method. The amount of nitrogen in the antigen prepared from *P. westermani* was much greater than in antigens prepared from other flukes and almost always about the same amount of nitrogen was detected from various lots of antigens prepared at different times. Considering that the active substance of the antigen is contained in the protein fraction of the worms, the antigen which has a constant activity can be obtained by the standardization of the amount of nitrogen in the antigen. Yokogawa also reported that the complement fixation test using the standardized serum of a patient with paragonimiasis is helpful for the standardization of the antigen for the I.D. test. Oshima and Yokogawa (1957) examined the relation between the concentration of the V.B.S. antigen and the strength of reaction (the size of weals), and found that when the concentration is between 1:2 500 and 1:40000 dilutions, all gave positive reactions. Yokogawa *et al.* (1955a) reported that the V.B.S. antigen is very stable, and is not affected by a temperature of 100° C for 30 min; there is no change for 3–5 years in antigen kept at 4° C. Yokogawa (1964) observed the effect of the I.D. test on partial immunity of sensitization of the skin. The I.D. test with V.B.S. antigen was performed repeatedly at about the same site on the left forearm in sixteen patients with paragonimiasis and two healthy individuals as controls every month for 1 year. With repeated inoculations of V.B.S. antigen it was found that there was no tendency for the weals to decrease or increase in diameter.

A total of 121 327 individuals were given the I.D. test using V.B.S. antigen in various endemic and non-endemic areas of paragonimiasis in Japan from 1954 to 1963 by Yokogawa *et al.* No side reaction was detected in these persons. Recently Yamamura (1959), Miyazaki (1959), Ishii *et. al.* (1959) and Yagura (1964) reported that the polypeptide fraction of adult *P. westermani* can be successfully used as the antigen for the I.D. test for paragonimiasis.

Preparation of the polypeptide (p.p.t.) antigen: Lyophilized material is extracted with 10 parts of 0·1 N HCl for 48 h at room temperature. The filtrate is brought to pH 5·0 with 5 N NaOH and kept at room temperature for 2 h. This filtrate is added to an equal volume of saturated picric acid and after standing overnight at room temperature a yellow precipitate is obtained. This precipitate is extracted with 3% HCl in 95% ethanol for 6 h at room temperature and then centrifuged. The supernatant is concentrated to 1/10 of its original volume. Then a white precipitate is obtained by adding acetone. This precipitate is washed repeatedly with acetone and dried *in vacuo*. This fraction is a basic polypeptide. For the I.D. test the polypeptide is dissolved with physiological saline so as to contain 20 μg/ml.

Yokogawa *et al.* (1960a) made a comparative study of the practical values of I.D. tests with V.B.S. antigen and p.p.t. antigen as the screening method for paragonimiasis in the endemic area. The I.D. tests with both antigens were performed on 1 045 individuals (96·5% of the whole population) in the Tsushima district, Ehime prefecture. The results were as follows. Two hundred and seventy of 1 045 individuals (25·8%) showed positive and 71 (6·8%) doubtful reactions with V.B.S. antigen, while 98 (9·4%) reacted positively and 35 (3·3%) doubtfully with p.p.t. antigen. The percentage of positive reactions with V.B.S. antigen was significantly greater than that with the p.p.t. antigen. However, 95 out of 98 which showed positive reaction with p.p.t. antigen also showed a positive reaction with V.B.S. antigen. Twenty-three out of 28 individuals who showed *Paragonimus* eggs in stool among 1 045 individuals were positive for both antigens and the remaining 5 of the 28 individuals showed positive reactions only with V.B.S. antigen and negative reactions with p.p.t. antigen. It was reported in another study that among 96 patients with paragonimiasis who showed eggs in their stools all were positive for V.B.S. antigen, but with p.p.t. antigen 3 of them showed a negative reaction.

From these results it was claimed that both antigens could be used successfully for the I.D. test. However, a few cases would be overlooked by the I.D. tests with p.p.t. antigen. It must be noted that the yield of the V.B.S. antigen is more than twenty times of that of p.p.t. antigen from the same amount of lyophilized material.

Yokogawa (1956b,c, 1964) summarized the antigenicity of the V.B.S. antigen for the I.D. test as follows: (a) the antigenic substance for the I.D. test does not pass through cellophane membrane; (b) it does not precipitate by centrifugation at 30 000 rev/min for 30 min; (c) it is located in the protein fraction and not in the polysaccharide fraction; (d) skin-sensitizing antibody is rendered evident in the serum of a patient with paragonimiasis by the Prausnitz-Küstner reaction (Yokogawa *et al.*, 1957b).

2. Precipitin Test

Very few reports have been made on the precipitin reaction of paragonimiasis. Ito (1956) tried the precipitin test with Coca's extract of adult *P. westermani* on fifteen patients with paragonimiasis and got positive reactions in all of them.

Kunieda (1957) reported that two patients showed positive reactions in the precipitin test with saline extract from adult *P. westermani*. Yokogawa, with the precipitin test using V.B.S. antigens, examined a lot of serum samples from those patients who were positive for *Paragonimus* eggs and for the complement fixation test, and concluded that it is not likely to be of practical use because the titres of antigen and antibody were usually extremely low.

3. Flocculation Test

Yokogawa (1956a) applied the Bentonite antigen method described by

Bozicevich (1951) to the flocculation test for paragonimiasis. This Bentonite antigen was prepared from the adult *P. westermani* and the flocculation test showed very good results: 55 out of 66 individuals (83·3%) with *Paragonimus* eggs in the sputum or faeces were positive, but all five cases which had a past history of paragonimiasis and showed a negative result for *Paragonimus* eggs at present were negative for this test: this result corresponded well with the result of the complement fixation test.

However, the flocculation test has a drawback: the Bentonite antigen is rather difficult to prepare and its stability is low.

Takano (1960) used the cholesterol-lecithin antigen described by Vogel *et al.* (1957) for this test and compared it with Bentonite antigen. The preparation was far easier but the sensitivity of cholesterol-lecithin antigen was a little lower than that of Bentonite antigen.

Koizumi (1956) obtained positive results with Middlebrook's haemolytic reaction in the serum of a patient with paragonimiasis using the antigen prepared from the adult *P. westermani*.

4. *T. M. Test*

Morishita (1955) obtained remarkable precipitation between the extract of faeces of a patient with ascariasis and the rabbit immune serum against *Ascaris lumbricoides* and called this the T. M. test. Morishita (1957) reported that the precipitation took place between the extract of faeces of patients with paragonimiasis and the rabbit immune serum against *P. westermani*. Okabe (1961) also proved that the precipitation took place between the extract of urine from patients with paragonimiasis and the rabbit immune serum against *P. westermani*.

5. *Complement Fixation Test*

Little has been written about the complement fixation test for paragonimiasis until recently. Ando (1917c, 1921) conducted the test for the first time on patients. He found that 23 out of 25 patients showed a positive reaction and all who recovered from this disease showed negative reaction, suggesting that this test could be used as a criterion of cure for paragonimiasis after treatment. Chung *et al.* (1955a, b, 1956) investigated the technique and the antigen for the complement fixation test. Their antigen was used in a concentration as high as 1:10 to 1:25. It was stated that in the animal experiments the positive reaction in the complement fixation test appeared 2–4 weeks after infection. There was mention also of the cross reaction of paragonimiasis with other trematode infections as follows: 28 out of 29 patients showed positive reactions with the antigen prepared from adult *Fasciola hepatica*; 25 of them showed positive reactions with the antigen from *Clonorchis sinensis* but they all showed negative reactions with the antigen from *Schistosoma japonicum*.

Using the same V.B.S. antigen (1:5 000 dilution) as for the intradermal test, Yokogawa and Awano (1956) used the 50% haemolysis end point titration for the complement fixation test for paragonimiasis. They investigated degrees of antigenicity of the various kinds of antigen for the complement fixation test, finding that V.B.S. antigen showed the highest antigenicity, protein fraction by semisaturated ammonium sulphate less, and polysaccharide and poly peptide fractions showed no antigenicity.

Yokogawa (1964) also reported that 4 out of 22 cases of clonorchiasis sinensis and 6 out of 25 cases of schistosomiasis japonicum showed positive reaction with V.B.S. antigen from *P. westermani*, while 10 out of 31 cases of paragonimiasis showed positive reaction with the antigen from *Clonorchis sinensis* and 8 out of 37 cases of paragonimiasis showed positive reactions with the antigen from *Schistosoma japonicum*. Chung *et al.* (1956) studied the complement fixation test in cerebral paragonimiasis. They reported that 20 out of 24 cases showed positive reaction for the complement fixation test in the cerebrospinal fluid, but all the cerebrospinal fluid samples from the patients with tuberculous cerebrospinal meningitis and general paresis showed negative reactions. Yokogawa (1956b) reported that the complement fixation test was negative in four cases who had recovered from paragonimiasis 20 years ago and yet remained positive for the intradermal test. He also reported that in one case of paragonimiasis in which the worm cyst in the lungs was resected surgically, the complement fixation test became negative about 4 months after operation.

Yokogawa *et al.* (1962b) specified that most cases treated with bithionol and completely cured became negative for complement fixation tests 3–9 months after treatment. It can be safely said that the results of the complement fixation test are closely correlated with the active infection. The intradermal tests with V.B.S. antigen can be used to great advantage for screening large populations because of its simplicity in use, safety, ease of application and low cost. However, it can be said that the result of the intradermal test does not always show the actual existence of lung fluke infection in the area examined because of the continuation of the positive dermal reaction for long periods after recovery from the disease. On the other hand, the complement fixation test is closely correlated with the existence of infection and not past infections. Therefore, for the epidemiological surveys the intradermal test should be used first and the complement fixation tests should be performed on individuals who show positive or doubtful dermal reactions.

C. X-RAY DIAGNOSIS

1. Characteristic Findings in Chest X-rays of Patients with Paragonimiasis

Numerous studies have been reported especially in the last ten years on the use of X-ray pictures for the diagnosis of pulmonary paragonimiasis. Ando and Yamada (1916) were first to report on this possibility, although X-ray pictures of paragonimiasis frequently give findings similar to those of pulmonary tuberculosis.

Miyake (1939) was the first to make use of tomography for five patients and proved in all of them the presence of nodular or ring shadows which are said to be typical of paragonimiasis.

Diaconita and Goldis (1964) reported that tomographic and bronchographic examinations are indispensable for the clinical diagnosis of paragonimiasis. In results reported by many investigators, abnormal shadows are found in the middle, upper and lower parts of the lungs, but are rarely seen in the apex. It can be said also that the abnormal shadows are seen more frequently in the right lung than in the left.

The nodular shadow is the one suggestive of a tuberculoma and it has a sharply marked rounded or oval contour. The ring shadow is a cystic form with a relatively thin wall and is round, oval or irregular in shape.

Iwasaki et al. (1956) reported on 145 patients that nodular shadows, ring shadows and infiltrative shadows, in that order, are considered to be the typical findings for paragonimiasis. They also stressed that the moving phenomenon of the abnormal shadow in the chest X-ray was probably due to the migration of the worm.

Shigeyasu (1959), using partly tomography and partly high voltage radiography, made statistical observations on chest X-rays of 510 patients and reported as follows: nodular and ring shadows, 256 cases (47·4%); infiltrative shadows, 63 cases (11·7%); localized bronchiectasia, 42 cases (7·8%); transparent figure like a tunnel, 5 cases (0·9%) (45 cases); increase of lung markings, 62 cases (11·5%); calcification, 3 cases; hilar shadows, 37 cases; combination with pulmonary tuberculosis 5 cases (0·9%); changes of pleura, 16 cases (2·9%) (49 cases); no findings, 91 cases (16·9%). (The number of cases in parentheses shows those combined with other shadows.)

2. Confusion with Pulmonary Tuberculosis

It is not easy to diagnose paragonimiasis solely by chest X-ray examination, and particularly to differentiate this disease from pulmonary tuberculosis. This is due to the fact that from the standpoint of pathology the changes in the lungs are not confined to paragonimiasis except in some cases which show typical modifications such as worm cysts. Indeed, the rate of appearance of nodular or ring shadows which are seemingly typical for paragonimiasis shows only 30% of the patients with paragonimiasis, and it is said that nearly 40% of them can hardly be distinguished from those of pulmonary tuberculosis.

It has been reported recently from Japan, China, Korea, Formosa, the Philippines and some other countries that there is an unexpectedly large number of patients with paragonimiasis in the endemic areas who had been wrongly diagnosed as cases of pulmonary tuberculosis and treated with drugs appropriate to this disease.

Recently, Iwamura (1964) found about twelve cases of paragonimiasis among the patients with pulmonary tuberculosis in west Nepal where paragonimiasis had not been reported.

When the general condition of the patients is not so poor despite severe changes in the chest X-ray picture, or when X-ray findings do not turn out better in spite of treatment for tuberculosis in endemic areas of paragonimiasis, particular attention should be directed to paragonimiasis.

Yokogawa et al. (1963a) periodically followed up the alterations in the abnormal shadows in the chest X-rays of seventy-eight patients with paragonimiasis during and after treatment with bithionol. Most shadows were absorbed from 1 to 3 months after treatment, only a few remaining unchanged for longer than 6 months to 1 year. It might be possible to evaluate the effect of treatment for paragonimiasis comparatively early by following periodically the changes of chest X-ray shadows after treatment.

XI. TREATMENT

The ideal type of an anthelminthic should be more effective against the parasite and not toxic to the host. The large size of *Paragonimus westermani* within cysts in the lung tissue of the host has added to the difficulties of finding a satisfactory treatment for paragonimiasis. In early studies of this disease in Japan a large number of different drugs was tried, none of which showed any promise except emetine hydrochloride. However, patients receiving repeated injections of this drug almost always have secondary reactions such as headache, weariness, temporary dizziness and nausea, and the drug is contraindicated in old people, pregnant women and in patients debilitated by other conditions. Furthermore, it has been reported by many investigators that a very large number of injections was necessary to produce a "cure".

An important advance in this treatment was made when S. Yokogawa and Ro (1939) found that a combination of emetine and prontosil gave much better results than emetine alone. Ro and Yokogawa (1941), Ro (1942) and S. Yokogawa and Ro (1942) studied the histopathological changes in the lungs of dogs that had been treated with a combination of emetine and prontosil. Some interesting observations were made of the effect on the worms. The earliest changes were in the reproductive system and affected the production of eggs. The ovary and testes degenerated at an early stage, while the vitelline glands were the last of the reproductive organs to degenerate. The possibility was suggested that some unknown toxic substance produced by the effect of the prontosil on the tissues was ingested by the worms and produced these profound changes in their reproductive systems. This, combined with the intense cellular reaction and the direct action of the emetine hydrochloride, killed the worms.

Narihara (1939) and Sato (1940) tried a combination of emetine hydrochloride and a home-made sulphonamid preparation and obtained favourable results.

Miyakawa *et al.* (1955a,b) reported clinical improvement following the combined use of emetine and sulphonamides. Furthermore they compared the blood and tissue concentrations in dogs receiving emetine alone and in those receiving it in combinations with sulphonamide. They found appreciably more emetine stored in the blood and tissues of the dogs receiving sulphonamides as well than in those receiving emetine alone. They suggested that aluminium hydroxide, kainic acid (extract of *Digenia simplex*) and santonin also have the same effect as sulphonamide.

Komiya *et al.* (1952) treated thirty-two cases of paragonimiasis with a combination of emetine and various kinds of sulpha drugs, such as sulphamine, sulphathiazole and sulphadiazine. The drugs were given daily over a period of 10 days. The 4% emetine solution was injected in doses of 1 ml/day to patients over 12 years of age. The daily dose of sulpha compounds was 4 g. The number of cases and the nature of the results did not warrant a comparison of the efficacy of the combination with the different sulpha drugs. Only three of the patients were completely free from side effects after treatment, viz. slight headache, weariness, temporary dizziness and nausea. To test the effect of the combination of sulpha drugs, the sputum and faeces of each patient were examined for eggs immediately after treatment, and also 1 month and 4 months later. In their investigations Komiya et al. (1952) found that 17 of their 32 cases were negative immediately after treatment, 10 were negative 1 month later, and 5 were negative 4 months later. Actually, only five cases remained negative throughout the entire series of examinations. Komiya et al. suggested that follow-up examinations after treatment would be carried out for periods exceeding 3 months after treatment to determine whether the patients had relapsed or not. Recently Chung et al. (1954) used chloroquine phosphate in very high doses in two children and one adult. There was clinical improvement and a rapid reduction in the number of eggs in the sputum. Later they used chloroquine on seven cases which had relapsed after apparently successful treatment with emetine: chloroquine was administered orally in doses up to 0·25 g twice a day to children and up to 0·5 g twice a day to adults. The period of treatment varied from 93 to 231 days for total doses of 27–86 g. All were completely cured clinically except for the persistence of cerebral paragonimiasis. Although Granz (1956) also successfully treated one case of pulmonary paragonimiasis, Kitamoto et al. (1958) reported discouraging results using chloroquine either alone or in combination with emetine.

With these conflicting reports in mind, Buck et al. (1958a, b) undertook an evaluation of chloroquine therapy on 116 patients, including twenty-four with extrapulmonary paragonimiasis. All the patients received the drug orally, intramuscularly and as an inhalation in aerosol form. From their observations, these workers concluded that the response to chloroquine was related to the duration of the disease and the location of the parasite. The success of therapy in pulmonary paragonimiasis was almost three times greater among patients with a history of disease up to 2 years than among those who had been ill for 5 years or more. Good results were obtained in several patients with Paragonimus empyema and pleurisy and in one case of renal paragonimiasis. On the other hand, negative results were obtained in patients with cerebral paragonimiasis, some of whom had increased epileptic attacks under therapy. Khoo (1961) tried three combination methods of treatment for nine paragonimiasis patients: emetine–stibophen–chloroquine combination; tetracycline–chloroquine followed 7 weeks later by nilodin–pentostam–chloroquine, and tetracycline–chloroquine–hetrazan combination. He reported that the treatment of pulmonary paragonimiasis was so far disappointing. Chloroquine diminished the quantity of sputum but did not eliminate ova from it. Five out of nine cases suffered side effects which included dizziness, blurring of vision, nausea, tightness and pains of chest, backache, numbness of limbs, loss of appetite and diarrhoea. Shih et al. (1958) found living worms in the brain at surgical intervention in cases previously treated with both emetine and chloroquine and concluded that surgery alone offers hope of curing cerebral paragonimiasis. H. W. Grauman (unpublished lectures, 1957) urged that surgery is often contraindicated, in both early and late cases.

Yokogawa *et al.* (1956) examined the effect of a number of drugs *in vitro* on the excysted metacercariae of *P. westermani*. They found that atabrine and chloroquine killed the excysted larvae in dilution of 1:300 000 within 24 h. Emetine hydrochloride in 1:200 000 dilutions and stibnal in dilutions of 1:20 000 to 1:50 000 also killed them in the 24 h period. However, under the conditions of their experiments, they failed to find any evidence of activity by hetrazan, terramycine, erythrocin, fumazillin, piperazine, gentian violet, carbarsone and sulphonamide. Soon after, Yokogawa *et al.* (1961b) found by the *in vitro* test mentioned above that bithionol (Bitin, Tanabe Co., Tokyo) killed the excysted larvae of *P. westermani* in dilution of 1:1 390 000 within 24 h. For paragonimiasis, bithionol seemed to be the most effective of any drugs which have ever been tested. Its structure is shown in Fig. 7, and it

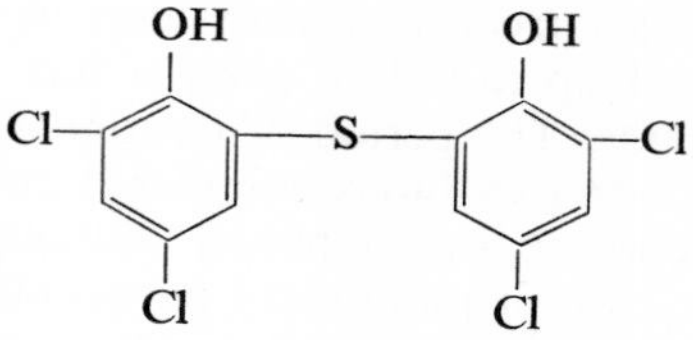

FIG. 7. Chemical structure of bithionol (2,2′-thiobis (4,6-dichlorophenol)).

has been used under the commercial name "Actamer" (Monsanto Co., U.S.A.) as an ingredient of cosmetics because of its skin-sterilizing effect. This agent was first found to have an excellent anthelminthic effect on the chicken tapeworm, *Raillietina kashiwarensis* (Sawada, 1957) and on the liver fluke, *Fasciola hepatica* (Ueno, 1959).

After confirmation of the excellent efficacy of this drug for animals infected with *P. westermani* and *P. ohirai* (Yokogawa *et al.*, 1961b), the first clinical trial was conducted on thirteen patients with paragonimiasis, most of whom had been treated previously with a combined method of emetine hydrochloride and sulphonamide (Yokogawa *et al.*, 1962a). As a result, it was found that paragonimiasis can be cured with bithionol (Bitin) given in a daily dose of 50 mg/kg on alternate days for a total of 5–15 doses, and that on relapses were observed in patients for 2 years after treatment. Eleven out of thirteen had mild and transient side effects, such as diarrhoea, abdominal pain, nausea or vomiting and two cases had an urticarial eruption. However, in no case was the blood, urine or liver function upset. The most frequent side effect was diarrhoea, beginning shortly after oral administration in most cases and subsiding spontaneously after the passage of one to several stools: there was neither tenesmus nor bloody stool. Yokogawa (1961) also reported that bithionol can be used for mass treatment of paragonimiasis in endemic areas as a control measure.

Since bithionol was reported as a new agent against paragonimiasis there are many reports that indicate that it has much value as shown in Table IV.

TABLE IV

Results of Treatment for Paragonimiasis with Bithionol* given by Mouth on Alternate Days

Reference	Daily dose** (mg/kg)	No. of doses	No. of patients Treated	Cured
Yokogawa *et al.* (1961a)	30–50	5–15	30	29
Amagishi *et al.* (1961)***	40–50	10	48	48
Katamine *et al.* (1961)	20–30	10	19	19
Sato *et al.* (1963)	10–50	10	45	42
Iwata *et al.* (1962)***	40–50	10–20	6	6
Oba *et al.* (1962)***	40–50	10	14	14
Yang *et al.* (1962)***	40–50	10–15	17	17
Kang *et al.* (1963)	20–50	15–30	61	61
Yokogawa *et al.* (1962a)	10–20	10–15	29	27
Yokogawa *et al.* (1963a)	30–50	10–15	60	60
Total			329	323

*Bitin (Tanabe Co., Japan).
**In two or three divided doses after meals.
***Unpublished reports.

Yokogawa *et al.* (1963a) studied the relationship between the amount of bithionol used and its efficacy, as well as the röntgenographic changes taking place in the chest after treatment with it. The results were as follows: apparent cure was obtained in 78 of the 80 cases treated, including all that received 50 mg/kg every other day 5, 10 or 15 times, 40 mg/kg 10 or 15 times, 30 mg/kg 7, 10 or 15 times or 20 mg/kg 15 times. The seventy patients given a total of 210–750 mg/kg of the drug over periods of 9–29 days and 8 out of 10 cases given 200 mg/kg in 9–19 days were apparently cured. The two patients in whom positive signs recurred had received 200 mg/kg, one in 9 days (40 mg/kg 5 times) and the other in 19 days (20 mg/kg 10 times). In these two cases blood-stained sputum containing a few *Paragonimus* eggs was noted for 7 and 3 months, respectively, after completion of treatment.

Diarrhoea, loose stools, abdominal pain, nausea, vomiting and urticarial eruption have been mentioned as the side effects of bithionol. Yokogawa *et al.* (1963a) observed that when bithionol was administered diarrhoeic stools were noted initially once to several times per day, but with continued administration in some cases they became normal and in no case was the discontinuation of the drug or other measures necessary for diarrhoea. Transient diarrhoea was noted in 32 out of 62 adults (51·6%) and in 3 out of 18 children (16·7%). Abdominal pain, anorexia, nausea, or vomiting also occurred, but always in mild form. Urticarial eruption or dermatitis as a noteworthy side effect was observed in six adults and one child. It was found that the smaller the amount of bithionol administered, the lower the rate of appearance of side effects became. They were less frequent in children than in adults.

The course of infiltrative, ring or nodular shadows which had been noted prior to treatment were examined by taking normal and tomographic X-ray pictures immediately after treatment and every month thereafter for 6 months. Of the 129 pathological shadows observed in 78 cases before treatment, 27 (21·0%) had already disappeared, and 83 (64·3%) had contracted a few days after treatment. Six months after treatment 98 (76·0%) had disappeared, 26 (20·2%) had contracted and the 5 remaining were unchanged. These five cases (unchanged at 6 months) were still unchanged 1 year after treatment. No definite relationship was consistently found between types of shadows and the time of disappearance or reduction. However, generally speaking, the order of absorption seems to be first uniform infiltrative shadows, then ring or nodular shadows and, lastly, uneven infiltrative shadows. It will be most interesting to investigate the relation between the shadows and the tissue lesions in the lungs by pathologico-anatomical studies. Iwasaki (1962), Katamine et al. (1963), Sato et al. (1963) and S. P. Yang (personal communication, 1962) also reported that X-ray shadows due to paragonimiasis were rapidly absorbed after treatment with bithionol.

Yokogawa et al. (1962a, 1963a) also reported that among 41 patients with paragonimiasis expectoration of blood-stained sputa and eggs ceased in 17 cases after the second dose (i.e. after the 3rd day of treatment), in 22 after 3–5 doses (5th to 9th day) and in 2 after 7 or 8 doses; i.e. after the administration of less than 5 doses of the drug in 39 of the 41 cases.

Katamine et al. (1961) treated 22 patients with bithionol. A dose of 20 mg/kg or 30 mg/kg per day was given to three different groups; i.e. (1) daily for 10 days, (2) every other day 10 times, and (3) every 4 days 10 times. Apparent cure was obtained in all cases without exception; stool and sputa became negative for Paragonimus ova within 3–8 days of treatment regardless of the intervals of drug administration, with one exception in which Paragonimus ova became negative in 15 days of treatment. It is interesting to note that there was no evident relationship between the time when production of blood-stained sputum or eggs ceased and the amount of drug given or intervals of administration. That is to say, in all groups given 20 mg/kg or 30 mg/kg every day, every other day or every 4 days, production of blood-stained sputum and eggs ceased within 4–9 days of treatment.

Kang et al. (1963) treated sixty-one patients with bithionol. They were divided into two groups, each of which were further divided into three subgroups as follows:

Group A. Relatively small daily dose for 30 days	Group B. Relatively larger dose on alternate days for 30 days
1. 20 mg/kg	1. 30 mg/kg
2. 25 mg/kg	2. 40 mg/kg
3. 30 mg/kg	3. 50 mg/kg

No significant difference between group A, 1–3, and group B, 1–3.

All sixty-one patients were cleared of eggs in the sputum and stool during and after treatment as follows:

Day of treatment	Clearance of eggs (%)
0–10	27·9
11–20	24·6
21–30	21·3
After 31	13·1

Total of negative conversion before day 30: 73·8%.

With regard to the side effects of bithionol, Kang *et al.* reported diarrhoea in 52·5%, lower abdominal pain in 31·1%, nausea, constipation and anorexia in 11·4% and urticaria in 14·8%. However, they stated that almost all of the side effects were transient, and did not necessitate any symptomatic treatment. Sato *et al.* (1963) reported that 42 out of 45 patients were completely cured when bithionol was given either in daily doses of 10–50 mg/kg on alternate days for 10 doses, or once a week 10 times. Three relapsed cases were all given 10 mg/kg bithionol every other day 10 times.

Yokogawa *et al.* (1961b) studied the pathological changes of the worms in the worm cyst of the lungs of dogs treated with bithionol. The shapes of the uteri of the dead worms were not distinguishable and eggs were never found, but there were many brown granules of irregular sizes. Even in the living worms there were only a few eggs or granules of various sizes, probably vitelline-granules.

Park (1962) conducted comparative studies of various drugs by treating 140 patients with chloroquine, emetine and bithionol (Bitin). The results were as follows:

Chloroquine and emetine. After five courses (one course: 13 mg/kg/day chloroquine for 10 days, followed by 1 mg/kg/day emetine for 10 days, i.v.) 35 out of 81 (43·5%) patients were completely cured.

Bithionol. After one or two courses (40 mg/kg on alternate days 15 times) 57 out of 59 (96·6%) patients were completely cured.

Waitz *et al.* (1963) stated that bithionol has good effect on the lung forms of *P. kellicotti* when given orally by gavage for 10 or 20 days at levels of 50 or 100 mg/kg/day, or when mixed with the diet at levels of 70 or 155 mg/kg/day for 14 days. Doses given twice a day for 10 days were more effectual than doses given once a day for 20 days where the total amounts of drug during the course of the treatments were equal. It was reported that the drug was not effectual against immature worms in the pleural or peritoneal cavities.

Yokogawa *et al.* (1961b) found that rats experimentally infected with *P. ohirai* could be successfully employed for chemotherapeutic studies of paragonimiasis in place of the dogs or cats infected with *P. westermani*. They studied the effects of bithionol on immature *P. ohirai* in rats, grouped as shown in Table V.

Bithionol was therefore effectual against immature *P. ohirai* when hosts were given 750 mg/kg. On the other hand, Yokogawa *et al.* found that bithionol was not effectual against immature *P. westermani* migrating through the muscle of rats and dogs, even when more than 750 mg/kg of bithionol was

TABLE V

Effects of Bithionol on P. ohirai in Rats (Yokogawa et al., 1961)

Rats infected with 10 metacercariae of P. ohirai	Dose	Survival rates (%) of P. ohirai
Group A	50 mg/kg orally every other day 13 times, beginning 11 days after infection. Total 750 mg/kg	17·3 (low)
Group B₁	50 mg/kg every other day, twice before and four times after infection. Total 300 mg/kg	58·0 (high)
Group B₂	50 mg/kg every other day, twice before and 13 times after infection. Total 750 mg/kg	25·0 (low)
Control		52·5 (high)

given. This parasite-host system appears to be most interesting in chemo-therapeutic studies. Yokogawa et al. (1962a, 1963a) studied serum concentration of the drug. Three healthy male volunteers were given bithionol and the serum concentration was examined at different times. Case 1 received the first and second one-third portions of the 50 mg/kg dose on the afternoon and evening of the 1st day (after lunch and after supper) and the final one-third immediately after breakfast on the 2nd day; after this no bithionol was given. In cases 2 and 3 a further 50 mg/kg bithionol was given after lunch and supper on the 3rd day and after breakfast on the 4th day. Blood samples were withdrawn at different times up to 75 h after initial administration. After the initial dose the blood concentration increased abruptly and reached 121·0–141·6 μg/ml in 27 h; during the next 24 h it decreased down to 83·13–97·0 μg/ml as measured at the 47th h. Following the second dose taken at this time, it increased again and reached 133·3–154·3 μg/ml at the 75th h. In case 1, where the second dose was not given, the blood concentration steadily decreased with time, yet it was as high as 68·0–105·3 μg/ml at the 75th h. From these results it seemed clear that the blood concentration of bithionol was unexpectedly high and that it remained so over a fairly long period. It is possible, therefore, that a high blood concentration is maintained by the administration of the drug at intervals of 2 or 3 days.

Yokogawa et al. (1962a) also examined the blood concentration of bithionol when 50 mg/kg was given every other day 10 times. They found no accumulation of bithionol. However, 80–180 μg bithionol per ml of blood was constantly detected throughout the period of treatment but was no longer present on the 5th day after the last dose.

Murakoshi (1962, unpublished) reported that bithionol seemed to inhibit the oxidative phosphorylation of the lung fluke.

Regarding surgical treatment of cerebral paragonimiasis, Kim and Walker (1961) stated that of 47 patients operated, 14 (30%) could be considered improved or cured for 2 years after the operation; in only eight cases were patients free from seizures after operation, and all of these had encapsulated abscesses removed, including, in five instances, a fluke. Ten patients with multiloculated firm cysts with adjacent necrotic brain tissue and gliosis continued to have seizures after operation. The conclusion was that although neurosurgical intervention removes cerebral paragonimiasis from the category of hopeless conditions, it is not the solution to this problem. The effective treatment of pulmonary paragonimiasis should eliminate most intracerebral infections.

As for the internal treatment of extrapulmonary paragonimiasis, especially cerebral involvement, several workers in Japan and Korea have suggested that good results can be expected with bithionol, although studies are not yet complete. Recently, another drug, 2-tris (*para*-aminophenyl) carbonium salt (Pararosanilin), which was first tried for schistosomiasis mansoni, was used in the dogs infected with *P. kellicotti* (Thompson *et al.*, 1962; Elslager *et al.*, 1961). Najarian *et al.* (1962) reported that when given orally to dogs infected with *P. kellicotti* tris (*p*-aminophenyl) carbonium chloride (TAC chloride) and tris (*p*-aminophenyl) carbonium salt with one-half 4,4'-methylenebis (3 hydroxy-2-naphtoic acid) (TAC pamoate) markedly decreased production and caused numerous abnormalities in worm eggs. They stated that the chemotherapeutic evaluation of these substances in human paragonimiasis is suggestive. However, Harada (1964) was unable to confirm the significant efficacy of pararosalinin against *P. ohirai* in experimentally infected rats.

XII. CONTROL

From what we know of the life cycle of *P. westermani* and of the epidemiology of paragonimiasis, a number of possible methods of control can be suggested. However, only a few offer practical possibilities. In a theoretical analysis, the following methods of breaking the life cycle of the lung fluke of man have been suggested: (1) destruction of the adults in the human host by treatment; (2) killing of reservoir hosts to destroy the adults; (3) disinfection of sputum and faeces of infected individuals to kill the eggs; (4) destruction of snail intermediate hosts to kill the larval stages; (5) killing of second intermediate hosts to destroy the metacercariae; (6) prevention of human infection by the metacercariae freed from the second intermediate hosts; and (7) prevention of human infection through eating the second intermediate host raw or partially cooked.

A successful clinical treatment would be of great value as a control measure only in situations where most of the infection of the snail intermediate hosts is from human sources.

Yokogawa (1952a, b) stated that the snails are chiefly infected with eggs from human sources and not from reservoir hosts in the endemic area of Japan. He found 187 out of 6 574 specimens of *Semisulcospira libertina* infected with cercariae of *P. westermani* from irrigation canals in a village in Shizuoka prefecture, but no infected snails were found from the main stream of the Kano river running through the village. He suggested that this was the highest incidence of infection in snails that had been reported in the endemic areas of

Japan and the high incidence was produced in this areas by miracidia from eggs in human sputum and faeces, which might have been introduced into the canal with nightsoil used as fertilizer.

Until recently the treatment of paragonimiasis was still in the experimental stage and the treatment itself was thought to be a complicated and difficult procedure. However, as a result of recent successful work, it can be suggested that mass treatment with bithionol as a control measure for paragonimiasis in the endemic area will work well. Yokogawa (1961) reported that the same efficacy of treatment with bithionol as seen in the hospitalized cases was found in the mass treatment of sixteen out-patients with paragonimiasis. These patients were allowed to lead an ordinary daily life during the treatment. 30 mg/kg of bithionol per day was administered in divided doses immediately after meals every other day to patients in their homes. Although they were given treatment during the busy agricultural period, the efficacy and side effects were not very different from what was found in hospitalized cases.

However, there have been no studies on the value of mass chemotherapy of paragonimiasis as a control measure. Clear evidence as to whether or not transmission of the infection can be interrupted by mass treatment with bithionol in the endemic area is strongly needed. It has been suggested that wild or domesticated animals were an important source of infection of the snail, but no evidence has been obtained. Most of the adults worms found previously in wild animals in Japan were identified as *P. ohirai*, *P. iloktsuenensis* and *P. miyazakii*.

The control of trematode disease by the elimination of the snail intermediate hosts, by the use of chemicals or by making their habitats unfavourable for them, has been frequently suggested. The type of habitats in which the snail intermediate hosts of *P. westermani* live would seem to make this method of limited application in the control of paragonimiasis. The killing of the crabs that transmit the infection to man is an obvious possibility and has been frequently suggested. This method, however, would be difficult to apply in most of the endemic areas and no evidence has been found that it has actually been used extensively as a control measure.

At one time it was thought that a considerable amount of human infection came from drinking water containing the encysted metacercariae that had been freed from crabs. The epidemiological studies by Yokogawa (1952b) in Japan and by Yogore (1956) in the Philippines suggest that this method of infection may not be common. Their investigations suggested the possibility of infection from cysts freed from crabs in the preparation of food. Efforts to induce people to be more careful in handling the crabs when preparing them could reduce this danger.

In Japan the lack of food and the evacuation of people to the rural districts during and after the Second World War have increased the incidence of paragonimiasis, and studies made during the past ten years have shown that it is still a significant public health problem in certain areas of Japan. However, very recent work by Yokogawa et al. has clearly shown that this disease in man will gradually die out in areas where mass treatment with bithionol has been thoroughly carried out.

REFERENCES

Abbott, R. T. (1948). *Bull. Mus. comp. Zool. Harv.* **100**, 245–328.
Akaiwa, H., Hatta, T. and Hayashida, M. (1931). *Geka* **32**, 657–709.*
Ameel, D. J. (1932). *J. Parasit.* **18**, 264–268.
Ameel, D. J. (1934). *Amer. J. Hyg.* **19**, 279–317.
Ando, A. (1915). *Chugai Iji Shimpo* **856**, 1463–1487.*
Ando, A. (1917a). *Chugai Iji Shimpo* **884**, 71–87.*
Ando, A. (1917b). *Chugai Iji Shimpo* **885**, 162–167.*
Ando, A. (1917c). *Chugai Iji Shimpo* **889**, 417–427.*
Ando, A. (1921). *Nihon Biseibutsu-gaku Zasshi* **15**, 391–404.*
Ando, A. (1924). *Iji Shimbun* **1136**, 327–337.*
Ando, A. and Yamada, M. (1916). *Chuo Igaku Zasshi* **128**, 1–11.*
Basch, P. F. (1959). *J. Parasit.* **45**, 273.
Beaver, P. C., Malek, E. A. and Little, M. D. (1964). *J. Parasit.* **50**, 664–666.
Bozicevich, J. (1951). *Publ. Hlth Rep.* **66** (Reprint No. 3094), 806–814.
Buck, A. A., Sadun, E. H., Lieske, H. and Lee, B. K. (1958a). *Z. Tropenmed. Parasit.* **9**, 310–327.
Buck, A. A., Sadun, E. H., Lieske, H., Lee, B. K. and Haage, H. (1958b). *Z. Tropenmed. Parasit.* **9**, 328–334.
Chang, H. T., Wang, C. W., Yu, C. F., Hsü, C. F. and Fan, J. C. (1958). *Chin. med. J.* **77**, 3–9.
Chen, H. T. (1935). *Lingnan Sci. J.* **14**, 143–144.
Chen, H. T. (1940). *Lingnan Sci. J.* **19**, 429–530.
Chen, H. T. (1960). *Acta zool. sin.* **12**, 27–36.
Chiu, J. K. (1962). *Kyushu J. med. Sci.* **13**, 51–66.
Chung, H. L. and Tsao, W. C. (1962). *Chin. med. J.* **81**, 354–378.
Chung, H. L., Chen, C. H. and Hou, T. C. (1954). *Chin. med. J.* **72**, 1–14.
Chung, H. L., Weng, H. C. and Hou, T. C. (1955a). *Chin. med. J.* **73**, 1–14.
Chung, H. L., Weng, H. C., Hou, T. C. and Ho, L. Y. (1955b). *Chin. med. J.* **73**, 47–54; 368–378.
Chung, H. L., Hou, T. C., Li, T. H., Sheh, M. P. and Yang, C. L. (1956). *Chin. med. J.* **74**, 1–16.
Chung, H. L., Ho, L. Y., Tsao, W. C., Hsing, P. H., Tung, Y. C. and Mu, S. H. (1963). *Chin. med. J.* **82**, 712–717.
Cobbold, T. S. (1859). *Trans. Linn. Soc. Lond.* **22**, 363–366.
Daengswang, S. (1963). VIIth International Congresses of Tropical Medicine and Malaria, Abstr. 67.
Dawes, B. (1963). *Parasitology* **53**, 109–122.
Diaconita, G. H. and Goldis, G. H. (1964). *Acta tuberc. scand.* **44**, 51–75.
Dissanaike, A. S. and Paramananthan, D. C. (1962). *Ceylon J. med. Sci.* **11**, 29–45.
Domen, H. and Abe, Y. (1955). *Geka* **17**, 678–680.*
Elslager, E. F., Short, F. W., Worth, D. F., Meisenhelder, J. E., Najarian, H. H. and Thompson, P. E. (1961). *Nature, Lond.* **190**, 628–629.
Fan, P. C. and Khaw, O. K. (1963). *Chin. med. J.* (*Republic of China*) **11**, 207–214; 284–296.
Fan, P. C. and Khaw, O. K. (1964). *Chin. med. J.* (*Republic of China*) **11**, 55–64.
Garrison, P. E. and Leynes, R. (1909). *Philipp. J. Sci.* **4**, 177–183.
Granz, W. (1956). *Verh. dtsch. Ges. inn. Med.* **62**, Kongress.
Habe, T. (1942). *Venus* **12**, 32–56.*

*In Japanese.

Harada, Y. (1964). *Jap. J. Parasit.* **13**, 1–18.*

Harada, Y. and Mori, O. (1951). *Igaku to Seibutsu* **20**, 65–67.*

Harinasuta, T., Kruatra Chue, M. and Tandhanand, S. (1957). *J. med. Ass. Thailand* **40**, 227.

Hatano, K. (1960). *Jap. J. Parasit.* **9**, 294–308.*

Hirano, T. (1957). *Niigata Igakkai Zasshi* **72**, 189–200; 477–493.*

Ho, L. Y. and Chung, H. L. (1959). *Renmin Baojian* **1**, 987–997.

Hosokawa, S., Morita, K., Fujii, M., Mori, W. and Geshi, T. (1957). *Jap. J. Parasit.* **6**, 55–74.*

Hsü, C.-T., Ma, Y.-M. and Wang, T.-T. (1959). *Obstet. Gynec.* **14**, 416–466.

Hunter, G. W. III, Hodge, E. P., Johnes, W. W., Diamond, L. S. and Ingalls, J. W. (1948). *Bull. U.S. Army med. Dep.* **1948**, 128–131.

Ikeda, A. (1957). *Jap. J. Parasit.* **6**, 88–89.*

Inamoto, K. (1916). *Chosen Igakkai Zasshi* **16**, 245–261.*

Ishigaki, S., Morishita, K. and Suguro, T. (1954). *Nihon Naika Gakkai Zasshi* **42**, 48.*

Ishii, Y., Yamamoto, S., Morisawa, S., Mitsutomi, S. and Takizawa, K. (1959). *Jap. J. Parasit.* **8**, 377–378.*

Isshiki, O. (1953). *Bull. Naniwa Univ.* **313**, 61–73; 75–90.*

Ito, J. (1949). *Nihon Kiseichu Gakkai Kiji* **16–18**, 17.*

Ito, M. (1956). *Jap. J. Parasit.* **5**, 169.*

Iwamura, N. (1964). *Jap. J. Parasit.* **13**, 489–491.*

Iwasaki, M. (1955). *Rinsho Naika Shonika* **10**, 207–218.*

Iwasaki, M. (1962). *Chiryo* **44**, 115–124.*

Iwasaki, M., Matsuda, K., Sakamoto, Y., Hirose, H. and Okura, T. (1956). *Chiryo* **38**, 1374–1379.*

Jinnai, D., Yamane, S. and Sato, T. (1952). *J. int. College Surg.* **18**, 32–39.

Kaku, S. (1950). *Rinsho Geka* **5**, 592–599.*

Kamo, H., Nishida, H., Hatsushika, R. and Tomimura, T. (1961). *Yonago acta medica* **5**, 43–52.*

Kang, S. Y., Kyu, L. K., Keum, H. F. and Chyu, I. L. (1963). *J. med. Ass. Korea* **6**, 59–66. (In Korean.)

Katamine, D., Murakami, F., Motomura, K., Nishikubo, K., Ajisaka, S. and Takatsu, H. (1961). *Endem. Dis. Bull. Nagasaki Univ.* **3**, 130–138.*

Katsurada, F. (1900). *Beitr. Path. Anat.* **28**, 506–523.

Katsurada, F. and Fujiki, I. (1899). *Tokyo Igakkai Zasshi* **12**, 1–18; **13**, 8–29.*

Kawashima, K. and Miyazaki, I. (1963). *Jap. J. Parasit.* **12**, 94–97.*

Khoo, O. T. (1961). *J. trop. Med. Hyg.* **64**, 53–60.

Kim, S. K. and Walker, A. E. (1961). *Acta psychiat. neurol. scand.* Suppl. **153**, 36, 7–85.

Kitamoto, O., Okada, T., Ueno, A., Yokogawa, M. and Kihata, M. (1958). *Kokyuki Shinryo* **13**, 92–99.*

Kobayashi, H. (1921). *Keijo Isen Kiyo* **4**, 5–16.*

Kobayashi, H. (1926). *Nihon no Ikai* **16**, 7–9.*

Koizumi, K. (1956). *Jap. J. Bact.* **10**, 967–971.*

Komiya, Y. and Tomimura, T. (1964). *Jap. J. Parasit.* **13**, 132–138.*

Komiya, Y. and Yokogawa, M. (1953). *Jap. J. med. Sci. Biol.* **6**, 207–211.

Komiya, Y., Yokogawa, M., Schichijo, K., Nishimiya, H., Suguro, T. and Yamaoka, K. (1952). *Jap. J. med. Sci. Biol.* **5**, 433–445.

Komiya, Y., Suzuki, R. and Ito, J. (1961). *Jap. J. Parasit.* **10**, 65–70.*

*In Japanese.

Kruidenier, F. J. (1953). *J. Morph.* **92**, 531–543.
Kubo, N. (1912). *Cbl. Bakt. Parasit.* Abt. Orig. **65**, 115–135.
Kunieda, T. (1957). *Gifu Ikadaigaku Kiyo* **4**, 753–763.*
Kuroda, T. (1958). *Gloria maris* **5**, 17–20.
Lei, H.-H. and Yen, C.-K. (1957). *Chin. med. J. Peking* **75**, 986–1003.
Lewert, R. M. and Lee, C. L. (1954). *J. infect. Dis.* **95**, 18–51.
Mannoji, N. (1952). *Igaku Kenkyu* **22**, 1191–1196.*
Mitsuno, T., Takeya, S., Managa, M. and Zimmerman, L. E. (1952). *J. nerv. ment. Dis.* **116**, 685–714.
Miyakawa, M., Tanaka, S. and Nakase, M. (1955a). *Igaku to Seibutsu* **36**, 221–224.*
Miyakawa, M., Tanaka, S., Nakase, M. and Shimizu, M. (1955b). *Igakuto Seibutsu* **37**, 25–27.*
Miyake, H. (1939). *Jap. J. Radiol.* **1**, 307–314.*
Miyake, H. (1952). *Nihon Rinsho Kekkaku* **11**, 315–318.*
Miyazaki, I. (1940). *Fukuoka Igakkai Zasshi* **33**, 336–344.*
Miyazaki, I. (1943). *Fukuoka Acta med.* **34**, 1150–1154.*
Miyazaki, I. (1944). *Fukuoka Acta med.* **37**, 195–202.*
Miyazaki, I (1955). *Igaku to Seibutsu* **37**, 11–15.*
Miyazaki, I. (1959). *18th Fukuoka Igakkai Sokai.* (Lecture.)
Miyazaki, I. (1961). *Kyobu Shikkan* **5**, 953–962.*
Morishita, T. (1954). *Gifu Idai Kiyo* **1**, 309–314.*
Morishita, T. (1955). *Nihon Iji Shimpo* **1946**, 16.*
Morishita, T. (1957). *Kiseichu no Shindan, Kanehara*, 85–90.*
Moriyasu, R. (1917). In "Collection of Articles in Honor of the 25th Anniversary of Professor Dohi."*
Muta, K. (1912). *Okayama Igakkai Zasshi* **271**, 28–35.*
Nagayoshi, Y. (1942). *Taiwan Igakkai Zasshi* **41**, 1012–1045.*
Najarian, H. H., Meisenhelder, J. E. and Thompson, P. E. (1962). *J. Parasit.* **48**, 237–240.
Nakayama, H. (1954). *Nihon Rinsho Kekkaku* **13**, 579–582.*
Nakagawa, K. (1916). *J. infect. Dis.* **18**, 131–142.
Nakagawa, K. (1917). *Taiwan Igakkai Zasshi* **13**, 366–368.*
Narihara, N. (1939). *Rinsho Shonika Zasshi* **13**, 953–965.*
Nicolaus, P. and Panning, A. (1933). *Akad. Verd. Ges. Leipzig.*
Noble, E. R. (1963). *J. Parasit.* **49**, 352.
Nonomura, T. (1941). *Okayama Igakkai Zasshi* **52**, 2368.*
Nunogami, M. (1931). *Kumamoto Igakkai Zasshi* **6**, 513.*
Ogida, K. (1954). *Igaku Kenkyu* **24**, 148–162.*
Okabe, K. (1956). *Kurume Igakkai Shi* **19**, 486–490.*
Okabe, K. (1961). *Rinsho Byori* **9**, 101–104.*
Okada, J. (1959). *Nihon Eiseigaku Zasshi* **13**, 783–788.*
Okamoto, S., Okada, J., Miyauchi, A. and Iwata, K. (1959). *No to Shinkei* **11**, 885–889.*
Okura, T. (1963). *Jap. J. Parasit.* **12**, 57–67.*
Omura, H. (1960). *Jap. J. Parasit.* **5**, 404–415.*
Oshima, T. (1953). *Jap. J. Parasit.* **2**, 35.*
Oshima, T. (1956). *Jap. J. Parasit.* **5**, 404–415.*
Oshima, T. (1957). *Seibutsu Kagaku* **9**, 62–66.*
Oshima, T., Yoshida, Y. and Kihata, M. (1958). *Rep. Inst. Publ. Hlth, Tokyo* **7**, 256–274.*

*In Japanese.

Otani, S. (1887). *Tokyo Igakkai Zasshi* **1**, 458–460.*
Park, C. M. (1962). *Yonsei Med. J.* **3**, 85–92. (In Korean.)
Prommas, G. (1928). *J. med. Ass. Thailand* **11**, 67.
Ro, M. (1942). *Taiwan Igakkai Zasshi* **41**, 1436–1439.*
Ro, M. and Yokogawa, S. (1941). *Taiwan Igakkai Zasshi* **40**, 268–307.*
Sadun, E. H., Buck, A. A. and Walton, B. C. (1958). *J. Parasit.* **44**, Sect. 2, 17.
Sadun, E. H., Buck, A. A. and Walton, B. C. (1959). *Milit. Med.* **124**, 187–195.
Sano, M. (1959). *Nihon Eiseigaku Zasshi* **14**, 84–95; 95–103.*
Sandosham, A. A. (1950). *Trans. R. Soc. trop. Med. Hyg.* **44**, 5.
Sato, T. (1940). *Taiwan Igakkai Zasshi* **39**, 371–391.*
Sato, H., Otsuji, Y., Hamada, M., Kubota, T. and Yonamine, Y. (1962). *Proc. Jap. Soc. trop. Med.* **3**, 44–45.*
Sato, H., Otsuji, Y., Hamada, M., Kubota, T., Muraoka, H., Maeda, M. and Seo, T. (1963). *Kyobu Shikkan* **7**, 922–932.*
Sawada, I. (1957). *Jap. J. Parasit.* **6**, 8–11.*
Shibata, T. (1951). *Saishin Kiseichubyo-gaku VII, Igaku Shoin.*
Shigemi, S. (1957). *Igaku Kenkyu Fukouka* **27**, 153–172.*
Shigeyasu, M. (1959). *Jap. J. Med. Radiother.* **19**, 173–202.*
Shih, Y. C., Chen, Y. S. and Chang, Y. C. (1958). *Chin. med. J.* **77**, 10–19.
Shimono, O. and Yamaoka, K. (1957). *Ehime-ken Eiseikenhyusho Hokoku.*
Suguro, T. (1959). *Jap. J. Parasit.* **8**, 518–522; 725–729.*
Takano, S. (1960). *Jap. J. Parasit.* **9**, 246–265.*
Takizawa, M. (1964). *Jap. J. Parasit.* **13**, 19–37.*
Tanabe, K. (1950). *Fukuoka Igaku Zasshi* **41**, 181–185.*
Tang, C.-T. (1940). *Chin. med. J.* Suppl. 3, 267–291.
Taniguchi, N. (1893). *Tokyo Iji Shinshi* **794**, 175–178.*
Thompson, P. E., Meisenhelder, J. E. and Najarian, H. H. (1962). *A mer. J. trop. Med. Hyg.* **11**, 31–45.
Tomimura, T., Terauchi, J. and Tarumoto, I. (1960). *Igaku to Seibutsu* **54**, 45–51,*
Tominaga, K. (1939). *Nihon Kiseichugakkai Kiji* **11**, 56.*
Tsuda, M. (1959). *Jap. J. Parasit.* **8**, 812–821.*
Tsuji, M. (1961). *Jap. J. Parasit.* **10**, 587–604.*
Tubangui, M. A., Cabrera, B. D. and Yogore, M. G. (1950). *Acta med. Philipp.* **6**, 371–372.
Ueno, K. (1959). Proceedings of the 48th Annual Meeting Japanese Society of Veterinary Science.*
Vajrasthira, S., Harinasuta, C. and Maiphoom, C. (1959). *Jap. J. exp. Med.* **29**, 159–166.
Vevers, G. M. (1923). *J. Helminth.* **1**, 9–20.
Vogel, H. (1963). VIIth International Congresses of Tropical Medicine and Malaria, Abstr. 67–68.
Vogel, H., Widelock, D. and Fuerst, H. T. (1957). *J. infect. Dis.* **100**, 40–47.
Waitz, J. A., McClay, P. and Thompson, P. E. (1963). *J. Parasit.* **49**, Sect. 2, 16.
Waitz, J. A., McClay, P. and Thompson, P. E. (1964). *Amer. J. trop. Med. Hyg.* **13**, 584–588.
Wakeshima, T. (1932). *Tokyo Iji Shinshi* **56**, 2922–2978.*
Wu, K. (1935). *Chin. med. J.* **49**, 741–746.
Wu, K. (1938). *Far East Ass. trop. Med. Dix. Cen. Hanoi* **2**, 689–713.
Yagura, T. (1964). *Osaka Daigaku Igaku Zasshi* **16**, 191–201.*
Yamagiwa, K. (1890). *Virchows Arch. Path. Anat. Physiol.* **7**, 447–460.

*In Japanese.

Yamaguti, S. (1943). *Jap. J. Zool.* **10**, 461–469.
Yamamura, Y. (1959). *Nihon Seikagakkai, Kyushu Chihokai.* (Lecture.)
Yamao, Y. (1952). *Jikken Seibutsu Gakuho* **2**, 159–162.*
Yogore, M. G. (1956). Thesis, School of Hygiene and Public Health. Johns Hopkins University.
Yogore, M. G. (1957). *Phillip. J. Sci.* **86**, 37–46.
Yokogawa, M. (1952a). *Jap. J. med. Sci. Biol.* **5**, 221–237; 501–515.
Yokogawa, M. (1952b). *Kosyu Eisei* **11**, 19–25.*
Yokogawa, M. (1953). *Jap. J. med. Sci. Biol.* **6**, 107–117.
Yokogawa, M. (1955a). *Jap. J. Parasit.* **4**, 57–63.*
Yokogawa, M. (1955b). *Jap. J. Parasit.* **4**, 128–129.*
Yokogawa, M. (1956a). *Bull. Inst. Publ. Hlth Tokyo* **5**, 7–10.
Yokogawa, M. (1956b). *Rinsho Byori* **4** 224–230.*
Yokogawa, M. (1956c). *Shindan to Chiryo* **44**, 88–95.*
Yokogawa, M. (1960). *Jap. J. Parasit.* **9**, 433–434.*
Yokogawa, M. (1961). *Kyobu Shikkan* **5**, 965–973.*
Yokogawa, M. (1964). *Kyobu Shikkan.* **8**, 441–456; 572–583.*
Yokogawa, M. and Awano, R. (1956). *Nihon Iji Shimpo* **1703**, 27–35.*
Yokogawa, M. and Oshima, T. (1958a). *Jap. J. Parasit.* **7**, 131–134.*
Yokogawa, M. and Oshima, T. (1958b) *Jap. J. Parasit.* **7**, 333–337.
Yokogawa, M. and Oshima, T. (1959). *Jap. J. Parasit.* **8**, 44–49.*
Yokogawa, M. and Tsuji, M. (1962). Proceedings of the First Regional Symposium on Scientific Knowledge of Tropical Parasites, pp. 194–206.
Yokogawa, M. and Yoshimura, H. (1956). *Jap. J. Parasit.* **5**, 449–456.*
Yokogawa, M. and Yoshimura, H. (1957). *Jap. J. Parasit.* **6**, 546–554.*
Yokogawa, M. and Yoshimura, H. (1960). *Jap. J. Parasit.* **9**, 173–186.*
Yokogawa, M., Oshima, T. and Suguro, T. (1955a). *Jap. J. Parasit.* **4**, 276–281; 282–287.*
Yokogawa, M., Oshima, T. and Kihata, M. (1955b). *Jap. J. Parasit.* **4**, 388–393.*
Yokogawa, M., Oshima, T., Sugawa, Y., Hirano, T. and Nakagawa, A. (1955c). *Nihon Iji Shimpo* **1634**, 19–23.*
Yokogawa, M., Oshima, T., Yoshimura, H. and Kihata, M. (1956). *Jap. J. Parasit.* **5**, 155.*
Yokogawa, M., Yoshimura, H. and Suzuki, J. (1957a). *Tokyo Iji Shinshi* **74**, 13–16; 403–406.
Yokogawa, M., Yoshimura, H., Oshima, T. and Kihata, M. (1957b). *Jap. J. Parasit.* **6**, 449–457.*
Yokogawa, M., Oshima, T. and Kihata, M. (1958a). *Jap. J. Parasit.* **7**, 51–55.*
Yokogawa, M., Yoshimura, H., Koyama, C., Sano, M., Tsuda, M., Suzuki, J. and Tsuji, M. (1958b). *Tokyo Iji Shinshi* **75**, 67–72.*
Yokogawa, M., Yoshimura, H., Sano, M., Okura, T. and Tsuji, M. (1958c). Transaction of 18th Branch-meeting in the East Division of Parasitology Society of Japan, pp. 12–13.*
Yokogawa, M., Yoshimura, H., Sano, M., Okura, T. and Tsuji, M. (1959). *J. Parasit.* **45** (Suppl.), 20.
Yokogawa, M., Okura, T., Tsuji, M., Suzuki, R., Shimono, O., Hatano, K., Amagishi, T., Ogida, K. and Yamaoka, K. (1960a). *Jap. J. Parasit.* **9**, 428–429.*
Yokogawa, M., Yoshimura, H. and Komiya, Y. (1960b). *Jap. J. Parasit.* **9**, 451–456.*
Yokogawa, M., Yoshimura, H. and Oshima, T. (1960c). *Jap. J. Parasit.* **9**, 636–640.*

*In Japanese.

158　　　　　　　　MUNEO YOKOGAWA

Yokogawa, M., Yoshimura, H., Sano, M., Okura, T., Tsuji, M., Takahashi, T. Inasaka, Y., Noguchi, M., Mochizuki, H. and Ishizu, H. (1961a). Transaction of 21st Branch-meeting in the East Division of Parasitology Society of Japan, p. 21.*

Yokogawa, M., Yoshimura, H., Sano, M., Okura, T., Tsuji, M., Takizawa, M., Harada, Y. and Kihata, M. (1961b). *Jap. J. Parasit.* 10, 302–316.

Yokogawa, M., Yoshimura, H., Tsuji, M. and Suguro, T. (1961c). *Jap. J. Parasit.* 10, 6–13.*

Yokogawa, M., Okura, T., Tsuji, M., Iwasaki, M. and Shigeyasu, M. (1962a). *Jap. J. Parasit.* 11, 103–116.

Yokogawa, M., Tsuji, M. and Okura, T. (1962b). *Jap. J. Parasit.* 11, 117–122.

Yokogawa, M., Yoshimura, H., Sano, M., Okura, T. and Tsuji, M. (1962c). *J. Parasit.* 48, 525–531.

Yokogawa, M., Iwasaki, M., Shigeyasu, M., Hirose, H., Okura, T. and Tsuji, M. (1963a). *Amer. J. trop. Med. Hyg.* 12, 859–862.

Yokogawa, M., Tsuji, M., Araki, K. and Nomoto, T. (1963b). *Jap. J. Parasit.* 13, 323.*

Yokogawa, S. (1915). *Taiwan Igakkai Zasshi.* 152, 685–701; 153, 728–735.*

Yokogawa, S. (1916a). *Taiwan Igakkai Zasshi* 163, 349–354.*

Yokogawa, S. (1916b). *Nisshin Igaku* 6, 323–370.*

Yokogawa, S. (1917). *Taiwan Igakkai Zasshi* 181, 703–778; 184, 311–354; 401–427.*

Yokogawa, S. and Ro, M. (1939). *Acta jap. Med. trop.* 1, 1–18.

Yokogawa, S. and Ro, M. (1942). *Acta jap. Med. trop.* 4, 1–58.

Yokogawa, S., Cort, W. W. and Yokogawa, M. (1960). *Exp. Parasit.* 10, 81–205.

Yoshida, Y. and Miyamoto, M. (1960). *Jap. J. Parasit.* 9, 211–216.*

Yoshimura, H. and Yokogawa, M. (1958). *Jap. J. Parasit.* 7, 363–369.*

Yumoto, Y. and Nagayoshi, Y. (1943). *Nettai Igaku* 1, 585–603.*

*In Japanese.

In vitro Cultivation Procedures for Parasitic Helminths

PAUL H. SILVERMAN

Department of Zoology, University of Illinois,
Urbana-Champaign, Illinois, U.S.A.

I. INTRODUCTION

The idea of maintaining and culturing metazoan parasites outside of their host has long held a strong fascination for many parasitologists. To some, it has represented a means of examining many implications of host–parasite relationships and possibly of determining the reasons for host-specificity and the nature of parasitism. This attitude was expressed most clearly by Read (1950) who concluded his monograph with the following statement: "It is imperative to develop techniques for cultivating intestinal helminths *in vitro*, and to make further study of intestinal physiology. It seems apparent that the cultivation of parasitic helminths outside the host presents one of the most *difficult and most challenging problems facing parasitologists today."* (Read's italics.)

Since Read made that statement, there has been substantial progress towards the successful cultivation *in vitro* of various parasitic Metazoa. With this success considerable information concerning parasite physiology and behavior has been accumulated; however, it is clear that the mere cultivation of these parasites *in vitro* will not produce the answers to the many questions we are asking about host–parasite relationships. Five years after publication of his monograph Read (1955) modified his views, stating, "More mature consideration has convinced me that though cultivation *in vitro* will answer many questions, it will probably not be a magic key to the secrets of the host–parasite relationship."

This view is strengthened by the experience of the bacteriologists and virologists who have long enjoyed the advantage of being able to cultivate their parasites *in vitro*. In a recent symposium, microbiologists critically examined the present state of knowledge of the mechanisms involved in *in vivo* host–parasite relationships with particular reference to bacteria, viruses, Protozoa and fungi and the contribution to this knowledge that has been made by *in vitro* studies using culture techniques which include defined, complex or tissue culture media (Smith and Taylor, 1964). The conclusion reached was that although *in vitro* studies have yielded much information on the nature and type of many physiological processes essential to micro-organisms, present knowledge of microbial behavior *in vivo is superficial.* Little is known about infection and disease processes or about the factors affecting the appearance and disappearance of pathogens in nature. It was concluded that because of wide divergences in behavior of micro-organisms *in vitro* and *in vivo* it was unwise to extrapolate from results obtained in the test tube to situations which obtain in the host. It was further pointed out that great caution should be exercised in extrapolating from results obtained with unnatural laboratory hosts to natural hosts; this is a view which has been strongly expressed also in studies of metazoan parasites (Silverman *et al.*, 1962).

Nevertheless, *in vitro* cultivation procedures can give us an insight into many of the essential physiological requirements of the parasite and when used intelligently in conjunction with carefully planned *in vivo* experiments they should help to elucidate some of the many aspects of the host–parasite relationship. Work on the metabolism and physico-chemical requirements of parasites, investigations of certain features of behavior in parasites, and studies of antigens and other materials secreted and excreted during growth and metamorphosis, can be implemented effectively by means of *in vitro* culture techniques. Other aspects of comparative and parasite biology which could be explored with this tool have been outlined by Weinstein (1958). It has become clear that when *in vitro* culture techniques are firmly established, readily available and *standardized*, so that one laboratory can compare its work with that of another, then it will be possible to make considerable use of this valuable aid in parasitology.

II. TERMINOLOGY

Bacteriologists have long described single species of microbes maintained on artificial media as being in "pure culture". The application of the term "pure culture" to Metazoa however, has not meant the same thing. For instance, a pure culture of third stage larvae of *Haemonchus contortus* is taken by helminthologists to mean that it is not contaminated with any other species of *nematode* larvae; yet such a "pure" culture will normally include an array of associated bacteria, Protozoa and molds.

In order to obviate this problem of nomenclature Baker and Ferguson (1942) introduced the term "axenic" to characterize the maintenance of a sterile organism free from *any other living organism*. Unfortunately, the term "axenic" has been used somewhat loosely by some workers as being equivalent to "*in vitro*" (i.e. in glass or artificial). Stoll (1959) pointed out that the term "axenic" should be restricted to its original meaning and should not even be applied to culture of Metazoa whose microbial populations are kept under static control by antibiotics. I heartily agree with Stoll and will use "axenic" to refer only to helminth cultures proven to be maintained in the absence of any other living cells.

Dougherty (1953) in support of the use of the term "axenic", and in order to extend the usefulness and specificity of it, suggested derivations of the root "zenic" to describe the number of organisms (xenites) in association in *in vitro* cultivation, e.g. monoxenic, dixenic, etc. to polyxenic. The root "xenic" is defined as the condition which obtains when an organism is in culture with an unknown number of associates (Dougherty, 1959). In the preparation of this review I have tried to apply Dougherty's terminology and conclude that at this stage in the development of this field of research it is not useful to apply these derived terms. Few workers have identified either the species or exact number of associated micro-organisms in *in vitro* helminth cultures. In most cases cultivation is carried out under a protective umbrella of antibiotics which maintains a bacteriostatic environment for the helminths under investigation. It is also clear that because of the variable source of helminth material there is considerable variation between individual cultures in the types of associated micro-organisms. The only meaningful environmental condition is the true axenic one, which for successful rearing of some helminths is an absolute prerequisite.

Dougherty (1959) further introduces three terms to "resolve nomenclatural ambiguity" of media or diets. He suggests the use of the term *holidic*, to pertain to media the constituents of which are *exactly* known chemically, *meridic*, to pertain to media consisting of an holidic base to which is added "one substance or preparation of unknown structure" (e.g. protein), and *oligidic*, to pertain to media which consist of *crude* organic materials.

Dougherty (1959) himself, recognizes the difficult problem of providing media constituents whose chemical composition and structure are exactly known so that the use of the term *holidic* as a type of media classification is highly relative and tends to lose its meaning. In practical terms it is not enough simply to characterize a medium, but it is necessary to detail the constituents and this detailing obviates the usefulness of the terms "meridic" and "oligi-dic". It might very well be that the introduction of specialized terminology will one day be of some help in the field of *in vitro* cultivation of metazoan parasites but at this stage I have not found it to be so.

III. PROBLEMS AND GOALS

Smyth (1955, 1959) and Silverman (1963a) have outlined some of the basic problems which face investigators attempting to develop *in vitro* cultivation procedures for helminth parasites. Obviously the problems and goals differ depending upon the point in the life cycle of a parasite from which the investigator starts.

Questions of obtaining a supply of biological material which is in a homogeneous physiological state, of sterilizing and maintaining in aseptic conditions various helminth stages and establishing criteria for assessing accurately the response of parasites in *in vitro* environments are common to all such studies. The selection of suitable media for early trials is usually based on an attempt to simulate as closely as possible the conditions which normally occur *in situ* in the host. This has not always proved to be a good guidepost and there is some evidence to suggest that the most likely candidate media which have been developed for the culture of animal tissues are deleterious or inhibitory for some helminth parasites. The experimental approach of many workers has been to test a wide spectrum of balanced salt solutions, complex tissue culture media, natural fluids such as serum and plasma and extracts of tissues alone and in combination. It is to be hoped that with the increasing accumulation of data this method of trial and error can be replaced by starting media whose composition can be tailored to the parasite with some predicted degree of initial success.

A wide variety of criteria have been used for assessing success in *in vitro* cultivation procedures and naturally depend on the parasite and the stage with which one begins. Some of the criteria which have been used may be enumerated as follows.

(1) Motility and reaction to stimulus.
(2) An increase in size.
(3) Changes in external morphology or evidence of metamorphic development, i.e. molting.
(4) Physiological criteria such as the utilization of substrates.
(5) Organogeny, gametogenesis and oviposition.
(6) Cytological evidence of an increase in mitotic division.
(7) Completion of the entire life cycle.

The suitability of some of these criteria is open to criticism. Motility and reaction to stimulus may be demonstrated by dying worms whose metabolism is depressed and because of this "survive" for prolonged periods. Oviposition of adult female worms may indicate that physico-chemical conditions are adequate, but before this can be accepted as proof that the media is *nutritionally* adequate sufficient egg production must be obtained to show that this is not due to utilization of reserves. Similarly, molting and growth may be responses to unfavorable conditions. Clearly, caution must be exercised in judging the adequacy of an *in vitro* environment if continuous reproduction is not obtained.

IV. REVIEW OF LITERATURE

This review is not intended to be exhaustive. To have compiled a list of all published work which dealt in one way or another with attempts to maintain or culture *in vitro* parasitic helminths would have meant quadrupling the number of papers considered here. Rather, it has been my intent selectively to illustrate what I judge to be significant contributions. Since the reviews of Smyth (1947a), Hobson (1948) and Baer (1952) there has been an exponential increase in the number of papers published in this research area. A more recent symposium, devoted to work on the development of axenic *in vitro* cultivation procedures for a wide variety of free-living and parasitic invertebrate Metazoa, has made a significant contribution towards unifying many diverse areas and providing a stimulus and a useful point of departure for workers new to the field (Dougherty, 1959).

Certain inherent difficulties should be mentioned, for instance the lack of standards and detail concerning the preparation of many media and tissue extracts. Terms such as "meat broth", "pea mash", "fish broth", "pulverized liver" or "liver extract" have little meaning unless adequate information is given to enable other workers to make similar preparations for investigation.

Another point of variance which makes comparison of work difficult is the differences between the ages, physiological state and preculture treatment of parasitic helminths in different laboratories working with the same species. Apparently slight differences in storage or handling can produce dramatic results in subsequent culture attempts (Silverman, 1963a).

A critic of this review may note the lack of non-English references, for which a special search has been made, with disappointing results. In his review, Krotov (1958) referred to only five Russian papers in a list of eighty-three references. In fact, with the notable exception of the Japanese parasitologists, active work in this area seems largely to be conducted in English-speaking countries.

A. MEDIA DESCRIPTIONS

The formulae and components of balanced salt solutions and other complex media which are referred to in this review by their common names, e.g. Hank's, Earle's, Eagle's, 150, 199, NCTC 109, etc., are described by Morgan *et al.* (1955), Parker (1961) and Penso and Balducci (1963) unless otherwise indicated or detailed.

V. NEMATODES

A. *Neoaplectana* spp.

The first report of successful *in vitro* cultivation axenically of a parasitic nematode through successive generations without return to its normal host is that by Glaser (1940) who accomplished this with *Neoaplectana glaseri*, the nematode parasite of the Japanese beetle grub, *Popillia japonica*. Ensheathed second stage larvae were sterilized by repeated washings in sterile water interspersed with several treatments of hypochlorite solution. Static culture tubes with 2% agar slants, prepared with 0·5% NaCl, and to which was added sterile mammalian tissues were found to be capable of supporting the growth, development and reproduction of *N. glaseri*. These tissues included mouse embryos, beef kidney, rabbit ovary and rabbit kidney. Rabbit kidney was adopted as the standard tissue because it proved the easiest to manipulate and gave the best growth. Petri dish cultures which contained 2% dextrose agar and living yeast were also found to support growth and reproduction.

Subsequently Glaser *et al.* (1942), were able successfully to apply the same technique to *Neoaplectana chresima* another nematode parasite of insects which included in its host range the corn borer *Pyrausta nubilialis* and the corn earworm, *Heliothis armigera*. *N. chresima* closely resembled *N. glaseri* in its culture requirements and it was found possible to obtain under bacteria-free conditions growth and reproduction in a semi-solid medium which consisted of 20% by weight of ground beef kidney or liver, 0·5% NaCl and 0·5% agar. This medium could be autoclaved and stored before use.

Stoll (1953a) succeeded in developing a fluid medium for the axenic *in vitro* culture of *N. glaseri*. After many failures with various supplements in a veal infusion broth, he found that an acidified (pH 4·0) aqueous extract of rabbit liver prepared without heat and sterilized by filtration provided the stimulus to induce *N. glaseri* cultures to thrive and multiply freely. He examined the effect of the size of inoculum, incubation period, pH, temperature and light as well as the effect of agitation of culture tubes. He was not able to confirm the finding of Glaser *et al.* (1942) that autoclaved unsupplemented medium was an adequate culture system. Stoll's standard axenic culture medium and procedure consisted of 9 ml veal broth, 1 ml of raw rabbit liver extract and 25 mg dextrose at pH 6·0–6·5. Each 10 ml of this medium was inoculated with twenty-five infective *N. glaseri* larvae and shaken for 3 weeks in the dark at mean temperatures between 22·5 and 24·1° C. At the end of 3 weeks a 100-fold increase in worm yields was obtained. Later, Stoll (1954, 1961) found that livers from rabbits in late pregnancy yielded an extract which doubled the yields previously reported with raw liver extract.

Stoll (1953b) was able to demonstrate that the long period of axenic *in vitro* cultivation of *N. glaseri* larvae did not affect its ability to infect its normal host. After an estimated 201 generations of axenic maintenance *in vitro* the nematodes were found capable of infecting and killing eight out of twelve grubs to which they had been exposed.

In 1959, Stoll reviewed his extensive work on the culture conditions of *N. glaseri* and reported that the activity of raw liver extract could not be replaced by yeast extract, casein hydrolysate, protogen, B_{12}, serum or ascitic fluid. The acid soluble extract of liver was found to be active after several weeks storage at refrigerator temperatures and most of the active component(s) was found in a precipitate which formed after such storage. *Neoaplectana* was found to tolerate a pH ranging from 4·5 to 7·5 with an apparent optimum at 6·0. Stoll pointed out that the normal pH of the host insect, *P. japonica*, is about 6·8. Darkness, which was found to increase culture yields by 35%, is correlated with the normal habitat of the insect grub host. He also confirmed that culture tubes agitated on a shaker resulted in almost twice the number of nematodes recovered from static cultures.

One of the most important findings reported by Stoll (1959) was the determination of the conditions that enabled him to carry out serial subcultures in fluid media. Stoll found that subcultures 3, 7 or 14 days old progressed poorly or not at all. Transfers "from cultures 3 weeks old may or may not be effective; if held 4, 5 or 6 weeks before subculturing, however, they are routinely satisfactory, especially if the worms are resedimented once or twice in water or salt solution before transfer to new media."

Recently, Jackson (1961, 1962) working in Stoll's laboratory attempted to examine more closely and to define the culture conditions and media for *N. glaseri*. He found that a medium originally designed for the insect stage of *Leishmania* by Trager (1957) provided, with some modification, a suitable culture environment. In this medium third stage larvae of *N. glaseri* developed to the adult stage with subsequent reproduction eventually yielding third stage larvae and thus completing for the first time in a defined medium the complete life cycle of a parasitic nematode. The media consists of eighteen amino acids, fatty acid, urea, Krebs cycle intermediates, purines, pyrimidines, vitamins of the B group and glucose. This medium yielded less than one-tenth the numbers of reproducing forms which resulted from similar inocula in Stoll's medium. Jackson did not determine the relative merits of the various components and cautiously pointed out the problems inherent in such studies. Culture experiments—especially in "chemically defined" media—could, because of a species' ability to "adapt", be misleading about the actual diet of parasites in hosts (Jackson, 1962).

The developments described above on the *in vitro* cultivation of *Neoaplectana* are unique. Similar success has not been obtained with any other parasitic nematode. This may be due to a lack of the kind of continuous effort that has been exercised with *N. glaseri* since its initial isolation in 1943. Baer (1952) and others have suggested that *N. glaseri* is saprozoic, or perhaps a facultative parasite rather than an obligate one. Stoll (1953b) forcefully makes the case for considering *Neoaplectana* as a true obligate parasite although admitting that further definitive supporting evidence is needed.

Irrespective of the merits of these views, which can only be evaluated in the light of further facts concerning the life history of this nematode in nature, there remains a very substantial accomplishment. In addition to Jackson's properly cautious remarks, I should like to add the further consideration that the suitability of Stoll's fluid media and of the defined media must be tested further to determine what role, if any, might be played by reserve substances and by symbionts. The finding of Stoll (1959), that successful transfer in his supplemented fluid media depends upon "seasoned third-stage larvae", is suggestive of a similar situation which was noted in insect nutrition studies and subsequently explained by the presence of intracellular symbionts (Roeder, 1953; Gilmour, 1961; Brooks, 1963).

B. *Nippostrongylus*

Nippostrongylus (*muris*) *brasiliensis* became the first nematode parasite of a vertebrate animal to be cultured *in vitro* through every stage of its development, although this still has not been accomplished through successive generations (Weinstein and Jones, 1956a). *N. brasiliensis* is a skin-penetrating parasite of rats and undergoes development during migration through the lungs and trachea to the small intestine where it attaches itself to the mucosa and feeds on tissues and sucks blood. Eggs are passed out in the feces of the host and undergo two molts before becoming third stage infective larvae.

1. *Free-living Stages*

Weinstein (1949, 1953, 1954) and Weinstein and Jones (1956b) began their studies by investigating the ability of heat-killed bacteria to support growth and development of the free-living stages, McCoy (1929a, b) and Lapage (1933a, b) having previously established that living bacteria provided an adequate diet for these stages. Attempts to use heat-killed bacterial cells supplemented with vitamins, yeast or liver concentrates as a culture media proved ineffectual. Eventually it was found that formalin-killed bacteria (unlike heat-treated cultures) would support growth of the larvae to the infective third stage. However, low yields and abnormally small larvae were obtained by this method.

After much further investigation Weinstein and Jones determined that unheated homogenates of either chick embryos or rat liver supported good growth and development to the infective stage. Fresh liver extract was found to be variable in its ability to support larval development, and some preparations proved to be inhibitory. On the other hand, chick embryo extract (CEE) gave consistently good results and was more convenient to prepare. When 50% CEE was dialyzed against Tyrode solution it was discovered that essential components were lost but the activity could at least be partially restored by supplementing the dialyzed extract with a mixture of acid-hydrolyzed casein (vitamin free) and water soluble vitamins. Further testing revealed that the important constituents lost during dialysis were water-soluble vitamins and not amino acids. Dilution of the 50% CEE resulted in reduction of the yield of third stage larvae, although up to 63% of the larvae developed when only a 12·5% CEE in Tyrode solution was used as a culture medium. Weinstein and Jones (1956b) concluded that the limiting factor, as far as the free-living stage was concerned in diluting CEE, was the level of vitamins.

Further studies on the vitamin requirements of the free-living stages revealed eight "essential" vitamins: choline, thiamine, pyridoxine, calcium pantothenate, nicotinic acid, *p*-aminobenzoic acid, folic acid and riboflavin. The following five vitamins could be omitted without effecting the growth response: pyridoxal, nicotinic acid amide, biotin, ascorbic acid and B_{12} (Weinstein and Jones, 1957a).

Successful cultivation with CEE depended upon the presence of particulate matter. No growth could be achieved unless some fresh tissue were included.

The first successful non-particulate medium developed by Weinstein and Jones (1957a) consisted of a mixture of sodium caseinate, yeast extract and serum. In this medium high yields of filariform larvae were obtained although they were slightly smaller than normal larvae. No further definition of this medium for the free-living stages of *N. brasiliensis* has been reported.

2. Parasitic Stages

Concomitantly with their work on the free-living stages, Weinstein and Jones undertook an investigation of the parasitic stages. They began their investigations with sterilized infective filariform larvae obtained from fecal cultures. Because of their previous work on the free-living stages, they felt that CEE would be the most useful medium constituent to study. Weinstein and Jones (1956a) determined that no detrimental effects resulted from continuous rotation and all culture work was carried out with roller-tube apparatus.

In chick embryo extract medium alone (i.e. 50% CEE) they obtained considerable survival and some development up to the first parasitic molt. Cultures were transferred five times during an 8-day period at approximately 32–40 h intervals. In control cultures of Tyrode solution alone, larvae remained active for approximately 3 days and all were dead by the 4th day, none ever showing any signs of development. This early result indicated that an increase in temperature plus certain environmental conditions supplied by the CEE enabled the parasitic stages to undergo their preliminary development. Whether these environmental conditions were physico-chemical or nutritional was not clear. In this medium molting was much delayed and the stage of growth obtained was roughly comparable to the advanced lung stage which normally occurred in the rat about 48 h after infection. After much experimentation, they were able to obtain development of the young adults in a stunted form in media which combined the following components in several ratios: (a) caseinate or casein hydrolysate; (b) extract of powdered yeast or liver; (c) 50% CEE; (d) mammalian serum. Sexually mature males containing sperm and females containing infertile eggs were found in a medium containing caseinate, liver filtrate, CEE and rat serum. In 1956, when they first reported the results of their work on *in vitro* cultivation of the parasitic stages, it took approximately three to four times longer for fifth-stage worms to develop in culture than in the normal rat host. This report by Weinstein and Jones gave impetus to the work carried on by others with other species of parasites. It also firmly established CEE as one of the primary components of media for parasitic nematode in *in vitro* culture studies. By 1959, Weinstein and Jones had improved their technique and reared several thousand worms through to the adult stage in a time which roughly approximated to that spent in the normal host. They were puzzled by the considerable variation which they obtained using various batches of media and concluded that this was due to variations in vitamins and amino-acid mixtures. They also demonstrated that filariform larvae which they had reared axenically from eggs to the infective larval stage were capable of developing to sexual maturity in *in vitro* cultures. In spite of this very considerable success, they were unable to obtain mating and continuation of the cycle so as to carry out successive generations in *in vitro* cultures. Their improved technique also resulted in an increase of the size of the worms obtained *in vitro* which more nearly approximated to those recovered from the normal host rat. One of the most interesting findings reported by Weinstein and Jones (1959) was the simplification of their four-component medium. Using a basal medium containing only chick embryo homogenate and serum in much higher concentrations than had been previously employed, they obtained growth and development equal to if not better than that previously reported with the more complex medium. They also found that human serum gave better results than homologous rat serum. Supplementation of this basal medium with vitamin mixtures or Eagle's medium or liver concentrate increased the percentage yields of fifth-stage worms. Chemically defined media, such as 199, Eagle's, or NCTC 109 alone or with various supplements added, did not support the growth and development of infective filariform larvae. They were able to eliminate the use of antibiotics and thereby obtained growth and development under strict axenic conditions.

c. *Haemonchus contortus*

1. *Free-living Stages*

Lapage (1933a, b) was one of the early pioneers in attempts to culture *in vitro* the various stages of nematode parasites. He worked with various species of parasites of economic significance and undertook to standardize culture procedures for the free-living stages of nematode parasites of sheep and cattle. Following McCoy's (1929a) work based on studies with dog hookworm larvae, Lapage determined that cattle and sheep nematode larvae similarly required living bacteria as their sole source of food. He isolated a species of *Bacillus coli* (probably *Escherichia coli*) from the intestines of infective nematode larvae and prepared successful cultures with it. The cultures consisted of petri dishes that had been filled up to 3 mm in depth with an inorganic salt solution containing some glucose and which were inoculated with the strain of *B. coli* isolated previously. A short time was allowed for some bacterial multiplication to take place and then eggs, which had been sterilized by a hypochlorite solution, were added. About 5 000–10 000 eggs were put into each petri dish and kept covered with cloth or black paper. No attempt was made to control the ambient temperature. Lapage experimented with agar as an additional medium-component but he discontinued the use of this substance. He reported that his cultures developed with considerable uniformity in spite of the lack of temperature control. He concluded that once a larval hatch took place in a medium reasonably favorable and containing plentiful food, larvae developed in a uniform manner.

Glaser and Stoll (1938), using a medium which had been developed by Glaser and Copia (1935) for culturing *Paramecium* and the housefly, *Musca domestica*, under sterile conditions, succeeded in rearing *H. contortus* larvae from egg to infective third stage larvae in the absence of any living material. Their medium consisted of a semi-solid gel which contained 0·5% liver extract together with some extract of baker's yeast that had been prepared by first subjecting the yeast cells to a temperature of 75–80° C for 1 h, and then grinding for 2–3 h in a mechanical grinder before extracting with water. Small sterile test tubes, 100 × 13 mm, were used and 0·2–0·3 g of fresh sterile rabbit kidney were placed in the bottom of each tube, over which the liver-extract-agar was poured. Two drops of the sterile baker's yeast was added to each tube and then inoculated with *H. contortus* eggs. A variety of experiments were carried out in which the various constituents were varied. The amount of liver extract was altered or omitted, kidney tissue was omitted in some cases and different species of killed and ground micro-organisms such as brewer's yeast, *B. coli* and an unknown species of *Staphylococcus* was substituted. After inoculation with *H. contortus* eggs, the tubes were placed in a darkened humidor and held at room temperatures which varied between 22° and 27° C. This technique met with immediate success. Fourteen days after sowing eggs in their first sterile culture tubes well-nourished and active infective larvae were recovered from the surface of the agar. The larvae recovered from the initial cultures were stunted in length and ranged from 440 to 690 μ with a mean value of 569 $\pm$ 9 μ. This compared with larvae reared under normal conditions in sheep feces with a range of 605–752 μ and a mean value of 679 $\pm$ 4 μ. Bacteria-free larvae reared in this manner were found to be infective for sheep.

2. *Parasitic Stages*

Lapage (1933a) stated, "Attempts have been made to cultivate the parasitic larval stages, a method having been found by which the free-living infective third stages may be exsheathed and sterilized, so that the first parasitic stages may be obtained and studied further in sterile media of known composition. Although these first parasitic stages have been studied in hanging drops in more than 200 media designed to imitate environmental factors to which the parasites are presumably exposed in the body of the host, no success has been obtained." Later, Lapage (1935) gave details of his extensive experimentation with the exsheathed sterilized infective larvae. Lapage learned tissue culture technique at the Strangeways Research Laboratory at Cambridge and for this reason was influenced to use the hanging drop method which had been so successfully applied to various organ and cell cultures by the workers at that laboratory. His main technique was to test individual larvae in hanging drops although some larvae were also tested in Carrel flasks, petri dishes and other devices. He found that the exsheathed parasitic larvae could not tolerate a pH much below 5 and he tended to work near neutrality. All test cultures were maintained at 38–40° C.

Included in the list of media which he examined are the following: horse serum, sheep serum, sheep serum diluted with water, sheep serum and saline, whole blood, de-fibrinated blood, blood clot, fibrin, hemoglobin and hematin, peptic digest of blood, pancreatic digest of blood, chick extract, tissue cultures of chick caecum or intestine, starch (solid and in solution), dextrose, lactose and other hexoses, a variety of amino acids (either as the products of hydrolysis or prepared in their pure form), a number of broths (including serum broth and meat broths), ox bile, bile salts, mucin, gastric and pancreatic juices, fragments and extracts of sheep abomasum, duodenum or caecum,

K

liver extracts, digests with artificial gastric juice or pancreatic juice of liver or grass, cultures of cellulose-splitting bacteria with filter paper or with grass and yeast extracts, Meyer's stomach broth, etc.

Larvae were transferred daily and a maximum survival of 41 days was obtained in one medium consisting of a balanced salt solution and serum in a ratio of 3:1, whereas in most other media the larvae survived from 18 to 30 days. In practically all of the media there was evidence of some development although no growth was observed. This development consisted primarily of the formation of the sheath which is cast at the time of the first parasitic ecdysis. Out of approximately 2 000 larvae so examined about ten actually underwent the third ecdysis. In each case, however, after emergence of the parasitic fourth stage larva, they died very quickly. Lapage reported that media containing either liver or yeast extract appeared to be toxic. In some instances, he noticed a slight increase in the size of the genital primordium but in the majority of worms this did not occur. From Lapage's work it appears that provided certain environmental conditions meet minimum physico-chemical requirements larvae have the capacity to utilize their own reserves to undergo sufficient development to enable them to complete their first parasitic ecdysis without any external source of nutrient. In Lapage's words, "The occurrence of these third ecdyses did not, however, appear to be related to the composition of the media in which they occurred."

Further proof that third stage *H. contortus* larvae are able to make the transition from the third to the fourth stage without an exogenous source of food was provided by Stoll (1940). Stoll investigated the ability of sterilized exsheathed third stage *H. contortus* larvae to undergo development and ecdysis in a variety of balanced salt solutions. His results indicated that the first parasitic ecdysis of *H. contortus* may be obtained *in vitro* under sterile conditions with higher yields of ecdysis occurring in sealed rather than un-sealed tubes and that the process might be accelerated with certain concentrations of an aqueous liver extract prepared from Difco bacto-liver. He found that Ringer's and Tyrode's were the most successful balanced salt solutions whereas sodium chloride alone appeared to be toxic. Significant percentages (20–50%) of ecdysis and appearance of the fourth larval stage did not occur until the 3rd to 5th week of storage of the culture material. This is in contrast to the appearance of the fourth larval stage which normally can be found *in vivo* between the 48th and 72nd h after infection. Stoll concluded that the best results could be obtained under low oxygen tensions, in that a larval inoculum of 100 larvae in 2–3 ml of medium was the most favored condition. Stoll did not record any development beyond the first parasitic ecdysis and confirmed the report of Lapage that larvae died very soon after this stage.

Silverman (1959) reported on attempts to apply the media described by Weinstein and Jones (1956a) to the parasitic stages of *H. contortus*. Initial attempts with the Weinstein and Jones' medium ended in failure and as a result a systematic testing of various nutrients was undertaken. These nutrients included CEE, Hela cells, various liver extracts, sodium caseinate, casein hydrolysate, serum and various balanced salts solutions. A roller tube method was used and compared with static culture techniques. The effect of transferring media on successive days was also investigated. Success was eventually obtained with a medium consisting of CEE, autoclaved sheep liver extract, sodium caseinate and sheep serum in a 2:2:2:1 ratio. This medium, which is very similar to that described by Weinstein and Jones, and using a roller tube technique, supported growth and metamorphosis of larval stages up to the adult stage which was reached in about 24–30 days. The worms were stunted however, and no fertile eggs were observed. It was subsequently determined that the early failure of applying Weinstein and Jones' medium to *H. contortus* was apparently the result of certain toxic materials in the original fresh liver extract. This is a phenomenon of toxicity of liver extracts which has bothered a number of workers (Leland, 1963). Later Silverman (1963), in an attempt to produce on a large scale fourth stage *Haemonchus* larvae for immunological purposes, undertook a detailed study of the factors which affected the third parasitic ecdysis. It was found that the physiological age of the larvae and the type of pre-culture exsheathment had a bearing on the rate at which these larvae underwent further metamorphosis. Silverman placed emphasis upon the need to trigger off the larval biological clock by the use of stimuli which induce in nature the exsheathment of third stage infective larvae. Previously, Glaser and Stoll (1940) and Lapage (1933b) had used hypochlorite solution to induce exsheathment and to obtain sterilization. Sommerville (1957), Taylor and Whitlock (1960) and Silverman and Podger (1964) have shown, however, that the stimuli which are important in nature are carbon dioxide and certain reducing agents. Using balanced salt solutions under a saturated carbon dioxide gas phase, exsheathment and development of *Haemonchus* larvae to an extent which replicated that which occurred in nature was obtained. In 48–72 h between 60 and 90% of the larvae so treated could be induced to reach their fourth stage *in vitro* (Silverman, 1963a). Large numbers of fourth stage larvae were produced in a relatively homogeneous physiological state. Transfer of these fourth stage larvae to complex medium resulted in the development *in vitro* of over 50% of the original inoculum of larvae to the fifth stage in approximately the same time as that observed to occur *in vivo*.

Leland (1963), who used a medium consisting of CEE, serum, sodium caseinate, vitamins, a hog liver extract and balanced salt solution, successfully repeated Weinstein and Jones' (1956a) results with *N. brasiliensis* but failed to obtain the results reported by Silverman (1959) with *Haemonchus*. It might be that the pretreatment of third stage larvae may have affected his success. Leland used sodium hypochlorite solution for exsheathment and sterilization and also reported certain differences in the liver extract.

Douvres (1960a) using a clarified medium, described in the section on *Hyostrongylus*, and modified by the addition of the vitamin supplements described by Weinstein and Jones (1959), cultured two strains of *H. contortus*, one of which was resistant and the other susceptible to phenothiazine. He obtained fourth stage *H. contortus* (of bovine origin) 9 days after inoculation into the vitamin supplemented media. He observed ovine *H. contortus* in the fourth molt 27 and 7 days after initiation of the cultures for the resistant and non-resistant strains respectively. There was no clear indication in this work that vitamin supplements enhanced *in vitro* development although there appeared to be a significant difference between strains of nematodes.

D. *Hyostrongylus*

Diamond and Douvres (1960, 1962) investigated the possibility of cultivating the swine nematode *Hyostrongylus rubidus in vitro* with the aim of making available for study in the laboratory a parasitic nematode of economic importance. The swine stomach worm, *H. rubidus*, was used because of its availability and because the morphology of its histotropic (parasitic) stages was known. Since it was Diamond and Douvres' goal eventually to make observations during the cultivation procedures, they took special pains to clarify their complex medium. Their final complete medium consisted of a nutrient broth which contained trypticase, yeast extract, glucose, cysteine, ascorbic acid and salts and to which was added a clarified extract of rabbit embryos (22–24 days old), pig liver extract and inactivated sheep serum. Extraction of mammalian tissues was made with an acidified aqueous solution (100 ml 0·02 N HCl to each 10 g of tissue). Clarification of the extract was effected by filtration through paper and Seitz pads.

Infective larvae were exsheathed by the hypochlorite technique and added to static culture tubes (agitated twice a day) and transferred to fresh media every 48 h. The majority of larvae did not undergo any changes during 35–42 days of cultivation, however, individuals in the third molt were recovered after the 35th day (as compared to 5 days *in vivo*) and fourth stage larvae were observed after the 42nd day of cultivation. Study of those larvae which underwent the third molt revealed that the majority of these fourth stage forms contained genital primordia which were developed only to the level of third stage parasitic larvae as recovered from guinea-pigs.

E. *Ostertagia, Cooperia* AND *Trichostrongylus* spp.

Ostertagia spp. of ovine origin were first cultured to the fifth stage by Silverman (1959) in the complex medium developed for *Haemonchus*. Using a roller tube mechanism and changing the medium every 72 h, metamorphosis to the adult stage occurred in various successful cultures 24–30 days after inoculation of the exsheathed infective larvae. It was later found that the prior culture in CO_2-gassed balanced salt solution of *Ostertagia ostertagia*, *O. circumcincta* and *O. trifurcata* induced rapid development to the fourth stages. When these fourth stage larvae were transferred to complex media, they underwent metamorphosis and development to the stunted adult stage in 14–30 days (Silverman, 1959, 1963a, British Patent 894,603, and unpublished data).

Leland (1961a, b, 1963), using mixed as well as monospecific cultures of ovine and bovine *Ostertagia* spp. in CO_2-gassed complex media in a roller tube apparatus, obtained fifth stage adults after 30 days cultivation. Cultivation in excess of 48 days was required before eggs or sperm were observed. Leland obtained equal success in this medium with *Cooperia onchophora* and *C. punctata*, although *Trichostrongylus axei* failed to develop in the same conditions. In our laboratory *T. axei* failed to undergo early fourth stage development in any of a variety of balanced salt solutions but eventually did so in tissue culture medium 199 (Silverman and Podger, 1962).

Using *C. punctata* as his main test organism, Leland showed that omission of CEE resulted in a complete loss of growth-promoting activity of the media. On the other hand, serum was not an absolute requirement and growth to the adult stage could occur in its absence. Vitamin supplementation was observed to enhance considerably the yield and rate of development. Both liver extract and sodium caseinate were found to be necessary for development of the egg laying stages.

In contrast to his success with *Cooperia* and *Ostertagia*, results with *Haemonchus* in the successful *Cooperia* media was poor and only fourth stage forms were obtained.

Douvres and Alicata (1961) reported successful cultivation of *C. punctata* to the fifth stage in the cell-free medium developed by Diamond and Douvres (1962) for *Hyostrongylus*. Stunted adults appeared after 14–19 days in culture. As with *Hyostronglyus*, Douvres and Alicata observed that the genital primordium lagged behind somatic differentiation.

One of the most remarkable results on nematode *in vitro* cultivation is that of Leland (1962) who inoculated media with fertile *C. punctata* eggs and obtained development of adult worms which contained eggs and sperm. More details of this accomplishment will be welcomed as well as further work on *Cooperia* and other nematodes along these lines, i.e. to begin culture attempts with fertile eggs rather than infective larvae. Leland concluded that exsheathment stimuli, at least for *C. punctata*, were not an essential requirement in the life cycle. This result suggests that completion of the entire life cycle of parasitic nematodes through successive generations *in vitro* may soon be accomplished.

F. *Oesophagostomum* AND *Stephanurus*

The first report on attempts to culture the parasitic stages of nematodes of the genus *Oesophagostomum* is that of Diamond and Douvres (1960), who encountered *O. quadrispinulatum* as a contaminant in their work with *Hyostrongylus rubidus*. In the same medium described for their work with *H. rubidus*, Diamond and Douvres observed third stage *O. quadrispinulatum* larvae to persist unchanged up to 42 days after inoculation. After the 42nd day, however, some fourth stage *O. quadrispinulatum* larvae were noted. Since this species made up less than 1% of the total population in the culture, the number of observations which could be made were limited. Nevertheless, they were able to determine that the fourth stage larvae which they recovered after the 42nd day of *in vitro* cultivation was comparable to the stage of *O. quadrispinulatum* found in the swine on the 17th day after infection.

Douvres (1960a, b) furnished some details of his work with *Oesophagostomum radiatum* from calves. He reported that *O. radiatum* underwent the third molt 14 days after inoculation in the medium used for *Hyostrongylus*. When this medium was supplemented with a vitamin mixture, as described by Weinstein and Jones (1959), late fourth stage larvae appeared by the 27th day.

Douvres (1960b) obtained a marked improvement in his results when the medium was supplemented with a phosphate or water extract of mucus and mucosal surface material, and inactivated serum derived from helminth free, or lightly infected calves. In this supplemented intestinal-extract-serum medium, fifth stage larvae were obtained by the 24th day after inoculation of exsheathed infective larvae. When the mucosal extract consisted of material derived from nodules resulting from the host tissue reaction to the *O. radiatum* infection, it inhibited the rate of development *in vitro*. Tissue extracts from infected hosts produced precipitates and coatings of debris on the nematodes within 24 h after each transfer to fresh media.

Douvres (1962a) detailed much of his earlier work with *O. radiatum* and reported on the results of further modifications of the medium originally developed for *H. rubidus*. The media ingredients included rabbit embryo extract, swine liver extract, bovine serum nutrient broth, intestinal extract of the mucosal and submucosal tissues of a helminth-free calf and a vitamin mixture which included thiamine, pyridoxine, calcium pantothenate, nicotinic acid, *p*-aminobenzoic acid, folic acid, riboflavin and choline chloride. Incubation temperatures varied between 35° and 38·5° C and the interval between medium changes varied between 2 and 7 days.

In this cell-free clarified medium, vitamin supplemented cultures appeared to enhance the rate of development of the larvae; larvae in the fourth molt were observed as early as the 19th day in supplemented medium as compared with a 24 day minimum in unsupplemented media. No differences in rates of development were observed between cultures which contained (1) serum from helminth free or infected yearling calves, (2) liver extract from pigs of different ages, (3) different aged or concentrations of infected larvae, or (4) which were transferred to fresh media at different time intervals. However, 38·5° C was found to be superior to 35° or 37° as a culture temperature and the percentage yield was much greater in vitamin supplemented media diluted by a bovine intestinal tissue extract as compared to cultures diluted with a buffer. Subsequently Douvres (1962b) used this *in vitro* culture technique to investigate the effect of intestinal extracts from variously susceptible and resistant calves and demonstrated that antibodies can be extracted from such tissues and that they react specifically with antigens produced by the larval stages grown *in vitro*.

Silverman (1963a, and unpublished data) worked with an Australian strain of *O. radiatum* and found that it exsheathed readily in a CO_2-saturated balanced salt solution at pH 5 and subsequently underwent development to the fourth stage in Earle's or Hank's solution which had been gassed with CO_2. Over 60% of the *O. radiatum* larvae completed the third molt by 96 h of cultivation in a roller-tube mechanism and when transferred to a complex medium consisting of CEE, bovine liver extract, serum and sodium caseinate development to the fifth stage took place 14–21 days later. This rate of development is more rapid than that reported by Anantaraman (1942) for the naturally infected animal; however, this might be due to the absence of the intense host reaction which usually occurs *in vivo*. There is no indication in Douvre's work of the use of CO_2 as an additive.

Leland (1961a, b, 1963) cultivated *O. radiatum* and an *Oesophagostomum* spp. from an ovine source in a medium gassed with CO_2 and consisting of CEE, liver extract, serum, sodium caseinate and a vitamin mixture which supported *Cooperia* spp. to the fifth stage, and obtained fourth stage *Oesophagostomum* in large numbers although no subsequent molt was observed.

The vitamin supplemented medium of Douvres (1962a) used for the *in vitro* cultivation of *O. radiatum* was employed by Douvres and Tromba (1962) in attempts to culture *Stephanurus dentatus*, a nematode parasite of swine. By doubling the amount of swine liver extract and bovine serum of the above medium and culturing at between 39–40° C, they induced exsheathed third stage larvae to molt to the fourth stage by the 15th day of culture. Survival of these stages was excellent but no further development was noted.

G. *Dictyocaulus*

The genus *Dictyocaulus* includes the lungworm parasites of calves and sheep, *D. viviparus* and *D. filaria* respectively. In the calf or sheep, third stage larvae penetrate into the host tissue in the upper intestinal tract and migrate to the lungs via the lymph system. Larvae arrive in the lungs as third stage forms and there undergo further development to fourth and fifth stages. The adult forms live in the bronchi and pass out eggs which are coughed up and swallowed and undergo embryonation and hatching during passage down the gut so that they are found in the fresh feces as first stage larvae. The first reports on attempts to culture *in vitro* the parasitic stages of *Dictyocaulus* species was that of Silverman and Podger (1962), Silverman *et al.* (1962) and Silverman (1963a). Initial work on the *in vitro* cultivation of *D. viviparus* infective larvae with the aim of obtaining fourth stage larvae was carried out with the use of media which had been described by Silverman (1959). These media included tissue homogenate and extracts, sera, protein hydrolysates, and tissue and organ culture systems. Until pre-culture storage conditions were standardized and optimal exsheathment stimuli determined, larval development tended to be erratic and of a low order (Silverman, 1963a, b).

By progressive steps, it was found possible to omit most of the macro-molecular additives and homogenates with the exception of an extract obtained from a liver autolysate. This material when added to a balanced salt solution such as Tyrode's, Hank's or Earle's, proved to be remarkably active in inducing ecdysis and metamorphosis of *D. viviparus* third stage infective larvae to the fourth parasitic stage.

D. viviparus infective larvae were found to have a relatively short shelf life and survival was generally poor after 10–14 days at 4° C in water. It was found that the effect of the active liver extract was considerably more dramatic if fresh rather than stored larvae were used. For these reasons, *D. viviparus* larvae which had been stored for less than 7–10 days were used in most of the experiments. The autolyzed liver extract when dried to powder form and stored in a desiccator retained its activity for many months even when kept at room temperatures. Preliminary attempts to determine the nature of the ecdysis stimulating factor in the liver extract included comparative tests between fresh liver extracts and autolyzed liver and various commercial liver and peptone preparations. This was later extended to include various growth factors and vitamins and proteins such as casein, ovalbumin and insulin. An example of the results obtained is summarized in Fig. 1 which records data obtained from one of the comparative tests. Ecdysis stimulating activity was obtained with a commercial peptone preparation manufactured by Difco. Comparable preparations available from other manufacturers did not demonstrate any measurable activity even when tested at higher concentrations.

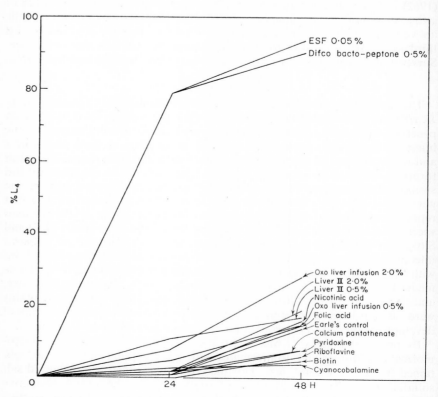

Fig. 1. Comparative effects of various supplements on the stimulation of ecdysis of exsheathed third stage *Dictyocaulus viviparus* larvae to the fourth stage. In each test the liver autolysate preparation (ESF) was replaced by the substance indicated.

The ecdysis stimulating factor (ESF) was found to be active at low concentrations with a threshold of activity between 50 and 100 $\mu g/ml$ (Fig. 2). Replicate titrations with different larval batches showed excellent agreement even when the time required for maximum L_4 conversion varied between 48 and 144 h.

Repeated efforts to determine the method of manufacture and the nature of the materials used in preparation of Difco bacto-peptone were not successful. It was learned indirectly that liver might be one of the raw materials but

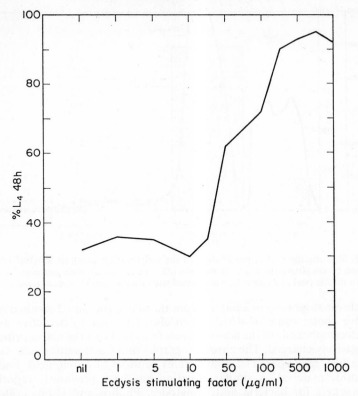

FIG. 2. Effect of various concentrations of a partially purified preparation of the ecdysis stimulating factor. The dose-response curve indicates a threshold of activity for *Dictyocaulus viviparus* at about 50 μg/ml.

this could not be confirmed. Tests of liver infusions and other products from commercial sources containing liver extracts did not show any activity (see Fig. 1).

Further attempts to fractionate and concentrate by chemical means the ESF in liver autolysate indicated that it was not destroyed by deproteinization but was destroyed by ashing. It could be concentrated following delipidization and it appeared in the supernatant when ethanol and salt precipitation techniques were used. It was partially destroyed by pancreatic and papaic hydrolysis and completely destroyed by ficin and acid hydrolysis.

Following delipidization an extract of Difco bacto-peptone was placed on a column of Sephadex-G25 and eluted with 0·2M NH$_4$OH. Over sixty 8 ml fractions were collected and the optical density of samples from each collection were measured at 280 mμ and also tested for ESF activity. The results of one such chromatographic run are summarized in Fig. 3. A distinct peak of activity coincided with a profile peak at fraction 2. All fractions were lyophilized and were compared on an equivalent weight basis. Two dimensional

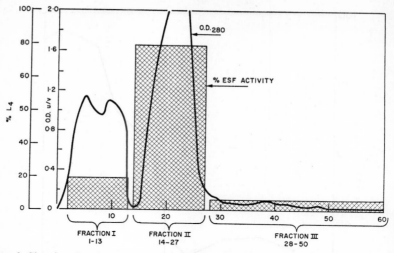

FIG. 3. Showing the partial purification of the ecdysis stimulating factor (ESF) obtained by column chromatograhpy using Sephadex-G25. The histogram indicates activity associated with a profile peak, Fraction II, when tested with *Dictyocaulus viviparus* larvae.

paper chromatography of samples from the active fraction 2 resulted in eight to twelve spots; some of which when eluted proved to be active as ESF. Paper electrophoresis of the active eluents indicated that the active principle(s) was negatively charged. The chromatography and fractionation data suggests that the ESF may consist of a mixture of peptides or amino acids and some polypeptide material. A similar situation has been previously reported by other workers for bacteria and nematodes. Phillips and Gibbs (1961) and Florsheim *et al.* (1962) fractionated peptides from casein and found that they behaved as growth stimulating factors for *Streptococcus equisimilis* and *Pediococcus cerevisiae* respectively. Sayre *et al.* (1961), who worked with the free-living nematode *Caenorhabditis briggsae*, isolated and partially characterized a growth control factor from fresh autolyzed liver extract. In this later case, however, they were able to show that they were dealing with a discrete proteinaceous substance which yielded on hydrolysis twelve amino acids.

Using balanced salt solutions supplemented by the ESF obtained from autolyzed liver extract or from Difco bacto-peptone, it was possible to induce rapid molting of the first parasitic stage of both *Dictyocaulus viviparus* and *D. filaria*. When such fourth stage larvae were transferred to a medium consisting of CEE, sodium caseinate, serum and liver extract about 50% of the inoculum developed to the fifth stage. The time of development was roughly comparable to that observed in the normal host. No eggs or reproductive adults have been observed, however. Since the above experiments and cultivation procedures were primarily designed from the point of view of producing parasitic stages which elaborated antigenic materials for immunological studies, full advantage was not taken of the culture opportunities for investigation of growth and maturation under various conditions. Of interest, however, is the fact that these culture systems were carried out on a very large scale, in some cases 10 liter culture vessels containing over 1 liter of fluid and revolving on a ball mill type of apparatus were employed.

H. *Trichinella*

McCoy (1936), who was interested in cultivating the parasitic stages of several species of helminths, expressed the view that the failure to obtain successful cultivation in an artificial medium was due to the small biochemical differences in the host environments which determined host specificity. For this and other reasons, he felt that *Trichinella spiralis* was a most favorable parasite to use for this type of investigation. He pointed out that (1) *Trichinella* is able to develop in a wide variety of hosts, which include most mammals and certain species of birds, (2) the infective larvae grow to sexual maturity in the short period of 3 days, (3) since the infective larval stage develops in the muscle tissue of the host, the intestines of the larvae do not contain bacteria and consequently it is quite easy to obtain sterile worms for inoculation into artificial media.

McCoy was unable to obtain development of the trichinae larvae in sterile cultures composed of minced 10-day chick embryos suspended in Tyrode's solution. Although most of the larvae remained alive for 4 or 5 days or longer, none of them showed any signs of development. McCoy did realize some success, however, when he injected sterile trichinae larvae into developing chick embryos. His best results were obtained in embryos which were from 12 to 14 days old. Examinations made from 1 to 8 days after inoculation of the worms revealed various stages of development in about 60% of the eggs in which the embryos still lived. Less than 5% of the number of larvae injected actually underwent any significant development. In one chick embryo examined on the 7th day, a female worm was found which had been fertilized and contained young larvae developing in the uterus. This mature female was significantly smaller than that which normally was found in the intestine of the normal host animal. In view of this success with living chick embryos, McCoy undertook experiments to determine whether the injection of trichinae larvae into the embryos of pregnant rats would yield improved results. Laparotomies were performed on pregnant rats on about the 12th to 14th day of gestation. Approximately 1 000 sterile larvae were injected through the uterine wall into the amniotic sac of the embryos. The results of this series of experiments were highly variable but indicated that normal adult trichinae worms would develop if the rat embryos were not killed by the operative procedure. On the basis of these results and the fact that pregnant rats so inoculated with trichinae yielded litters which contained infective trichina cysts, McCoy concluded that factors such as digestive enzymes, bacteria, or their products and the partially digested food materials usually present in the intestinal mucosa are not essential for the growth and maturation of adult *Trichinella*. McCoy also observed successful development of adult *Trichinella* when sterilized larvae were injected into the horns of the uterus. Such larvae developed to the adult stage and produced infective larvae which found their way into the muscle tissues of the mother.

Weller (1943) undertook a series of experiments to attempt to obtain development of *Trichinella* larvae *in vitro* using the roller tube culture apparatus which had previously only been used for tissue culture systems. His initial experiences with various sterilizing solutions seemed to indicate that they all had a deleterious effect on the larvae. For this reason, he prepared all his larvae by a simple washing procedure that was repeated a number of times to remove mechanically all contaminating bacteria. Weller's basic technique consisted of preparing fragments of minced 8- to 10-day-old chick embryo tissue in a chick-plasma clot which was distributed evenly over the wall of a 20 × 150 mm Pyrex test tube. A nutrient fluid consisting of Simms solution, CEE and chicken serum was added and the culture vessel sealed. Cultures were placed horizontally in the rotating device which revolves 8–10 times per h. The nutrient overlay fluid was removed daily and replaced with fresh fluid and the cultures aerated with sterile air. In nineteen cultures set up in this manner, 10–20% of the larvae completed their first molt; others failed to complete the first molt but began to show retraction and preparation for a second molt while still within the first sheath. On two occasions larvae were observed that underwent the second molt and this occurred 48 h after the initial inoculation of the culture. No sexual differentiation was observed in those larvae which had undergone the second molt. Retraction and formation of the third cuticular sheath was first seen at 38 h and occurred frequently by the 50th h of cultivation. Larvae that had retracted from the third sheath showed sexual differentiation with development of vulva, ovary and uterus in the female and the appearance of anal papillae in the male. Although a fourth sheath was observed on some male larvae, no further development took place and all larvae began to show degenerative changes by the 65th h of cultivation. Numerous modifications of this basic medium were undertaken to see if an improvement in development could be obtained. These included the use of different types of mammalian embryonic tissue extracts and tissues, the use of yeast extracts and other changes in the nutrient fluid such as liver extract, various supplements of vitamins, and the addition of standard bacteriological nutrient media such as bacto-tryptose, bacto-tryptone, peptones, and casein hydrolysates. Although most of these fluid nutrient media gave good tissue growth, they did not significantly affect the development of the *Trichinella* larvae.

Levin (1940), in a brief report, indicated that *Trichinella* larvae survived in Tyrode's solution for up to 11 days at 38° C. Although solutions containing glucose seemed to be more beneficial than those without, no sexual development occurred. He also reported that B-complex vitamin supplements had no effect.

Kim (1961) using the medium described by Weinstein and Jones (1956a) was able to obtain *Trichinella* larvae through the developing adult stage comparable to that reported by Weller (1943) in his chick embryo tissue culture system. The medium which Kim found to be of value consisted of 50% CEE in chicken, ox, rat or rabbit serum. He also found that 50% CEE could support development to the sexually differentiated stage. In a further study, Kim (1962) examined the effects of substituting mouse embryo extract for CEE and the effect of adding various kinds of sera, amino acid mixtures, as well as changes in the balanced salt solutions. This comprehensive study did not yield results significantly better than those obtained with CEE alone. Significantly, he observed, as had the other workers who previously used *Trichinella*, that the worms decreased in size during cultivation and underwent molts which resulted in the retention of the outer cuticle. It might well be that *Trichinella* larvae do not require any external nutrient but rather certain physico-chemical conditions for their development to an advanced stage and that feeding might only occur during the adult phase.

I. *Ancylostoma*

1. *Free-living Stages*

McCoy (1929a, b) undertook a study of larvae of *Ancylostoma caninum*, the hookworm of dogs, and attempted to determine the food which was required during their free-living stages. Using 250 ml Erlenmeyer flask cultures of bacteriological agar he grew twenty-five pure strains of bacteria and one species of yeast. He found that twenty-two species of the bacteria were suitable as a sole source of nutrient for the hookworm larvae. The yeast, *Torula rose*, was not a suitable source of nutrient and McCoy speculated that the yeast cells were probably too large to be ingested by the larvae.

His technique consisted of sterilizing eggs recovered from the feces of heavily infected dogs and inoculating the eggs onto 24 h bacterial cultures. At room temperatures the eggs required 36 h to hatch so that first stage larvae were presented with a heavy bacterial growth. The larvae grew to the infective stage in the normal 7-day period. They also underwent comparable development in physiological salt solutions containing suspensions of the various bacteria. Filtrates of the bacterial cultures were not a suitable nutrient for the growth of these free-living stages. Bacteria when killed by heat lost the capacity for supporting growth of the hookworm larvae. McCoy concluded that living bacteria constitute the essential food utilized by hookworm larvae in developing to the infective stage.

Lawrence (1948) working in Australia with *Ancylostoma braziliense*, the hookworm of dogs and cats, undertook a study with the aim of developing an easily reproducible medium in which the free-living stages would develop under aseptic conditions so that physiological and biochemical studies could be made without the complications introduced by the presence of bacteria. He found that a sterilizing solution consisting of 10% formalin in 10% "Milton" (a commercial antiseptic which contains 1% sodium hypochlorite) was the most effective and least deleterious solution of those tested for the cleansing of eggs. Lawrence confirmed that *B. coli* when provided in a living state was a suitable food for the larvae of *A. braziliense*. In either suspensions of bacteria or on agar plate cultures of the bacteria, practically all viable hookworm eggs developed to the infective larval stage. However, when the bacteria were killed by (a) heating at 65° C for 2 h, or (b) by irradiation with ultraviolet light (no details of UV source given), or (c) by treatment with acetone followed by aeration for 15 min at 57–60° C to get rid of the acetone, none of the larvae reached the third stage in any of the media containing dead bacteria. In one culture containing bacteria killed by ultraviolet irradiation, some development as far as the second stage was noted. Filtrates of 24–48 h cultures of *B. coli*, suspensions and extracts of baker's yeast did not support growth and development of larvae. Eventually success was obtained with the medium described by Glaser and Stoll (1938). This consisted of a semi-gel agar medium containing ground heat killed yeast, liver extract and pieces of fresh rabbit kidney. Experiments showed that the yeast and liver extract could be omitted without preventing the larvae from reaching the third stage. Lawrence concluded, "It is clear that the essential ingredient in Glaser and Stoll's medium is the fresh, sterile rabbit kidney and this, unfortunately, is the most complex one." Although Glaser and Stoll's medium provided the best conditions for development of *A. braziliense* larvae, the results were highly variable and always rather poor. Lawrence undertook a complex study of a variety of kidney extracts and preparations of peptones to determine whether there was any other possible readily available material which would be suitable for the growth of free-living stages. The materials investigated included extracts of kidney from the ox and rabbit, peptones and meat infusions, yeast extracts and veal powders and also Difco beef heart powder. Although many of the media and combinations of media yielded some encouraging results, none were quite as successful as the Glaser and Stoll technique. None of the media, including Glaser and Stoll's, permitted aseptic cultivation of the larvae comparable to that which was obtained with living bacteria.

Weinstein (1953) working with eggs of *Ancylostoma caninum* and *A. duodenale* which he obtained from a hospitalized Korean patient undertook to examine the media recommended by Glaser and Stoll as a suitable beginning for the preparation of aseptic *in vitro* cultivation techniques. He also undertook to confirm that heat-killed bacteria were not a suitable food for the free-living stages. Weinstein introduced the use of antibiotics which greatly simplified the cultivation procedures. He was able to demonstrate that although first stage larvae could be found with large numbers of bacteria in the lumen of their intestine, heat-killing of the bacteria seemed to make them undigestible. In fluid cultures consisting of Tyrode's solution and suspensions of bacteria with or without liver extract, as recommended by Glaser and Stoll, little development was found. However, when small amounts of 50% CEE were added, development of approximately 81% of the larvae to the filariform stage was obtained. These early results pointed to the importance of fresh CEE for the development of filariform larvae. Weinstein then determined that 50% CEE alone or rat liver extract in 50% concentration provided a suitable medium for the development of filariform infective larvae. These larvae proved to be infective in a laboratory puppy which had been reared helminth-free. In spite of this success, the range of sizes and of developmental stages was very considerable. Any dilution of either the CEE or the rat liver extract to below 25% resulted in inactive medium as measured by the number of filariform larvae which would develop. Transfer of cultures every 36 h greatly enhanced larval development. Heating of the tissue extract or its passage through bacteriological filters, fractionation by dialysis, or high speed centrifugation had marked deleterious effects on the ability of the media to support larval development. Weinstein also found that certain extracts of rat liver appeared to have a toxic material which was inhibitory to the development of the larvae. He was not able to identify or isolate the growth inhibitor in the rat liver extract. In 1954, Weinstein reported the successful application of this technique to *Necator americanus*, the human hookworm, when he reared filariform larvae from eggs under axenic conditions.

2. Parasitic Stages

Although there have been no reports to date of the successful *in vitro* cultivation of the parasitic stages of *Ancylostoma*, Weinstein and Jones (1959) reported on results obtained with the third stage filariform infective larvae of the hookworm, *Necator americanus*, which is closely related to *Ancylostoma*. Using a medium which consisted of 70% CEE, 20% serum, and without the use of antibiotics, fourth stage larvae were obtained after 22 days of cultivation. Although they observed an increase in the size of the worms, no fifth stages were reported. The culture conditions and roller tube apparatus used in this work were the same as that which they reported for their studies on *Nippostrongylus*.

Komiya *et al.* (1956) studied the conditions under which *Ancylostoma caninum* adult worms could be maintained *in vitro*. Adult hookworms were recovered from dogs 3–4 weeks after infection and sterilized with antibiotics. Three "couples" were placed in Carrell flasks, the medium was changed every 2 days and the criterion of survival was the motility of the worms as observed under a dissecting microscope. In physiological salt solutions alone, Krebs-Ringer (with bicarbonate) proved superior with an average maximum survival of 7 days as compared with 5 or less in Ringer, Locke or Tyrode (without glucose). The addition of 0·5% glucose increased survival of female worms to 15 days and male worms to 8 days. When placed in dog serum female worms survived for up to 35 days with no differences observed when the serum was diluted to 50% with Krebs-Ringer bicarbonate solution. In the same medium male worms survived for 20 days. The addition of red blood cells did not increase survival time in serum, nor did it seem to affect egg laying or copulation. In some experiments male worms were reported to survive for up to 6 weeks and female worms for 12 weeks. During the first 3 weeks copulation *in vitro* was observed frequently. Egg production continued up to the limit of survival, although many eggs were obviously abnormal. Numerous embryonated eggs and hatched larvae were formed during the first 4 weeks of maintenance.

Although not strictly concerned in the cultivation of hookworm, a recent description by Roche and Torres (1960) is of some interest to those who would wish to consider a close study of the digestion and physiology of adult hookworms. The technique provides for the maintenance of the adult worm in a double chamber which enables the anterior end to be separated from the posterior end. The living worm is threaded through a thin rubber membrane which separates the two parts of the chamber and prevents contact between the fluid contents. Worms were kept alive and under observation for periods of up to several hours. Indications are that this apparatus might lend itself to longer studies and provide means effectively to prevent the accumulation of metabolites.

J. ASCARIDOIDEA

1. Larval Development

Apparently the first attempt to cultivate *in vitro* the larval stages of an ascarid nematode was that of Ackert *et al.* (1938) who worked with the ascarid of chickens, *Ascaridia lineata*. Ackert and his co-workers point out that *Ascaris* is somewhat peculiar as a parasitic nematode in that it has no true free-living stage. The larval stages of the ascarid are completed almost entirely within the host except for embryonation of the egg.

The *in vitro* hatching conditions described by Rogers (1958) and Fairbairn (1960) were not known to Ackert and his co-workers, who recovered larvae which had hatched from eggs that had been fed to young chicks. Larvae were collected from the chicks' duodenum and were then used for *in vitro* cultivation studies. Larvae were kept in normal saline at normal bird temperature (106–108° F) and measurements for growth were made by taking the length of the larvae as a criterion. They found that if larvae were kept in a sterile saline solution which overlay a solid dextrose cornmeal-agar plate in a petri dish, larvae survived for nearly 2 weeks. The pH of the medium was found to be 6·93. When various peptone broths were added to the media, they were found adversely to affect the larvae which survived for much shorter periods than in the sterile saline solution. Larvae could be observed to be ingesting food materials.

Because of their initial failures with freshly hatched larvae, Ackert *et al.* allowed the *A. lineata* larvae to undergo periods of development in the chick gut before transferring to *in vitro* test media. As possible media they examined hens' eggs, various carbohydrate solutions, and isotonic salt dextrose as described by Stunkard (1932). With larvae that were allowed to develop for 19 days in the duodenum of a chicken, and then transferred to a carbohydrate solution consisting of 20 g starch, 10 g dextrose in 50 ml distilled water which gave a pH of 6·23 and which was overlaid on dextrose-cornmeal agar, the worms underwent an increase in length of about 20%. In the isotonic salt dextrose solution of Stunkard, larvae which had been allowed to age 23–36 days *in vivo* and were 22–56 mm in length when transferred to this medium, underwent an increase in length of between 0·2 and 25·9 mm (i.e. up to 50%). Of twenty-four larvae between the ages of 23 and 36 days, twenty underwent some kind of growth in this medium.

The interpretation of the results obtained with partially developed larvae is somewhat problematical because it is not clear how much of the material contained within intestinal cells as reserve substances are utilized for further growth and differentiation. There is no strong evidence in the work of Ackert *et al.* that the media provided any significant nutrient stimulus.

In a series of tantalizingly brief notices, Pitts and Ball (1953, 1955) and Pitts (1960, 1962) reported on the *in vitro* cultivation of freshly hatched larvae of the pig ascarid, *Ascaris lumbricoides*. Pitts and Ball obtained an increase in length of up to 50% with hatched *Ascaris* larvae cultured in a complex media consisting of CEE with supplements. This size of larvae compared with that obtained from the livers of mice by the 5th day of infection. Pitts (1960) reported that larvae, hatched in the intestines of mice and sterilized, did not grow or survive as well as the larvae which were artificially hatched by his technique (Pitts, 1948). Pitts (1960) used a roller tube apparatus and media consisting of hog serum and CEE (ratios and quantities not stated) and supplemented with "a variety of organic materials". He sub-cultured daily or every other day and reported growth and survival of newly hatched larvae showing an increase in length of 100–200% with a maximum size of 2 470 × 70 μ being obtained in an 18-day culture. His most successful result was obtained by using larvae recovered from the liver of a mouse on the 8th day after infection. Some free sheaths were found in the cultures but no active exsheathment was observed. Pitts (1962) further reported that by using a special culture chamber (Pitts and Ball, 1955) and Eagle's medium, supplemented with fresh rabbit serum, increases in length and diameter of over 100% were obtained. The maximum size obtained with newly hatched larvae was 965 μ in length and 59 μ in diameter (i.e. an increase of 304% in length and 500% in diameter). This was secured in a 42-day culture maintained at 35–36° C and in which the medium was changed at 7-day intervals. Mass exsheathment of up to 80% of the first stage larvae was noted during the first 4 days. Supplementation of the Eagle's and fresh rabbit serum medium with yeast or liver extract, amino acids or pyruvate did not yield significantly better growth. Fresh hog serum was reported not to be as good as rabbit serum as a supplement for Eagle's medium.

Cleeland and Laurence (1962) claimed that the methods of Pitts (1948), Haskins and Weinstein (1957) and Rogers (1958) for the hatching of *Ascaris* eggs results in damage to the fresh larvae and was partly responsible for the poor results secured in *in vitro* cultivation procedures. Cleeland and Laurence treated *Ascaris* eggs with sodium hydroxide and hypochlorite to remove the outer proteinacious layer and partially to remove the chitinous layer. Eggs were suspended in 1% neutral formalin and maintained at 22–26° C until a majority had reached the infective stage, which usually occurred within 30 days. The eggs were then washed in formalin and suspended in a balanced salt solution maintenance medium at 37° C and agitated by means of a magnetic stirrer until hatching occurred. Freshly hatched larvae were washed and concentrated by gentle centrifugation and transferred to 20 ml screw cap tissue culture tubes. By adjusting the screw cap some control over the diffusion of air into the tube was obtained. Tests in Earle's balanced salt solution or medium 199 resulted in the survival of larvae for 3–4 days in the BSS alone or 9–11 days in medium 199. Medium 199 when supplemented with 20% bovine serum supported survival of the larvae for 27 days during which time there was a change in the internal structure of many larvae and a slight increase in size. The largest larvae in this medium were measured to be 280 × 12 μ as compared with the freshly hatched larval size of 240 $\pm$ 15 × 11 $\pm$ 2 μ. These results were obtained under aerobic conditions. When the screw caps were tightened and the larvae maintained under "deep-tube" cultivation in 199 supplemented with 20% bovine serum, larvae survived

50–60 days and a slight increase in size was noted. In one instance after 40 days incubation, a living larva measuring 609 × 29 μ was found. Active ex-sheathing and development of internal structures was observed. Growth ceased when the incubation temperature was lowered from 37° to below 26° C. Larvae maintained in phosphate buffered saline containing 20% bovine serum showed no increase in size or change in internal structure. An increase in the serum supplementation of 199 did not have any marked effect on either the survival or growth of larvae.

Cleeland (1963) continued these investigations and studied the effects of different atmospheres and various supplements to Eagle's medium or medium 199 without 20% calf serum. He obtained growth of artificially hatched larvae only when an initial concentration of 20 000 or more larvae/10 ml of medium were cultured at 37·5° C under partially anaerobic conditions. Only 0·1–1% of the larvae ever showed a marked increase in size and their develop-ment was considerably behind that which occurs *in vivo* (80–100 days *in vitro* as compared to 9–12 days *in vivo*). When cultures were gassed with oxygen the larvae died in 10–20 days. After some initial growth took place, gassing with a nitrogen and 5% CO_2 mixture proved to be stimulatory if not essential to further development. Cleeland also demonstrated that when the amino acids and vitamins found in Eagle's medium were added to Earle's balanced salt solution containing glucose and serum, growth of larvae was obtained com-parable to that which occurred in the more complex medium 199.

2. Adult Maintenance

Because of its size, the adult *Ascaris lumbricoides* (*suum*) has been con-sidered to be an extremely valuable organism for the study of nematode physiology. Hobson (1948) and Hobson et al. (1952a, b) have investigated a number of conditions which were effective for maintaining adult worms in a viable condition. Fairbairn and Reesal (1950), Cavier and Savel (1953), Pollak and Fairbairn (1955), Ellison et al. (1960) and Harpur (1962) have studied the problem further. Although these studies are not strictly within the range of this review, they do give some indication of the requirements which might be needed for further development of the parasitic stages. One of the salient points which ought to be examined in detail appears to be the effect of carbon dioxide and oxygen. Cleeland and Laurence (1962) speculated that in their deep culture tubes the redox potential of the medium and/or the amount of the oxygen in the sealed tubes affected the different results which they noted. The importance of O_2 and CO_2 for developing ascarid larvae has been empha-sized by Cleeland's (1963) work. The studies of workers with adult worms indicate that oxygen is toxic for the ascarids and that 5% carbon dioxide is required as a stimulus for a more normal type of metabolic activity. The work of the investigators listed above with adult ascarids should be studied with care for clues of physical-chemical or nutritional requirements which may help with the cultivation *in vitro* of this important species.

Worthy of note in this connection is a review by Krotov (1958) on mainten-ance and cultivation of parasitic worms under artificial conditions which makes reference to a number of results by Russian workers, the original papers of which are not readily available. He records an interesting method used by Russian workers (Kovalevsky and Kurlov, 1927) who maintained adult *Ascaris* in normal saline and after 24 h "fed" them for 12–18 h on meat broth or boiled milk, and again replaced the medium with saline solution. They claimed that this technique did not require the use of aseptic methods and made it possible to prolong the survival time of the ascarids to 3 weeks. They reported that after each feeding, the females began to lay more eggs. Krotov reports that when ascarids were maintained in Locke's solution which was replaced twice a day, they lived for 5·7 days on the average, while when fed on a daily diet of pea mash they survived for 10 days!

K. FILARIOIDEA

Hobson (1948) credits the microfilaria with some of the longest survival records *in vitro* of any nematode species parasitic in warm-blooded hosts. His conclusions are based on reports by Fulleborn (1912) and Johns and Querens (1914) who observed the ability of microfilaria to continue in an apparently active state for up to 52 days in blood stored in an ice chest. In an excellent review of the literature on this subject, Earl (1959) critically evaluates the previous reports on survival and development of filariae in various types of media and conditions and points out that these reports should be treated with great caution. Although true survival might be obtained for some considerable periods, the reports of apparent growth may be the result of physical distortion and other changes in the nematodes but not genuine development.

1. *Microfilariae*

Earl (1959) reported the results of his experiments with microfilariae of *Dirofilaria immitis*, the heartworm of the dog. He successfully maintained microfilariae at 37° C in the chemically defined medium 199 for 4 days but this time was increased to 43 days when a 10% supplement of inactivated dog serum was added. Survival time was further increased to 61 days when the dog serum content of the medium was raised to 30%. In a mixture of 199 plus 10% inactivated dog serum and layered over sheets of dog kidney cells, microfilaria survived for about 40 days. A similar period of maintenance was obtained when the dog serum was replaced by heterologous cow or horse sera. When the temperature was reduced from 37° C to room temperature (18–22° C) survival time was reduced to 18 days. In some of his cultures, Earl included the red blood cells of the host dog but obtained no significant increase in survival time. He used milk dilution bottles or screw cap test tubes as static culture vessels which were incubated on their sides.

Earl found that microfilariae of *D. immitis* would tolerate freezing when snap frozen in a dry ice–ethanol bath when glycerol additive was used at a 1:9 ratio in a mixture of 199 plus 10% dog serum. After 30 min in the frozen state about 40% viable microfilaria could be recovered. Attempts to store frozen microfilaria for longer periods were not successful. The only time interval which he checked was that of 2 months so there is little to indicate what is the maximum period of survival under freezing conditions.

In 1960, Taylor reported on her attempts to cultivate the microfilariae of

Loa loa, Wuchereria bancrofti and *Dirofilaria immitis*. Taylor investigated the ability of a variety of balanced salt solutions and medium 199 supplemented with either horse serum, CEE or sodium caseinate to support the survival and development of microfilariae. She also reported on the first attempts at cultivation *in vitro* of the mosquito stages of *D. immitis*. Most of the media sustained the microfilariae from 8 to 14 days. In a medium consisting of dilute Tyrode supplemented with horse serum, she obtained her best results with the microfilariae of *Loa loa* and *D. immitis*. In this medium, the microfilariae remained alive and morphologically normal for 10–14 days when red cells were included. Supplementation with glucose, CEE, raw liver extract or mosquito extract failed to prolong survival of larvae or to induce them to develop further. The sole indication of development was observed in microfilariae of the human filarial parasite, *Loa loa*, in which after 10 days in medium 199 or in Tyrode supplemented with horse serum, she observed a division of certain cells. She obtained no success in either development or prolonged survival with the larval stages recovered from infected mosquitoes. The younger larvae were more difficult to maintain than those which had reached the infective stage. Medium 199 was sufficient to maintain the early stages alive but the later pre-infective stages died after only 1 day in this medium even when mosquito gut was included in the culture. She reported that infective larvae survived quite well in a roller tube tissue culture of puppy skin or heart tissue. In a medium consisting of Gey's fluid, supplemented with dog serum and CEE, the infective larvae usually molted but did not increase in size. Simplified media maintained the infective larvae for several days but did not induce the development observed in the more complex roller tube culture medium. The simple media cultures were carried out in Carrel flasks under static conditions.

The first significant success in the cultivation and development of microfilariae was that of Sawyer and Weinstein (1962) who reported that they obtained development of *D. immitis* microfilariae to a stage comparable to 3–4 days of differentiation in a mosquito host. The "sausage-form" microfilaria normally develops in the mosquito host where it is found in the Malpighian tubules. Their successful technique consisted simply of incubating heparinized whole blood from infected dogs at 27° C. Developing larvae of *D. immitis* could be recovered from such "cultures" as early as 3 days after incubation (Sawyer and Weinstein, 1963). When the infected heparinized whole blood was incubated at 37° C only typical undeveloped microfilariae were recovered. A technique which involved the separation of microfilariae from dog blood and transferring the parasites to blood or blood fractions derived from other mammals free of filarial infection also met with success, although not to the same extent as that obtained with infected dog blood. These experiments included human, rabbit and rat blood. No development was obtained in the rat blood and in several cases human blood appeared to be superior to that from the dog. Only slight (1·4%) development of microfilariae to the sausage form was observed in rabbit blood as compared to 11·5% (maximum) observed in dog and 10·3% in human blood. No development was obtained when the plasma fraction of blood was used as a culture medium. Low yields of sausage forms were recovered from blood cell and saline media without plasma. Plasma, however, provided a good medium for survival of microfilariae which continued alive for more than 18 days at which time there was a 50% viability. These data suggest the presence of a nutrient in the red blood cells required for initial development of *D. immitis* microfilariae. Success was also reported with the use of the chemically defined medium NCTC 109 when supplemented with horse serum. NCTC 109 medium supported survival of microfilariae for approximately 7 days but no development was observed. The addition of serum extended the survival time to 8 days and stimulated development to the sausage form. No attempt was made to renew the medium during the culture period and all cultures were gassed with 5% CO_2 every 2 or 3 days. Comparable development occurred at both 27° C and at room temperature (temperature unstated). At 37° C the survival time was reduced to 4 days and development did not occur. Horse serum was the only type of serum tested and was supplemented at various levels between 1 and 40%. Maximum yields of 5% late first stage larvae (sausage forms) were obtained at the 5% supplementation level with unheated serum. When the serum was heated, the yield of developing larvae doubled with increased serum content. Sawyer and Weinstein reported that after attaining the full sausage form, molting was not observed although larvae were seen in a premolt condition as evinced by a separation of the cuticle. At this stage the tail was tightly coiled and associated with a cuticular sac which surrounded the developing larvae.

2. Adult Filaria

Earl (1959) found that medium 199 and a modified Eagle's Hela cell medium containing 10% inactivated horse serum supported the adult filariae of *Dirofilaria immitis* in a viable state for several weeks with a maximum of 65 days. The media was changed at 12 h intervals. The female worms were found to ovulate and extrude ova and microfilariae. In one 4 h sample after 4 days *in vitro*, examination of the medium revealed that products of parturition consisted of 97% ova and 3% microfilariae. Ova and microfilariae were observed in all stages of development from the fourth cell stage to recognizable microfilaria. Earl determined that an anaerobic environment caused cessation of all activity after 3 days. Also, by keeping adult filariae at 4° C for 5 days, the worms were killed.

Taylor (1960) maintained adult *Litomosoides carinii in vitro* for 23 days and the females produced microfilariae for up to 18 days. The medium consisted of fresh rat serum in medium 199 in a static Carrel flask at 37° C. Cultivation at lower temperatures (35° or 31° C) or the use of horse or cotton rat serum instead of rat serum appeared to be of no benefit.

Taylor also worked with adult *Dirofilaria immitis*. She reported that when *D. immitis* was cultured in a Tyrode's or Ringer's balanced salt solution, supplemented with dog serum and 0·1% glucose and CEE, the adult worms remained alive for a maximum of 7 days and the females produced microfilariae for only the first 2 days. Weinstein and Sawyer (1961) reported their results with attempts to maintain adults of *Dirofilaria uniformis in vitro*.

They were able to maintain *D. uniformis* adults in medium NCTC 109 with or without a rabbit serum supplement. The medium was gassed with 5% CO_2 and air and changed daily to remove acidic metabolic products and also to determine microfilarial production. In medium 109 alone, the filariae lived for 10 days but when supplemented with 5, 10 or 20% serum, survival time was extended to 3 weeks. All were dead by the end of the 4th week. Production of microfilaria occurred during the first 13–16 days of survival with peaks on days 2 and 3. Adult worms derived from a Dutch rabbit and cultured in medium 109 which was supplemented with a low concentration of calf serum (concentration not stated) showed survival patterns similar to that obtained with the rabbit serum but microfilarial production was considerably lower.

VI. Cestodes

In an excellent comprehensive review Smyth (1947a) summarizes the work done on the physiology and *in vitro* maintenance and cultivation of tapeworms. Smyth's review which is supplemented by those of Baer (1952) and Wardle and McLeod (1952) are recommended for reference to work done before 1950.

A. PSEUDOPHYLLIDEA

The first report of *in vitro* cultivated tapeworm stages which resulted in apparently normal development of larval forms was that of Smyth (1946, 1947b) who worked with the progenetic plerocercoid larvae of *Schistocephalus solidus* and *Ligula intestinalis*. Smyth obtained maturation of plerocercoid larvae and development into sexually mature worms with oviposition taking place in the culture tubes. The medium was an isotonic salt solution (three-quarter strength Locke) or peptone broth and the critical factor appeared to be a temperature increase to 40° C; this being the normal temperature of the duck definitive host. For normal gametogenesis and oviposition of fertile eggs the required physico-chemical conditions are (1) the use of a highly buffered media to counteract the adverse effects of acidic metabolic products; (2) cultivation under anaerobic or semi-anaerobic conditions; (3) compression of the plerocercoids within dialysis tubing; and (4) agitation of culture media to assist diffusion of waste metabolites. Under optimal *in vitro* conditions the plerocercoids undergo maturation and development in the same time as in the bird host, and as many as 88% of the eggs produced are fertile. "The medium and culture procedures . . . merely provide suitable environmental conditions under which *differentiation*, but not *growth* (using the term in the synthetic sense), can take place; the medium contributes nothing to the metabolism of development" (Smyth, 1959). Baer (1952) has commented that such experiments should not be considered "as successful demonstrations of *in vitro* cultures. They indicate that optimum conditions for survival of the larvae were realized and that, thanks to the large amount of reserve materials, especially glycogen, at the outset, metabolism has proceeded normally to the extent of maturation of the gonads." Be that as it may, Smyth's work has undoubtedly been a considerable stimulus to this field of investigation apart from its obvious intrinsic scientific merit.

Smyth (1958) investigated the possibility of culturing plerocercoids of pseudophyllidean tapeworms which contained small quantities of reserve materials and which would not mature *in vitro* under the conditions which he had determined for *Schistocephalus* and *Ligula*. He selected for this investigation *Diphyllobothrium dendriticum*, a parasite of the seagull and other fish-eating birds, which passes its intermediate stage in fish where the plerocercoids develop in the viscera and may be removed by aseptic means. If fed to rodents they will undergo development in the intestine of the rat. Because of physical difficulties associated with attempts to culture *in vitro* the large plerocercoid larvae of *D. dendriticum*, Smyth conceived the idea of culturing fragments which were excised from the plerocercoid larvae. Fragments 1–2 mm long were cut from the posterior quarter of the larvae and were cultured at 40° C in static Carrell flasks or in screw top vials which were shaken continuously. In dilute duck embryo extract fragments became segmented and developed traces of genital anlagen but did not undergo further development although they survived for periods up to 20 days. Using more concentrated duck embryo extract (4 g tissue per 10 mm Tyrode) and continuously shaking the screw top vials, fragments became segmented by the 2nd day, developed genital anlagen by the 3rd day and by the 6th day had become differentiated into recognizable proglottids containing a cirrus and cirrus sac, a coiled uterus and testes capsules. Mature spermatozoa were found in some of the testes but cells representing the primordia of the ovaries were not detected. Although these fragments underwent considerable development and differentiation virtually no cytoplasmic growth took place in the tissues. As a result Smyth reported that the fragments gave rise to miniature proglottids each estimated to be about one-fifth to one-tenth the size of those which matured in a rat host. Further attempts to culture segments beyond this stage resulted in a rapid onset of autolysis which usually took place on the 7th to 8th day of culture. Smyth considered that this was related to the next stage of development, that of egg shell formation, a stage of intense protein synthesis, during which cells of the vitellaria are manufacturing the protein and phenolic precursors required for the egg shell. Smyth speculated that this onset of autolysis was due to the embryonic tissue attempting to satisfy its excessive nutritional requirements at the expense of its own cells. No advantages from the use of either the static or shaker cultivation method were observed. Smyth (1959) gave further details of his experimental technique and reported that renewal of medium at 24, 48 or 72 h intervals resulted in no significant difference in the rate or extent of differentiation and development of the tapeworm fragments. Among the constituents used in his complex media were included horse serum, chick amnion, chick yolk sac, concentrations of duck embryo extract ranging from 10 to 50%, and combinations of duck extract with horse serum, chick serum and lactalbumen hydrolysate in Earle's solution. His most successful development of proglottid maturation occurred in 20% duck embryo extract, as previously reported. In no case was there observed to be any development of vitellaria. Smyth (1959) also attempted to culture the stages of *S. solidus* which normally occur in the invertebrate intermediate host. Starting with freshly hatched coracidia and using a variety of media he was unable to obtain any development *in vitro*.

Mueller (1958) first reported the successful cultivation of the procercoid stages of the pseudophyllidian tapeworm *Spirometra mansonoides*. Procercoids were dissected from copepods and cultured in media consisting of mixture 199 plus 10% calf serum to which fresh CEE was added to form 50% of the total volume. The procercoids increased in size from 0·15 mm to approximately 7 mm in 60 days. Subsequently, Mueller (1959a) confirmed that this size sparganum is infective to cats; adult worms were obtained after oral infection. By this means, Mueller was able to eliminate the second intermediate host required in the normal life cycle of this parasite. In 1959b, Mueller gave further details of his technique which includes a description of the apparatus which he uses for transfer of media and is recommended as a model to those who would enter into this field.

Two points of interest should be noted: (1) Mueller used a roller tube system which revolved the culture tubes at 12 times per h; (2) he took special precautions to ensure that CO_2 was retained within his media. He found it necessary to change media daily and by using careful techniques, was able to keep cultures for 90 days with minimal contamination. Initially, Mueller obtained procercoids from infected copepods which he dissected with minute dissecting needles, but found that he was able to obtain large quantities of relatively clean procercoids by feeding mice with the infected copepods and then recovering procercoids from the abdominal cavity of the mice 5–10 days later. Using 1 000 or more procercoids per test tube in a medium consisting of 199, calf serum, extract of an 11-day-old chick embryo and Hanks' solution, Mueller obtained dramatic development of procercoids to the infective plerocercoid stage with an increase in length from approximately 0·1 mm to 10·0 mm in 1 month and to 20 mm or more in 2 or 3 months. Mueller recounts his earlier experience when he attempted to culture sparganum recovered from experimental mice and which were in a further stage of development than the procercoids with which he had obtained such success. Using Earle's salt solution or 199 supplemented with calf serum he obtained no increase in size or advance in development although survival up to periods from 9 months to 1 year was noted. He later returned to this examination of the *in vitro* requirements of the more highly developed spargana and discovered that when CEE was added to the 199, calf serum medium, containing 9- and 10-month-old scoleces, the tip of the head grew out to a needle nosed shape in 24 h and then the worms died as though the effort "had exhausted the starved tissues". When fresh scoleces from large spargana were placed in a similar 199, calf serum, CEE medium no such effect was demonstrated. Mueller remarks that this lack of effect of the CEE on fresh scoleces as opposed to starved scoleces is reminiscent of cultures of procercoid origin which seem to slow down markedly after a length of 5–7 mm is reached. It would appear as if the development of this mass of tissue triggers off a new phase of the biological clock mechanism which may require a new type of stimulus not available in the medium. Evidence for the requirement of such a stimulus was given in a report by Berntzen and Mueller (1963) on their successful attempt to culture *Spirometra* from a procercoid to the young adult stage. Using the apparatus described by Berntzen (1961, 1962), Berntzen and Mueller successfully cultured young adults from the plerocercoids which Mueller had previously produced by his *in vitro* technique. The process involved treatment with an evaginating solution of either whole cat or hamster bile or sodium taurocholate with trypsin. After inducing evagination and culturing the sparganum in a medium which contained a gas phase of 5–10% CO_2, they obtained scolex differentiation, shedding of the larval body, growth and early segmentation of the strobila. Whenever oxygen was incorporated into the gas phase or the CO_2 content was less than 5% only dead or dying spargana were found. If the evaginating solution was omitted no scolex differentiation or other development occurred. Complete details of the media are not given in their brief report however; it appears that the medium used by Berntzen for the cultivation of *Hymenolepis* is adequate for *Spirometra* provided that the gas phase and evaginating stimulus is incorporated in the procedure. As Berntzen and Mueller (1963) concluded, the life cycle of *Spirometra* which involves two vertebrate hosts and an invertebrate stage can be two-thirds duplicated in an artificial culture system. The problem now remaining is to culture the coracidium to the procercoid stage, which normally occurs in the invertebrate copepod intermediate host. When this is achieved the first complete tapeworm life cycle *in vitro* will have been accomplished.

B. CYCLOPHYLLIDEA

1. *Taenia*

One of the first records of an attempt to culture under sterile conditions a taeniid tapeworm is that of Mendelsohn (1935) who worked with *Taenia taeniaeformis* (*Taenia crassicollis*). Mendelsohn removed under sterile conditions the early developing strobilocercus from the liver of a rat. This strobilocercus which was in the early blastocyst stage was transferred with a few small fragments of the host's tissue reaction to sterile test tubes and attached to the interior surface by means of a thin layer of clotted chicken plasma. An overlay composed of a balanced salt solution, CEE and filtered horse serum was added. The sealed test tube was then placed in a rotating drum in an incubator at 37·5° C. Mendelsohn reported that although it was possible to cultivate the early larval stage alone, better results were obtained when small pieces of the cyst wall were included. He reported that a few (number unspecified) larvae of *T. taeniaeformis* were kept alive for 35 days and that they had proceeded to invagination of the head (scolex) with no evidence of sucker formation. Wilmoth (1945) investigated the ability of the strobilocercus stage of *T. taeniaeformis* to survive in a wide variety of media. These included Tyrode's solution and mammalian Ringer's solution to which was added various nutrient materials such as tryptone, peptone and liver digests with and without sodium taurocholate and/or agar as well as many other additives. No evidence of development to the strobilar stages were noted and the criterion of viability was the ability of the larvae to move once the static culture container was shaken. Five-month-old larvae of *T. taeniaeformis* were maintained in sterile medium containing a trace of glucose for a maximum of 24 days during which time they continued to show motility. Larvae survived longer in simple rather than in complex media and appeared to prefer aerobic to anaerobic conditions. They were able to withstand temperature ranges from 14 to 37° C as well as changes in pH from 9·3 to 4·6.

With the availability in recent years of the taeniid species *T. crassiceps*, which undergoes vegetative reproduction during its larval stage in the peritoneal cavity of the intermediate rodent host, a useful parasite has become available for the study of larval cestodes in *in vitro* culture conditions. In a brief note, Robinson *et al.* (1963) reported on the successful culture of *Taenia crassiceps* larvae. They found that larvae maintained at 38° C in roller tube cultures under a 5% CO_2 in air gas phase in medium 199 underwent budding and developed scoleces and hooks with suckers. Strobilization of mature cysticerci was also obtained. Similar attempts by Taylor (1963) with the same strain of *T. crassiceps* resulted in survival of the various stages of cysticerci but with little apparent development or differentiation. Taylor's results indicated that Waymouth's medium, 199 and NCTC 109 were less favorable for the survival and partial development of *T. crassiceps* larvae than Eagle's medium. Almost comparable survival was obtained in Hanks' saline solution alone. Taylor's attempts to adapt Berntzen's (1961) continuous flow apparatus for *T. crassiceps* were also unsuccessful. Voge (1963) reported development of buds of *T. crassiceps* cysticerci which were maintained in screw cap roller tubes at 37° C in a tissue culture medium consisting of Earle's balanced salt solution, lactalbumen hydrolysate, gelatin, yeast extract and γ-globulin calf serum. Survival of cysticerci varied from 1 to 4 months. She found that the media which Berntzen and Mueller (1963) used successfully for the pseudophyllidian cestode, *Spirometra*, was not successful when used with the cyclophyllidean *T. crassiceps*. Voge was careful to insure that the gas phase contained at least 5% CO_2 and that the medium was buffered with sodium bicarbonate. She also reported that antibiotics appeared to have an adverse effect on growth and found it necessary to carry out her studies under axenic conditions.

2. *Hymenolepis*

Historically, one of the first records of successful growth of a cyclophyllidean cestode *in vitro* is that of Schiller *et al.* (1959) who used *Hymenolepis diminuta* as a test organism. They severed the scolex and a small portion of the neck from the strobila, washed it in several changes of sterile Ringer's solution and inoculated it into Gey's solution in a roller tube at 38° C. In a mixture of Gey's balanced salt solution with glucose and 50% horse serum and in a similar media which was supplemented with a mixture of vitamins, amino acids, pyrimidines, salts and glucose, they recorded an increase in size by the 11th day with strobilization occurring in most media. Addition of an extract of cestode tissue to the 50% horse serum supported best growth with a thirty-fold increase in size. As many as 130 segments formed with some differentiation of reproductive organs in the best cultures. The report adds support to the findings of Smyth (1958) who originally used fragments of larger tapeworms as test organisms for studies of media and culture technique.

Taylor (1961) reported on an extensive series of experiments in which she attempted to cultivate the early stages of *H. diminuta* and *H. nana*. She used both sterilized cysticercoid and precysticercoid stages which were dissected from the beetle intermediate host. In addition to balanced salt solution the media included such components as CEE, extracts from *Tribolium* larvae, extracts of the intestine of rat or mouse, and extracts of whole tapeworms as well as bacterial metabolites from bacteria isolated from the small intestines of rats and mice. Both static and roller tube cultures were used but no significant development of the cysticercoid or precysticercoid stages was obtained. Cysticercoid larvae of *H. diminuta* were maintained *in vitro* for 6 days at 25° C in a simple media containing proteose-peptone, Ringer's solution, and glucose. After this time *in vitro* the larvae were still infective to rats. When rat serum was added to the medium, the larvae remained infective for 6 days at 30° C but not at 25° C. Cysticercoid larvae of *H. nana* survived for 5 days *in vitro* at 25° C and were still infective to mice at the end of this period. Juveniles of *H. diminuta* and *H. nana* survived for 7 and 9 days *in vitro* respectively at 38° C. Some growth of *H. nana* juveniles occurred when an extract of mouse intestine was added to a medium containing horse serum and medium 199 supplemented with amino acids. No information on the gas phase was given in this report. Prior to cultivation of the cysticercoid stages they were artificially excysted by the technique of Rothman (1959).

Berntzen (1960, 1961) reported a dramatic breakthrough on the *in vitro* culture of excysted cysticercoids of *H. diminuta* through to the adult stage containing developing onchospheres. Using a continuous flow culture apparatus, Berntzen succeeded in obtaining adult worms which after 15 days *in vitro* showed normal segmentation, scoleces and mature segments containing well-developed gonads which could not be differentiated from worms which were grown in the normal rat host. The medium consisted of two main parts: (1) a base medium which consisted of human plasma and Tyrode's balanced salt solution, to which was added (2) cysteine hydrochloride, thyroxin, thyamine, nicotinic acid, methyl testosterone, riboflavin, bacto-yeast extract and 10% by volume of CEE. The base medium was prepared by mixing human plasma with Tyrode's solution in a 1:1 ratio and allowing it to stand until a gel formed. This gel was broken up by violent shaking and the resulting liquid filtered. It is Berntzen's view that this medium contains an aggregate of essential materials which must be added in the proper sequence. Serum was used to replace whole blood plasma but without success in inducing development of the cestode. If CEE or yeast extract were omitted or added before the blood plasma and Tyrode's solution had gelled, no active growth occurred. The methyl testosterone was added because of studies by previous workers who observed that gonadectomized hosts did not support optimal growth of the tapeworm *in vivo*. Some growth was obtained *in vitro* without methyl testosterone but differentiation of the young proglottid was inhibited. Experimentation revealed that when larvae were cultured in flask tubes or petri dishes with the same medium and temperatures, no growth or differentiation was obtained. Berntzen suggests that the continuous moving of the medium and the constant removal of metabolic waste products are essential for success. He pointed out that this closely simulates the conditions which the cestodes encounter in the intestine of the host animal. He also observed that if single individuals were inoculated into the culture tubes, no growth was obtained. Usually twenty larvae per tube were inoculated and resulted in the successful recovery of two to six adult worms. No information was indicated as to the control of the gas phase but 1 N NaHCO₃ was used during the excystment process.

Berntzen (1962) applied the technique which he used for *H. diminuta* to the *in vitro* cultivation of *H. nana* beginning with the cysticercoid stage. He improved the culture apparatus and developed a re-circulation system which enabled him more adequately to control the gas phase and to re-utilize media if desired. Using a medium which consisted of balanced salt solution, amino acids, carbohydrates, Kreb cycle intermediates, vitamins and agamma calf serum, he cultured from the cysticercoid stage of *H. nana* apparently normal adult tapeworms which contained viable eggs that were proved to be infective for the beetle intermediate host. The *in vitro* culture period was only slightly longer (1–2 days) than that which took place in the normal definitive host. Investigation of the gas phase underlined the importance of CO_2 and the sensitivity of these organisms to too high a concentration of oxygen. The optimal gas phase consisted of 95% nitrogen and 5% CO_2. Air or 100% CO_2 or 100% nitrogen were found to be deleterious to the cestode. Contrary to the apparent experience of Taylor (1961), Berntzen found that antibiotics were inhibitory, if not toxic, to both *H. nana* and *H. diminuta in vitro*. He further determined that 39° C was a better culture temperature than 37° C, obtaining 11% more positive cultures at the higher temperature. Also the average number of recovered worms per unit or per culture tube, was 6% higher at 39° than at 37° C. With *H. nana* and *H. diminuta* he found that the first 3–5 days were critical and if worms survived this early period they could be carried to egg bearing adult stage without further loss. B vitamins and carbohydrates as well as amino acids and ribonucleic acid components as well as adenosine triphosphate were found to be essential elements of the medium. If sodium chloride was raised beyond a concentration of 7 g/l, only dead worms were found after 48 h of culture. In a more completely defined medium the agamma calf serum was found to be necessary and in its absence the cestodes could be maintained for 5 days or more; however, any increase in calf serum beyond this point had no effect. When Kreb cycle intermediates were omitted from the more completely defined media, survival for only 4–5 days was achieved. One further point of interest in the culture technique should be mentioned and that is the method of lining the culture tubes with filter paper to give the strobilar scolex a site for attachment. It is possible that the physical situation of the worm as well as the gas phase and other aspects of this continuous flow apparatus are essential elements in triggering the growth and stimulating differentiation even if the media components are not entirely satisfactory for the optimal physiological state of the developing worm. Berntzen's technique should be exploited in the investigation of many aspects of host–parasite relationships with other parasitic helminths.

3. *Echinococcus*

Echinococcus granulosus and *E. multilocularis*, as parasites of public health importance, have been the object of much study since the end of the 19th century. Dévé and Coutelen in the early 1920's published reports on the survival of larval scoleces in a variety of host fluids. This work is reviewed in detail by Rausch and Jentoft (1957) and by Smyth (1962b).

The first report on significant success in the *in vitro* cultivation of an *Echinococcus* species was that of Rausch and Jentoft (1957) who worked with *E. multilocularis* in Alaska. This is a parasite which is found in a wide variety of mammals including man. Rausch and Jentoft experimented with a variety of culture media. Their basic medium consisted of 40% human ascitic fluid and Hanks' basic salt solution. A second variety was one in which Hela cells were maintained under normal tissue culture conditions. Other media contained various concentrations, not specified, of extract of vole embryo (*Microtus*) or human plasma. Static culture tubes were used and maintained at 35° C. Media were changed every 3 or 4 days whenever the drop in pH indicated that this was necessary. In some cases the pH was adjusted by the addition of 5% carbon dioxide in air. Preliminary experiments with the larval scoleces of *E. multilocularis* indicated that they were able to maintain them in an apparently normal appearance for up to 60 days, although motility was observed only for the first seven days *in vitro*. Some of their most interesting experiments were with cestode larval tissue which was removed from the liver of recently infected rodents and which was divided into small pieces with scissors and introduced into culture tubes through a pipette. The finely divided cestode larval tissue developed vesicles *in vitro* which were recognized on the 22nd day in tubes which contained Hela cells and vole embryo extract as a culture medium. The cestode vesicles were embedded in the layer of the Hela cells on the surface of the tubes. On the 29th day the proliferation of larval vesicles was well advanced, and by the 30th day some of the larger vesicles contained in their walls bodies identified as calcareous corpuscles which appeared to be identical in structure and appearance with those seen at a similar stage of development *in vivo*. Observations on the 34th day revealed that the germinal membrane was well developed and appeared cellular. An immature, but well developed, scolex was also seen in one of the sectioned vesicles removed for histological observation. After 42 days of cultivation in the Hela cell and vole embryo extract medium numerous separate vesicles were seen and scoleces were readily observable in the larger vesicles.

When *in vitro* cultivated vesicles and cestode tissue were injected into lemmings, they were found to be infective and produced masses of vesicles in the subcutaneous tissues at the site of injection.

Rausch and Jentoft reported that the longer periods of cultivation resulted in problems of overgrowth from the Hela cells and these observations were best carried out with a medium which consisted of human ascitic fluid and Hanks' solution. In this medium from the 73rd to 120th day vesicles with scoleces were also observed. Although this rate of development was slower than that observed in the Hela cell and vole embryo extract medium, the physico-chemical conditions and nutrient material were apparently adequate for the development of vesicles and scoleces from macerated larval cestode tissue. Rausch and Jentoft point out that the larvae of *E. multilocularis* are capable of proliferating in a variety of mammals which are widely separated phylogenetically and that this potential capacity might be the reason why they obtained their success in *in vitro* conditions since it would follow that this cestode enjoys a wide tolerance of adverse circumstances.

Yamashita *et al.* (1962) utilized the technique described by Rausch and Jentoft (1957) to investigate *in vitro* secondary vesiculation of intact larval scoleces of *E. multilocularis*. (For those who are not familiar with this species of tapeworm it should be mentioned that when larval scoleces, "hydatid sand", is injected into the peritoneal or thoracic cavities of a suitable inter-mediate host it leads to the development of secondary hydatidosis. When hydatid sand is ingested by a definitive host the scoleces strobilate and became adult worms. Larval scoleces therefore possess this double potential depending upon the environment to which they are exposed.)

Yamashita and his co-workers investigated a variety of media whose ingredients included 0·5% lactalbumen and Hanks' basic salt solution to which bovine serum, bovine bile and mouse liver extract were added at various concentrations. The serum was inactivated at 56° C for 30 min before use and all other materials were Seitz filtered. Media was changed at intervals of 1–3 days as was indicated by the pH which they attempted to maintain at 7·4. They found that bovine serum was a necessary constituent for the survival of scoleces. The highest yield of vesiculated scoleces was obtained in a medium which consisted of 0·5 lactalbumen and Hanks' solution combined with 20% bovine serum and 10% liver extract. In this medium they were able to dis-tinguish three different types of vesiculation. By about the 45th day, they obtained complete hydatid cysts with recognizable germinal layers resembling early alveolar hydatid cyst formation. In cysts of 60–100 days of age, germinal layers could be definitely identified since they gave rise to early brood cap-sule formation. In some cysts the thick cuticular layer was lined with germinal cells. Calcareous corpuscles were found similar to those reported by Rausch and Jentoft. Not all larval scoleces tended to vesiculate into alveolar hydatid cysts, some apparently were predisposed to develop into adult stages. In these forms, scoleces evaginated and movements comparable to the undula-tions observed with adult tapeworms was observed. No formation of seg-ments nor any indication of strobilization was seen. By about the 40th day all movements of non-vesiculating scoleces ceased and hooks became detached from the rostellum. This process was quickly followed by degeneration, swelling and disintegration.

Smyth (1962b) in a carefully executed series of experiments undertook to develop a technique and to investigate the conditions for the *in vitro* culture of *E. granulosus* protoscoleces (= scoleces of Yamashita *et al.*, 1962). Smyth's work, which was carried out with *E. granulosus* protoscoleces obtained from the lungs or livers of sheep or cattle, is remarkably similar to that of Yamashita and his co-workers. Brood capsules were recovered from hydatid cysts and treated with a protease for short periods of time until the germinal layer was disintegrated and the protoscoleces freed. These were then inoculated into a variety of media which were maintained under two different conditions of agitation and rotation. Smyth indicates in his paper that he used rather high concentrations of antibiotics in his media which are stated to be 10 000 units of penicillin and streptomycin per ml. The media consisted of various combinations of the following components: bovine amniotic fluid, hydatid fluid, bovine serum, beef embryo extract, chick embryo extract and medium 199. Smyth determined that a medium consisting of 10% bovine embryo extract plus 50% hydatid fluid plus 40% bovine serum provided the greatest degree of mitotic stimulation, growth and differentiation. CEE appeared to be unsatisfactory and inhibitory to the development of the protoscoleces. Smyth's best medium is remarkably similar to that of Yamashita *et al.* and development time was approximately the same. Smyth did not observe any predisposition of the protoscoleces to develop into adult stages, they either underwent vesiculation or degenerated. The types of vesicular formation described by Yamashita *et al.* were also observed by Smyth. The plates illustrating the work of these two studies show marked resemblances in the formation of the two major types of vesicles from the protoscoleces and also the development of laminated membranes around the developing vesicle. It appears that Smyth did not have access to the paper by Yamashita since he points out that the differences between the unilocular and multilocular forms of cyst formation might be due to the way in which the laminated membrane is formed by the secretion process of the parasite. Basing his discussion on the work of Rausch and Jentoft (1957) who studied macerated tissues and *not* intact scoleces, he suggests that since under *in vitro* culture conditions *E. multilocularis* does not secrete a laminated membrane, this envelope formation "*appears to represent a fundamental difference in the growth pattern of the two species*" which could explain the form of the hydatid cysts in the intermediate host..." (Smyth's italics, 1962b). Unfortunately the photographs by Yamashita *et al.* clearly demonstrate the formation of laminated membranes around the vesiculated *multilocularis* cysts cultured *in vitro* indistinguishable from those illustrated by Smyth around *granulosus*.

Since the above was written (July 1964), Smyth (1964) has confirmed the similarities between his results and those obtained by Yamashita *et al.* Smyth points out that the scoleces represent embryos whose subsequent differentiation is stimulated and controlled by environmental factors. In this context they offer a challenge to experimental embryologists. It is to be hoped that more workers will take up the challenge offered by the *in vitro* culture approach to invertebrate embryology.

Webster and Cameron (1963) published an account of their extensive experiments carried out over a 4-year period during which they investigated the ability of forty-six different media to provide a suitable *in vitro* environment for the further development of (1) intact scoleces of *E. granulosus* and *E. multilocularis*, of (2) minced tissues obtained from *E. multilocularis* and of (3) hatched onchospheres of *Echinococcus*. They also experimented with intact cysts of *E. multilocularis*. One of the chief aims of their work was to induce scoleces to develop into adult tapeworms. The full details of the media, their techniques and the types of experiments which they undertook are difficult to summarize and interested workers are urged to consult the original text.

Webster and Cameron (1963) obtained *E. granulosus* cysts from man, elk and reindeer. *E. multilocularis* was maintained in laboratory rodents and most of the work was done with this species. Because of evidence that the parasite alters physiologically during maintenance in the laboratory by consecutive serial passages, they worked only with material of primary cystic origin or first transfer origin. The cestode material to be cultured was held under a loosely fitting layer of perforated cellophane in tubes which were kept stationary in an upright position. When studying the development of vesicles it was found that any type of agitation caused new vesicles to break off from the original cyst and for this reason tubes were kept stationary. When minced *E. multilocularis* tissue was used for experiments they were kept under a layer of perforated cellophane in a flask and held in a horizontal position either stationary or on a rocking machine. They investigated the use of a perfusion apparatus similar to that described by Berntzen (1961) but found it impractical and unnecessary for their purposes. Using synthetic medium 150, they found that small intact *E. multilocularis* cysts (0·32, 0·5 cm) produced new vesicles in culture. The production of vesicles was greatly enhanced by the substitution of glycogen for glucose as described in the original medium (Morgan *et al.*, 1955). The optimum pH for vesicle development was at 7·4 with no vesiculation taking place at a pH lower than 7. They found that when any concentration of serum was added ranging from 2·5 to 20%, no vesicles developed. In their modified Morgan medium, M 150, proliferation of vesicles first appeared on the 4th or 5th day. The fragile thin walled vesicles appeared to be restricted to one specific area on the parent cyst, gradually they increased in size and in a single instance scoleces developed. Vesicle formation usually ceases after 14 days and the cysts rapidly degenerate. When new vesicles become separated from the original cystic mass, they continue to develop and produce secondary vesicles. Webster and Cameron noted that cysts of definite primary origin which had been removed from liver had a greater capacity for vesicle production than the small cysts which they found throughout the abdominal cavity of the rodent host. Of all the cysts cultured only a maximum of 5% of any inoculum underwent development as described above.

Using undifferentiated cystic material in the same media as described above, Webster and Cameron obtained development of massive new vesicles within 3 weeks.

Webster and Cameron obtained evidence which suggests that the use of antibiotics for the washing or maintenance of bacteristatic conditions had an adverse effect on the development of the tapeworm. When penicillin and streptomycin were used for washing purposes and in the media, *E. multilocularis* scoleces developed abnormal appendages and secondary heads with suckers. Once the practice of using antibiotics was discontinued no further abnormal developments of this sort were observed.

E. multilocularis scoleces vesiculated in most culture media that were tested and Webster and Cameron concluded that this was a normal response to an unfavorable habitat. They observed the same type of vesiculation that was described by Smyth (1962b) and Yamashita *et al.* (1962) with the formation of laminated envelopes and vesicles either by swelling of the scolex or protoscoleces or by secondary constriction and vesiculation. Ultimately the vesiculated cyst absorbs the suckers and sheds the rostellar hooks.

In cysts which were maintained for 3 or 4 weeks localized internal thickenings developed which they interpreted to represent areas of future scolex formation.

Using a medium which consisted of Morgan's M 150 and including supplements of biotin, vitamin C, vitamin B_{12}, a co-enzyme solution consisting of TPN, co-enzyme A, cozymase and Na taurocholate, glucosamine, cholic acid, ADP, glucose, bacto-yeast, bacto-peptone, lactalbumen hydrolysate and 5% bovine serum, the scoleces evaginated and remained motile for 7 weeks increasing in size and developing two or three segments. The medium was changed daily and some of the used medium was reserved for metabolic studies and chromatographic analysis. Two segments appeared at the end of 14 days and three at the end of 3 weeks which is comparable to the rate of development within the normal canine host. The worms attained a maximum length of 0·55 mm. No development occurred beyond this stage and the scoleces remained in this state for another 4 weeks before degenerating. No evidence of gonad development was observed in any of the media which they employed. Experiments with synthetic medium CMRL-1066 described by Parker (1961) gave them the best result in their attempts to strobilate *E. multilocularis* scoleces. In this medium by the end of the first week the scoleces increased in size from 0·25 to 0·42 mm and in most cases the granules disappeared from the tissues of the scoleces and the excretory system became well developed but no further development was evident, with vesiculation and degeneration occurring after 14 days. However, in one case a single worm which had segmented was collected from a culture tube that had been lined by paper. This worm had developed to the 3 segment stage after 17 days. The third and most mature segment showed evidence of organogeny. Addition of meat digests and other extracted materials to the CMRL-1066 medium increased the longevity of the scoleces and initiated segmentation as early as 3 or 4 days after culture. By the 7th day, the length of the worms had increased to 0·57 mm and the excretory system was well developed with segmentation becoming apparent. Both horse and human serum were unfavorable in the medium and when serum was useful, the result with pooled bovine serum was equal to that obtained with agamma calf serum. As previously stated concentrations of over 5% serum produced adverse effects on the developing cestode.

The pH of the medium was critical in determining the developmental course of the scoleces. A slightly acid condition was necessary for tapeworm development with an optimum of about 6·8. If the pH of the medium was raised to neutrality, vesiculation occurred. At pH of 5 or 8 all scoleces died within 48 h. The number of worms in a solution was important and too few or too many produced early death and degeneration with vesiculation. No significant differences were noted between the development of *E. granulosus* and *E. multilocularis* scoleces in the media which they tested.

They also undertook attempts to cultivate hatched oncospheres of *E. multilocularis* and obtained early thin walled vesicles after 13 days in a medium which consisted of M 150 plus biotin and glycogen.

Using two of their simplified media, they carried out paper chromatographic studies to determine metabolic changes occurring during cultivation of the scoleces. They noted that there was a decrease in arginine, glutamine, aspartic acid, threonine, phenylalanine and increases in glycine and alanine when used media were compared with control media. Chromatograms to investigate changes in carbohydrates were negative for sugars when the control medium was tested which contained only glycogen; however, when glucose was added evidence of the presence of maltose was obtained.

Webster and Cameron found that segmentation occurred only in media in which sodium taurocholate had been present. They associated this with the fact that the canine host in which scoleces normally develop into adult tapeworms contains no glycocholate in the bile and only sodium taurocholate. They suggested that the sodium taurocholate bile salt acts as a surface active agent which allows freer exchange through the cestode cuticle, and they speculated that although the scoleces grew and segmented the development of the genital structures might require a specific substance such as a hormone.

VII. TREMATODES

A. STRIGEIDAE

Ferguson (1940) reported on the maturation of the progenetic larvae of *Posthodiplostomum minimum in vitro* to the egg- and spermatozoa-producing stages. *P. minimum* is normally infective for the heron which ingests the metacercariae from various species of fish. It is possible to maintain this parasite in chicks as well as heron and for this reason Ferguson felt that it might be a more useful parasite for study in attempts to induce maturation under artificial conditions. The metacercariae were recovered from fish where they encysted in a hyaline membrane. They were treated with a sterile pepsin solution which digested the cyst wall and freed the worms which were washed a number of times in sterile Ringer's solution to free them from any adhering bacteria. Static culture conditions were used and anaerobic and aerobic conditions were tested. An advantage of working with *P. minimum* was that excysted and sterilized metacercariae could be stored for up to 1 month in Tyrode's solution in a refrigerator for use when convenient. Of the various physiological salt solutions investigated, Tyrode's appeared to be the most suitable for survival. To Tyrode's solution was added varying amounts of horse serum, rabbit serum, extracts of chicken liver, kidney, duodenum, muscle, ovary, pituitary gland and extracts of 10-day-old chick embryos. Sterilized excysted metacercariae were inoculated into the chorioallantoic membrane of some 10-day-old chick embryos and some were inoculated into the liquid below the membrane. In all of the media described above the metacercariae died without any sign of development after 2 days of incubation. No improvement in these results were observed when the viscosity of the medium was increased either by means of agar or coagulated blood serum or egg white. Survival up to 2 weeks without development was obtained in a medium consisting of Tyrode's solution to which was added some defibrinated blood from unfed 3-day-old chicks. With Tyrode alone survival of metacercariae was of the order of 2 or 3 days. Success was finally obtained in a medium which consisted of Tyrode's solution to which was added either 2% bovine ovarian extract or yeast extract or ground heat-killed yeast. In this medium marked development took place after about 10 days of incubation and a few worms became adults producing eggs and spermatozoa. It was subsequently determined that dilution of the Tyrode's solution with distilled water in the ratio of 5:3 was advantageous. When serum from chicks up to the age of 6 months and unheated yeast extract was added conditions were obtained that were suitable for the survival of large numbers of metacercariae which developed into adult stages. The pH of this medium was about 6·5, which Ferguson points out is comparable to the pH near the middle of the duodenum where the adults of *P. minimum* are found in chicks. When serum was used which had been obtained from young black-crowned night herons, the trematodes were inhibited and it was suggested that the serum contained toxic substances, probably antibodies. In the normal heron host *P. minimum* produced about eight eggs whereas in the chick the number of eggs are reduced to between two and six. In the heron the fertile eggs normally appear in the feces 35–40 h after infection whereas in the chick this does not occur with such regularity but may be found in the feces 2–7 days after infection. The usual time for development of eggs in *in vitro* cultured metacercariae was about 10 days. The time of development *in vitro* was somewhat improved and this was eventually reduced to about 4 days which brings it to within the chick period. When compared with the normal adults found in the heron, gametogenesis of chick forms and those which develop *in vitro* were definitely abnormal. No active spermatozoa were recovered from the *in vitro* cultured forms and adults maturing in chicks and *in vitro* showed conspicuously less vitellaria when compared with the heron forms. Eggs which were obtained in culture, although normal in size, were not normal in shape and no development of miracidia was obtained under the conditions which normally would have been satisfactory for eggs recovered from the feces of the heron.

Later, Ferguson (1943a) working with the eye flukes of fishes showed that the cercariae of these species of *Diplostomum* were infective for a wide variety of animals including frogs, turtles, birds and mammals. When *Diplostomum* cercariae were injected into the orbit of the eye or were placed on the cornea, they penetrated and found their way into the lens where they developed into metacercariae which were later found to be infective for baby chicks. They developed into normal adult worms in the chick and eggs were recovered after 1 week. This technique was used to produce large numbers of axenic cercariae for *in vitro* culture conditions. Ferguson (1943b) prepared tissue cultures of various lens tissues obtained from fishes, rats, rabbits and cattle which together with Tyrode's or frog Ringer's solutions provided a suitable environment for the *in vitro* development of the cercariae to the meta-

L*

cercariae stage. The combination of salt solutions and source of lens tissue was critical since it was found that metacercariae failed to develop in lenses obtained from trout or rabbit or a bovine source when Tyrode's solutions was used. However, development was successfully obtained when the salt solution was replaced with frog Ringer's. Tyrode's was effective as a salt solution when either sunfish or rat lenses were used. The infectivity of the metacercariae developed in *in vitro* culture experiments was tested by feeding large numbers of these larval worms embedded in the bodies of small rainbow trout to laughing gulls or by injecting them directly into the duodenum of 2-day unfed baby chicks. No adult stages were recovered in any of these experiments. It would appear that the metacercariae which appeared morphologically normal were, for reasons not apparent, not infective to the vertebrate host. The reasons for this failure in obtaining fully infective progenetic larvae are difficult to understand since the size of the metacercariae were well within the normal range and the survival rate after development appeared to be good. The lens tissues appeared to provide the nutrient material required, because the addition of chick serum or yeast extract or bovine aqueous or vitreous humor did not improve the rate of development or survival time. Development of metacercariae took place even when the lens tissue had disintegrated or became opaque. Because of the considerable amount of work which has recently been done on the nature of lens tissue this would appears to be a useful medium constituent for further investigation.

Bell and Hopkins (1956) studied *in vitro* culture conditions for the strigeid metacercariae of *Diplostomum phoxini*. This species occurs as an adult in the duodenum of ducks and its metacercarial stage occurs in the brains of minnows. The metacercaria is apparently much less developed than that of *Posthodiplostomum minimum* with which Ferguson (1940) worked and the maturation of the adult form in the definitive host requires 3–4 days. Initial attempts to discover the conditions necessary for the maturation of these metacercariae were concerned with determining whether an exogenous energy substrate in balanced saline solutions was required. It was soon found that using salt solutions at either normal or three-quarter strength which included Locke, Tyrode's or Earle's and Hanks', the metacercariae died within 18 h. When 1% glucose was added to the various balanced salt solutions longevity of the flukes was greatly increased. In some cases they were still active after 144 h. The larvae in cultures were not affected by pH differences between 6·3 and 7·5. Using Tyrode's salt solution with 1% glucose as a basic medium various serum and embryo extract supplements were added. A standard set of cytological criteria were determined. This involved the use of colchicine to inhibit metaphase chromosomes which were then stained for microscopic examination. Media which contained serum showed a definite stimulus to nuclear activity. The addition of CEE added at a 4% level appeared to have no effect. Subsequent experimentation revealed that a medium consisting of duck serum plus approximately 10% of unfertilized duck egg yolk and incubated at 39° C in roller tubes which were rotated at 15 rev/h in aerobic conditions stimulated a higher degree of development than that previously obtained in the more fluid media. In this medium, flukes examined after

48 h showed the presence of a few active sperm. No further development took place although the flukes were still alive after 5 days. Bell and Hopkins speculated that *D. phoxini* normally ingests only solid food and believed it possible that in a liquid medium the necessary substances could not be absorbed. No development of vitellaria or of eggs were observed in the *in vitro* cultured larvae.

The stimulatory effect of the complex viscous medium of egg yolk was confirmed by the work of Bell and Smyth (1958) and the results obtained by Bell and Hopkins (1956) were improved upon when the culture system was shaken discontinuously to simulate intestinal movement. Under these conditions mitosis counts increased to that approximating the range which occurred under *in vivo* conditions and the production of active spermatozoa and abnormal eggs took place. Bell and Smyth's (1958) most successful medium included yolk and albumen. Soon afterwards Hopkins, and his students investigated the nutritional factors supplied by the yolk medium and reported in a paper by Wyllie *et al.* (1960) that the effect of yolk in a medium consisting of glucose, balanced salt solution and albumen could be partially replaced by horse serum plus yeast extract and amino acids. Whereas in the albumen, glucose, balanced salt and yolk medium, 43% of the flukes showed development of eggs when cultured for 6 days at 40° C, when the yolk was replaced with the horse serum-yeast extract and amino acid mixture only 5% produced eggs. If the amino acid addition was omitted, only 1% of the flukes showed any evidence of eggs. If the yeast extract was omitted, no eggs were found. However, the effect of the amino acids apparently depended on the presence of horse serum and this combination together with yeast extract gave the best result in the absence of yolk. They noted great variability even in their best cultures between the individual flukes examined.

Williams *et al.* (1961) undertook to determine which fraction of the yeast extract was active and to discover to what extent a chemically defined supplement could replace it. They used as their basal medium balanced salt solution with 0·6% glucose, 25% horse serum, and 12% fresh hen egg albumen. They discovered that the yeast extract contained two active fractions, one of which was dialyzable and the effect of which could be replaced by the amino acids. The non-dialyzable fraction was found to be resistant to acid and alkaline hydrolysis and was basically charged. The activity of the non-dialyzible fraction appeared to be associated with a substance of a small molecular size and possibly bound to a larger molecule, since if the dialysis was preceded by mild acid hydrolysis, the activity was lost. The only B-vitamin which appeared to fit this description, vitamin B_6, when tested alone required a concentration greatly in excess of that which normally occurs in the yeast extract for any activity. Williams *et al.* concluded that there is some substance(s) in yeast extract other than the B-vitamin which is active in stimulating *D. phoxini* to mature.

The unpublished work of Bell and Smyth on the undifferentiated metacercariae of *D. phoxini* is detailed by Smyth (1959). He reported that after 1 h cultivation of the metacercariae in a semi-solid egg yolk medium, the fluke gut was filled with solid material. It was evident that this organism possessed enzyme systems which were capable of metabolizing highly complex media, because the results of mitosis counts rose to 50–100 after 1 h cultivation and approached the figure of approximately 150–200 obtained *in vivo*.

B. FASCIOLIDAE

1. *Fasciola*

Although *Fasciola hepatica*, the liver fluke of sheep and cattle, is one of the most readily available parasites, no systematic attempts at culturing *Fasciola in vitro* were made until Stephenson (1947) undertook work on the conditions under which adults survived *in vitro*. Flukes were obtained from the bile ducts of sheep or cattle which had been dead for 1–6 h. They were transferred to the laboratory in cold bile and washed repeatedly in saline before survival experiments in various solutions were started. Solutions were changed every 16–24 h and observations were made on the number of surviving worms.

Stephenson showed that Ringer's solution was a far from suitable inorganic salt medium and determined that the pH most favored for longevity was 8·2–8·6. The salt solution determined by Stephenson to be the most favorable included borate, the effect of which he felt was to control bacterial contamination which had a deleterious effect on the flukes. Survival was considerably prolonged by adding sugars to the salt solution and he found that monosaccharides were more effective than disaccharides. By using a ligaturing technique he was able to determine that monosaccharides and disaccharides entered the body of the adult through its cuticle and not necessarily through the digestive tract.

Wide ranges of various physico-chemical conditions were studied and no strong preference for osmotic conditions, potassium and sodium or calcium and sodium ratios were noted. However, a definite optimum pH of about 8·4 was determined and a temperature optimum of about 36° C was also observed. He noted that any attempt to reduce the aerobic conditions also decreased survival time.

The most satisfactory medium determined by Stephenson included NaCl, 150 mм; KCl, 10 mм; CaCl$_2$, 1 mм; borax, 6 mм; and glucose, 30 mм at pH 8·6. In this medium worms survived for about 60 h at a temperature of 36° C.

Dawes (1954) improved considerably on the survival time by using Hédon-Fleig solution. In this buffered, borate-free medium it was found that worms continued to live for more than 3 days and sometimes for 5 or 6 days without loss of movement or natural coloration. Dawes used an aseptic technique for the removal of flukes which were recovered from intact livers that were kept warm after their collection at the abattoir. He concluded that borate had an adverse effect on the fluke and that the shock of drop in temperature encountered by the technique described by Stephenson may have accounted in part for the short survival time. Dawes reported that in exceptional cases some flukes remained active for as long as 12 days.

Rohrbacher (1957) reported on his attempts to duplicate Stephenson's experiments and to improve on them by the addition of various additives to the salt solution described by Stephenson. Rohrbacher dissected flukes immediately from the livers which were removed from the carcass and transferred them to sterile saline solutions. They were maintained at approximately 37° C while collecting and during transit to the laboratory. The flukes were then transferred to a basic saline solution containing antibiotics in which they were held for 18–24 h. After this treatment period it was usually possible to remove bacteria-free flukes because those that were contaminated gave the appearance of small blanched areas. He found that several balanced salt solutions including Tyrode's were satisfactory in permitting the survival of the flukes *in vitro* for up to 21 days, although at this time they were in a deteriorating condition. Flukes that had no glucose or other substances available in solution failed to survive more than 72 h *in vitro*. The addition of a variety of amino acids either individually or in combination had no value for the prolongation of the survival period. The addition of cholesterol did not prolong survival but did extend the period of normal motility and color for $1\frac{1}{2}$ weeks. When the salt solution was supplemented with an autoclaved liver extract the period of normal motility and color was extended to 2 weeks and survival to 3 weeks. A commercial extract of liver was added and this together with the autoclaved extract plus glucose enabled the flukes to remain in good condition for 3 weeks and to survive up to 30 days. Tests with various tissue culture materials such as chicken plasma, horse serum and beef embryo extract had little beneficial effect on the *F. hepatica* adults. Rohrbacher repeated Stephenson's ligature experiments and confirmed his results. He found that glucose, fructose, and glycerol were the only compounds that would support the parasite for a 6-day period during which the ligature experiment was carried out. Lactose, ribose, maltose, lactose, and sucrose had little or no beneficial effect. His studies were also in agreement with Stephenson over the wide range of physico-chemical environments which the flukes tolerated. His observations also suggested that the flukes preferred an aerobic type of respiration. Although flukes were able to survive as long in anaerobic solutions as in aerobic ones, the motility, color and shape of the worms indicated a preference for an aerobic state.

The criteria for the maintenance of the adult condition used by Stephenson, Dawes, and Rohrbacher were approximately the same; motility, color, and general appearance. Dawes and Muller (1957) and Smyth (1962a), in reporting the results of Clegg have indicated, however, that physiological abnormalities can be detected after only 3 h of cultivation and that a more critical test of survival should be used. Clegg (unpublished, 1957) using Hédon-Fleig saline and fresh specimens of *F. hepatica* obtained from experimentally infected rabbits found an average period of survival of 18 days with a maximum of 34 days. Clegg used cellulose tubing as an artificial gut for *F. hepatica* which helped to give the flukes a surface for attachment.

Dawes and Muller (1957) extended the use of Hédon-Fleig saline solution as a suitable balanced salt solution for *in vitro* studies. Using the lung fluke of frogs, *Haplometra cylindracea* and adjusting the phosphate buffer to pH 8·2–8·4, they were able to maintain flukes in an active condition for up to 105 days at 20° C. The addition of 0·5% glucose seemed to have no effect, in contrast to their results with *Fasciola* which died after 48 h without glucose. Supplementation with beef extract or tryptose had only a slight beneficial effect increasing survival to 110 days. Histological examination of the testes revealed abnormalities of spermatogenesis but this first appeared after 5 days *in vitro* which is much later than the time observed in *Fasciola*.

2. *Fascioloides*

Friedl (1961a) was one of the first workers to attempt to culture *in vitro* the larval stages of a fascioloid parasite. Friedl worked with *Fascioloides magna* and recovered rediae from infected laboratory-reared snails, *Lymnaea stagnalis*. The rediae were washed in antibiotic solutions and in the experimental media to be tested. The criterion of survival was movement of the rediae which appeared to correspond with their general appearance of viability. Several physiological salt solutions were tested and a modified Ringer's was found to be the most satisfactory and was used as the balanced salt solution. It was found that rediae *in vitro* appeared to tolerate a pH range of 7–8. Antibiotics did not appear to have any effect on survival of rediae. The addition of a variety of complex media which included yeast extracts and peptones did not appear to have any beneficial effect on survival over that obtained in control salt solutions. The yeast extract, however, appeared to exert a very slight stimulatory effect. Tests with a number of single amino acids in the modified Ringer's solution resulted in longer survival times than in controls. Hydroxyproline, proline and serine appeared to be the most effective in enhancing survival times over that of the control. Other amino acids such as arginine glycine, isoleucine, leucine, lysine, methionine, threonine, valine, and the amide glutamine were indifferent or did not prolong survival as long as that obtained in the control balanced salt solution. Phenylalanine and tryptophane appear to have an adverse effect on the rediae. Since under optimal *in vivo* conditions, *F. magna* requires 49–58 days for cercarial production in the normal host, the survival period of up to 7 days did not allow for observations of significant development as distinct from survival times. Later, in a more careful repetition of this work Friedl (1961b) confirmed the activity of the amino acid and slightly improved the survival time when the concentration of the active amino acids was increased. Hydroxyproline and serine gave the most consistent increase in survival time over saline controls. He found that the inclusion of sugars and acetates had little if any effect on prolongation of survival.

It would appear most appropriate to mention here the work of Ingersoll (1956) who also studied the survival of rediae of *Cyclocoelum microstomum*. Ingersoll investigated a wide number of simple and complex media in various combinations. In these media all rediae behaved in a consistently similar manner—they show elongation and contraction for short periods of time but did not undergo any appreciable growth or development. Rediae lived in culture medium for as long as 14 days increasing in some cases from an initial length of 150 μ to approximately 300 μ after 8 days *in vitro*. Rediae maintained *in vivo* measured about 660 μ after 8 days. Ingersoll used a hanging drop technique and he began his cultures by using the miracidia that had been hatched from eggs. Although rediae emerged from the miracidial coat within a few hours after being placed in the culture medium, some remained partially or entirely enclosed in the coat for 3 or 4 days and some died before they emerged. It might be that a stimulation for development is required which is normally encountered *in vivo*.

C. SCHISTOSOMATIDAE

1. *Adults*

Because of the medical importance of the human blood fluke, there have been many attempts to maintain the adults for the purpose of testing anti-helminthic drugs. The first notable advance was that of Lee and Chu (1935) who describe a simple technique for maintaining schistosome worms *in vitro* for weeks and even months under sterile conditions. Lee and Chu's work was undertaken with *Schistosoma japonicum* adults recovered from rabbits 8–10 weeks after infection. The worms, after removal by aseptic techniques, were washed in sterile saline solutions and then transferred to various media. They found that almost any animal blood serum served as a satisfactory medium. Horse, sheep and rabbit serum as well as human ascitic fluid from cases of cirrhosis of the liver were employed with success. The addition of Locke's solution or dextrose did not improve the efficiency of the medium in prolonging survival time. None of the sera appeared to be superior in their ability to support survival. In ascitic fluid or serum, which apparently was not changed, worms lived for up to 21 days. When the medium was changed, however, it was possible to prolong the life of the schistosomes for more than 2 months. The best survival result was 82 days in rabbit serum which was renewed at 1- or 2-week intervals.

Ross and Bueding (1950), working with *Schistosoma mansoni* which they recovered by aseptic techniques from mice 6–8 weeks after infection, tested survival in a completely defined medium, in whole serum, and in serum ultrafiltrate. The chemically defined medium consisted of a balanced salt solution and buffer, amino acids, vitamins, and glucose. In this medium the schistosomes survived for only 12–18 h; whereas in the whole serum they survived for 14–18 days and in the ultrafiltrate serum 10–12 days. Ross and Bueding concluded that protein and other non-dialyzable components of serum were of little significance to the survival of the worms. The pH of batches of serum-ultrafiltrate varied considerably, from 7·8 to 9·5. In order to stabilize the pH, carbon dioxide was driven off by aeration and the pH adjusted to 8 with NaOH. However, this did not appear to improve the survival time of *S. mansoni* in the ultrafiltrate. By adding various components of the chemically defined medium to the serum medium no inhibition of survival was noted and it was concluded that the brief survival of worms in the defined medium was due to a nutritional inadequacy of the medium rather than to a toxic effect. Addition of certain aqueous extracts of muscle tissue resulted in an increase in survival time obtained with the ultrafiltrate. They also found that schistosomes could survive in 100% nitrogen for at least 5 days suggesting that they were capable of an anaerobic existence.

The development of a successful continuous flow apparatus for the maintenance of *S. mansoni* worms was described by Newsome and Robinson in 1954. In this apparatus and using horse serum and worms recovered 8 weeks after infection from hamsters, *S. mansoni* were maintained for 28 days during which time they retained their normal motor behavior patterns. Newsome and Robinson reported that some of their experiments were successful in sustaining activity in *S. mansoni* for up to 2 months. The rate of flow or withdrawal of fluid from their apparatus was approximately 5 ml of medium per day which satisfied the environmental requirements of five worms maintained in the observation chamber.

Robinson (1956) gave more details of the techniques for (1) recovery of the worms from the hamster, (2) the method of preparation of the apparatus, and (3) sterilization and introduction of the aseptically prepared schistosomes. He used a heparin-Tyrode solution which was sprayed over the viscera in the region of the portal vein to prevent coagulation of the whole blood during removal of the worms. Using horse serum as a basic medium, various modifications were tested. In a horse serum-Tyrode solution medium survival of worms for a few weeks was obtained, but the results were considered unsatisfactory because experiments were not apparently reproducible. Dilution of horse serum by the Tyrode's appeared to reduce its buffering capacity and pH changes were considerable. No improvement in survival was obtained when small quantities of hemoglobin were added. The addition of 0·1% glucose, however, significantly enhanced the activity of worms in horse or human serum as compared to serum medium alone. Egg-laying and copulation in *in vitro* cultures occurred in the manner described by Chu (1938) for *S. japonicum*. Any increase in temperature above 37° C was found to be deleterious to the worms, resulting in their death. On the other hand, if the worms were subjected to temperatures as low as 20° C for 12 h they survived and showed normal motor behavior patterns for a further period of 3 weeks when returned to their normal temperature of 37° C. Fluctuations in the pH of the serum glucose medium did not appear to have any harmful effects on the worms. In view of the significant enhancement effects of glucose an investigation was undertaken into the reserve of glycogen and the effect on this reserve during various period of *in vitro* maintenance. After 17 days in culture there was little significant loss in glycogen content of cultured worms when compared to worms removed at the same time from the hamster host.

Robinson (1958, 1960) modified the original continuous flow apparatus and made further observations on the conditions which affected copulation and egg-laying of the schistosomes maintained *in vitro*. He compared the activity of worms which were recovered from the hamster, mouse and multimammate rat. In addition to horse serum, he tested the effect of rat serum, rabbit serum, human serum, baboon serum, cotton rat serum and guinea-pig serum. Egg-laying appeared to be associated with copulation and Robinson suggested that the stimulus for egg-laying is a tactile one. Guinea-pig serum was by far the most suitable medium in which to obtain maximum egg production. Robinson concluded that the greatest number of eggs were laid in serum from animals which are poor hosts to *S. mansoni* and the smallest numbers are laid in serum from good hosts. He also reported that a small number of experiments were carried out on the maintenance of *S. japonicum in vitro* and egg-laying was seen to occur.

Ito *et al.* (1955) and Ito and Komiya (1955) reported on their attempts to maintain *S. japonicum* in blood or serum medium and also in chemically defined artificial medium. Adult *S. japonicum* worms were recovered from rabbits and guinea-pigs 6–11 weeks after infection. (The animals were killed by injecting air into blood vessels.) The schistosomes were maintained in Carrel flasks under static conditions. Antibiotics were used and aseptic techniques were employed. The motility of worms was used as a criteria for survival. Whole blood, defibrinated blood, red blood cells and serum derived from the horse were used in the natural medium constituents. The most effective medium was undiluted horse serum in which worms survived for up to 33 days without change of medium. When the medium was changed at regular intervals the life of the worms could be prolonged up to 64 days. The addition of pig embryo extract to the serum did not enhance survival. They claimed that the most effective temperature for maintaining the worms was 28° C. Sera from different horses were compared and found to yield slightly different survival results ranging between 10 and 60 days. The pH also varied in the various sera between 7 and 7·6.

In their studies on chemically defined medium they compared physiological saline, Locke's solution, Tyrode's and Ringer's. Ringer's solution was found to be the most effective salt solution for sustained survival of worms, and with the addition of 5% glucose and 1% asparagine female worms survived for 8 days (range of 5–12) at 28° C and males for 2·7 days (range of 2–4 days). The use of bovine serum albumin in a 50% Ringer's solution was not found to be better than the balanced salt solution alone. Ito and his co-workers investigated the effect of various culture temperatures including 8°, 18°, 28° and 38° C. Although the results at 28° were consistently better than those obtained at 38°, the use of this lower temperature is open to question.

The results obtained by those Japanese workers are quite remarkable when considered in comparison with those described by Ross and Bueding (1950) who used a chemically defined medium but got no more than 12–18 h survival. More recently Senft and Senft (1962) have utilized medium NCTC 109 which consists of twenty-six amino acids, a series of enzymes, co-enzymes, nucleic acid derivatives, vitamins, glucose, and glutamates in a balanced salt solution. A detergent agent, pH indicator and antibiotics were added to facilitate technical handling of the medium and introduction of the worms. In this medium adult *Schistosoma mansoni*, which were recovered from infected mice, survived 8–45 days with most worms being maintained between 15 and 25 days. Whole worms or fragments of worms seemed to survive with equal facility. The criterion of survival was movement of the somatic tissue and continued flexing and action of the gut. Worms were kept in tubes incubated at 37° C and the medium was changed every 2 days. The age of the worms was not indicated and this might, in part, be responsible for the great variation which was obtained. Egg-laying continued up to the 24th day and usually started after an initial "shock" period of 2–3 days; however, in one instance egg-laying did not occur until after the 17th day. Senft and Senft point out that the medium is far from optimal but that this offers a useful beginning for the development of a good chemically defined medium. As the eggs which were produced up to the 24th day *in vitro* must have been based at least partially on the ability of the worm to utilize medium constituents and to synthesize proteins, this medium offers the most hopeful experimental system yet devised for further investigation. Maximum production of eggs appeared to be about 100/day and occurred after 4–6 days *in vitro*. The eggs were uniformly non-viable and had an amorphous cell organization. On only a few occasions was any flame cell motion detected within individual eggs.

2. *Immature Forms*

One of the first recorded attempts to induce growth in young schistosomulae is that of Senft and Weller (1956) who worked with a culture medium which was used for the maintenance of human cells *in vitro*. It consisted of 45% bovine amniotic fluid, 45% Hank's balanced salt solution, 5% inactivated horse serum and 5% beef embryo extract together with antibiotics and a pH indicator. The medium was adjusted to about pH 7·4 prior to use by gassing with 5% CO_2 in air. Cultures were incubated at 37° C and medium was changed at 2–4 day intervals. Two age groups of schistosomulae were used in these experiments; one group was collected 6–10 days after infection in mice, and the second group was recovered on the 16th day after infection. The 6–10-day-old juveniles survived 3–10 days and increased in length several fold. Sixteen-day-old schistosomulae were found to survive much longer *in vitro*, some appearing to be active after 35 days of observation. By this time they had increased in length by up to 360% and worms which had lost part (one-half to one-third) of their body during handling underwent regeneration of the missing parts within 10–20 days of *in vitro* cultivation. Caeca and excretory canals were seen to regenerate in this medium. Red blood cells seemed to have a stimulatory effect and increased activity when added to the medium. In spite of the substantial increase in size and survival of the schistosomulae no significant differentiation or development was observed.

Robinson (1957) experienced similar difficulty in obtaining any significant development of young schistosomulae when maintained *in vitro*. He used immature forms recovered from the hamster 11 days after infection. The medium consisted of one part horse serum and two parts Tyrode's solution, to which was added 0·2% glucose. In this medium the young worms were extremely active, and although numerous additives were tried and the schistosomulae maintained *in vitro* for up to 58 days, few did more than double their size.

Cheever and Weller (1958) followed the lead provided by Senft and Weller (1956) and investigated various media and supplements in a complex series of experiments. Schistosomulae were usually recovered from mice 16–18 days after infection, and experiments were observed over a routine 4 week period. It was confirmed that the addition of red blood cells to the tissue culture medium as described by Senft and Weller stimulated the growth of schistosomulae. Most of this growth promoting activity appeared to be in the red cell membranes although the possibility of some residual hemoglobin could not be ruled out. The supernatant containing hemoglobin after hemolysis of red cells possessed only limited stimulatory activity. CEE was found to replace and to be superior to the red blood cell membranes. In a medium of horse serum, red blood cells and CEE, several worms increased in length from 1 mm to 7–8 mm. Human serum was found to be superior to horse serum and to the tissue culture medium. In medium 199, to which an equal volume of human serum had been added, an increase in the length of schistosomulae of over 600% in 3 weeks was obtained as opposed to a 300% increase when human serum and Hanks' solution was used. In spite of this considerable growth and development of schistosomulae *in vitro* no sexual maturation was observed. No growth occurred in mixture 199 alone and schistosomulae did not survive for more than 12 days. The addition of crystalline serum albumen to either 199 or Hanks' solution significantly prolonged survival of worms but no growth occurred.

In a medium consisting of serum, Hank's balanced salt solution and red blood cells and 0·25% lactalbumen hydrolysate, Clegg (1959) obtained rapid growth of young schistosomulae recovered from the lungs of mice. He reported development of young male worms with observable sperm, but although females formed a small ovary they did not develop vitellaria or lay eggs.

Later, Clegg (1964) improved on his 1959 results using an altered basic culture medium. His basic culture medium consisted of equal volumes of inactivated rabbit serum and Earle's saline plus 0·5% lactalbumen hydrolysate, 0·1% glucose, 1% rabbit red cells and antibiotics. Young schistosomulae recovered from mice 7 days after infection, were introduced into a cellulose-sac culture tube. The schistosomulae and rabbit blood were placed inside the sac which was immersed below the surface of the basic medium inside a screw top culture tube. By the use of CO_2 the pH of the medium was maintained at 7·4. The cellulose-sac culture apparatus was agitated in a water bath at 37° C to insure the rapid disperson of metabolites. The culture tube was spun at intervals so that the sedimented blood cells within the dialysis sac would form a source of nutrients available to the schistosomulae. The optimum development obtained *in vitro* compared favorably with that which was observed *in vivo*. The lung form developed to the second stage (gut formation stage) at a similar time; however, the difference between *in vitro* and *in vivo* development became apparent during the 3rd and 4th weeks. The worms cultured *in vitro* required 6 weeks to reach the stage which normally occurred in the mouse by the 4th week, although many of the *in vivo* stages might not be any further developed than those which were obtained *in vitro*. Individual female worms were found with developed eggs, but it was more usual to obtain worms showing signs of gametogeny and egg shell development only. Supplementation of the basic medium with 10% CEE and 100% liver extract or 0·1% purified liver extract did not prove to be effective and in fact appeared to be inhibitory when compared with the normal control medium.

Clegg attempted to apply his technique also to the cercarial stage and found that without prior penetration in mouse skin as a required stimulus, the cercaria would not undergo development *in vitro*. After allowing large numbers of cercariae access to the skin of the mouse and recovering them 30 min after penetration, it was found possible to induce their development *in vitro* at the same rate obtained with the schistosomulae recovered from the lungs. Clegg's investigation confirmed that the red cells stimulate growth of cultured *S. mansoni*, as was originally discovered by Cheever and Weller (1958). It was also found that the use of the lactalbumen hydrolysate as a source of amino acids provided an important nutrient source. When glucose was increased in concentration from 0·1 to 0·45% the rate of development was considerably slowed if the cultures were left in a static condition. Clegg's interpretation was that the conversion of glucose to lactic acid resulted in an inhibitory effect and required agitation to ensure the rapid removal of this metabolite. These results merit close attention and suggest strongly that the culturing *in vitro* of stages of *Schistosoma* which normally occur in the mammalian host is not far from achievement. Recent results by Chernin (1963) with the stages of *Schistosoma* which normally occur in the snail may mean that within the foreseeable future it will be possible to culture all stages of this trematode *in vitro*.

A technique of interest in the cultivation of cercariae is that reported by Jensen and Stirewalt (1963), who used a diffusion chamber with cellophane membrane sides within which the cercaria were maintained. When bathed by medium 199 and maintained on a tissue explant, cercariae were reported to live for up to 22 days with some evidence of development. Another medium employed consisted of medium 199 plus 20% calf serum and 5% whole egg ultrafiltrate plus antibiotics. Unlike the results reported by Clegg, the cercariae cast their tails and evacuated their acetabular glands assuming the appearance of schistosomulae recovered normally from the lungs of an infected animal.

D. OTHER TREMATODES

Special mention can be made of the work by Yokogawa *et al.* (1955, 1958) with metacercariae of *Paragonimus westermani* recovered from infected cats. In Tyrode's solution regulated at a pH 7·4 and supplemented in various ways with horse serum, CEE and red blood cells, the excysted metacercariae were maintained for up to 203 days, by which time they had increased tenfold in size. Using cat serum and Tyrode's solution with red blood cells, the medium being changed at irregular intervals, metacercariae survived up to 75 days. No significant differences were found between serum from rabbit, horse, cattle, dog or cat, provided that it was inactivated.

Mention should also be made of the work by Fried (1962) who studied the survival of metacercariae of the ocular trematode *Philophthalmus* recovered from infected snails. Metacercariae did not survive in sea water for longer than 2 h; whereas, in 0·45 and 0·48% NaCl they survived for 12–24 h. In glucose sea water, flukes survived for up to 3 days. Longest survival was obtained in a serum-Tyrode's solution mixture in which one metacercaria survived for 7 days in unchanged medium. Another fluke survived for up to 9 days in a culture tube, the medium of which was changed every 3 days. In Tyrode's solution containing yolk albumen, the flukes were seen to ingest the proteinaceous nutrients and, although they survived for only 6 days, the posterior genital primordium appeared to show an increase by the 4th or 5th day. Work with immature adults resulted in survival for up to 5 days in medium 199 which was changed daily.

VIII. Acanthocephala

Work on the *in vitro* cultivation of species of *Acanthocephala* has been almost entirely restricted to the maintenance of adult or mature forms. Of the few papers in this area of research, the most significant is that of Dunagan (1962) who studied the survival of *Neochinorynchus emydis* and *N. pseudemydis* which are parasites of turtles. Mature worms were recovered from the small intestine of infected turtles and washed several times in sterile solutions containing antibiotics. Using Tyrode's solution, the survival of the Acanthocephala at various pH values was tested, and at pH 7·2 and 8·2 there was little difference in their ability to maintain motility for 19–21 days. When rendered sterile, mature acanthocephalan worms were placed in dialysis tubing immersed in a medium consisting of Tyrode's solution at pH 8·2 plus 11% turtle serum and 0·1–1% glucose and the worms survived for 71–75 days. The medium was changed every 7 days. In 100% turtle serum, without the dialysis tubing, the worms survived for up to 66 days with a mean survival period of 51 days. When tissue culture medium 199 at pH 7·8 was supplemented with 3·0% turtle serum and the media changed only once, the worms survived for as long as 90 days with a mean period of 64 days. Under these same circumstances if the media were not changed, survival was reduced to an average of about 33 days. In Eagle's Hela cell medium at pH 8 supplemented with 20% calf serum, survival was as good as that obtained with the 199 plus turtle serum medium. In view of the stimulatory effect of glucose, a further series of tests were carried out to see if this substance could be replaced by other carbohydrates. It was found that galactose, maltose and trehalose at the 0·1% concentration could replace glucose, no apparent differences being observed. Throughout the study no indication of growth was observed, but copulation and egg maturation occurred. Female worms which were examined during the 51st to 73rd day of survival contained motile sperm which were attached to developing ovarian balls. Eggs did not show any physical abnormalities, although their viability was not tested by feeding them to the intermediate ostracod hosts.

IX. Discussion

This review of recent literature shows good progress from the state of research summarized by Hobson (1948), who concluded that attempts to cultivate parasitic helminths *in vitro* "have met with an almost uniform lack of success". Today, although the task is " . . . not an easy one, there is little doubt that all parasitic organisms will be induced to survive, develop and reproduce *in vitro* when sufficient intelligent effort is applied" (Silverman, 1963a).

A. PRECULTURE TREATMENT

Work with progenetic cestode larvae (Smyth, 1946, 1959), infective nematode larvae (Silverman, 1963a) and trematode metacercariae (Ferguson, 1940) show that many infective stages contain substantial reserves which are capable of supplying the nutritional needs during early parasitic development. In such cases, for successful development *in vitro*, proper storage and preparation of the helminths and the provision of a suitable physico-chemical environment is all that is required to stimulate development and even maturation. Too much emphasis cannot be placed on the need to prepare carefully the helminth material so that it is in a suitable developmental and physiological state. In some instances, the primary challenge to the investigator is to simulate the conditions which operate *in vivo* to activate the biological clock and which "triggers" certain developmental processes (Rogers, 1962).

The excystment of metacercariae with the appropriate enzyme system, the hatching of eggs and exsheathment of nematode infective larvae with *natural* stimuli, the pretreatment of spargana with an evaginating solution (Berntzen and Mueller, 1963), all have been found to be necessary prerequisites to successful cultivation procedures. The use of "natural" stimulants as opposed to "unnatural" materials (e.g. CO_2 instead of hypochlorite for nematode exsheathment) is to be preferred. The finding, that schistosome cercariae require a penetration stimulus before further development *in vitro* takes place, would fit in well with the general picture (Clegg, 1964).

B. STERILIZATION

The introduction of antibiotics has contributed greatly to the successes accumulated since the 1940's in the field of parasitic helminth cultivation. Antiseptic solutions such as hypochlorite, formalin or White's (1932) solution had to be used at concentrations that may have been deleterious for the helminths or at best were on the borderline between a bactericidal and anthelminthic effect.

At the same time, caution must be exercised in the use of the antibiotic "umbrella" or "crutch". An impressive list of observations has been recorded concerning the adverse effects of antibiotics on helminths *in vitro*. Berntzen (1962) working with *Hymenolepis*, Voge (1963) working with *Taenia crassiceps* and Webster and Cameron (1963) who studied *Echinococcus* reported on the effects of penicillin and streptomycin which appeared to be inhibitory and to induce growth aberrations. Clegg (1964) found that *Schistosoma mansoni* was sensitive to chloromycetin. It is possible that antibody sensitivity may account for some of the failures reported, particularly with cestodes and trematodes.

C. MEDIA AND CULTURE CONDITIONS

During the early development of mammalian tissue culture techniques and media, natural fluids, tissue homogenates and extracts played an important role in demonstrating the possibility of maintaining organ fragments and cells *in vitro* in a viable state. With the establishment of tissue culture procedures as a standard laboratory technique there followed the development of a number of chemically defined media which have provided a basis for the comparison of work carried out in different laboratories. The science and art of parasitic helminth cultivation is presently at the stage in some quarters of demonstrating its feasibility, but there are a number of encouraging signs of a still more sophisticated approach.

The lack of standards and the difficulty in reproducing even in the same laboratory comparable extracts of liver, or chick embryo, etc., limit the significance of important results. Reproducibility and standardization of media constituents depend upon the development of chemically defined media. In this regard, the work of Jackson (1962) with *Neoaplectana*, Berntzen (1962) with *Hymenolysis* and Cheevers and Weller (1958) with *Schistosoma* have special merit. Also of considerable importance to parasitologists are the nutritional studies that are being carried out with the free-living nematode, *Caenorhabditis briggsae*. These workers have developed a chemically defined basal medium which sustains partial growth but not reproduction until supplemented with small amounts of a liver protein fraction (Sayre *et al.*, 1963). This supplement has been purified and prepared as a discrete proteinaceous substance which, when added at the rate 100 μg/ml to the basal medium, supports serial subcultures. The use of the chemically defined medium for the cultivation of the free-living stages of *Nematospiroides dubius* has sustained development from the egg stage to the third stage infective larva (Hansen *et al.*, 1964). More recently this medium has been used to culture the parasitic stages of *Haemonchus contortus* and at the time of writing vigorous late fourth stage larvae showing signs of the fourth molt to the young adult stage have been observed (Hansen and Silverman, unpublished data). This defined medium has so far proved to be superior to the complex type previously used, as judged by the viability, vigour and stage of development obtained. It appears to offer to investigators a standard culture system for studies concerned with the metabolism, physiology and immunology of developing parasites. It is urgently suggested that this medium be tested for its ability to support growth of a wide range of parasites.

Experiences with complex media have indicated that success with one parasite will not necessarily lead to success with another in the same medium. Weinstein and Jones (1957b) found that the technique and media used successfully to culture *Nippostrongylus brasiliensis* was not suitable for either *Strongyloides ratti* or *Strongyloides* from the rhesus monkey. Leland (1963), using the medium which he developed for *Ostertagia*, was able to culture *N. brasiliensis* but not *Haemonchus contortus* or *Trichostrongylus axei*. In our laboratory *H. contortus*, *T. axei* and *Strongyloides papillosus* underwent parasitic development in simplified media after the appropriate exsheathment stimuli were provided, and subsequently they reached the young adult stage when transferred to complex media (Silverman and Podger, 1962; Silverman, 1963a). Our results indicated that direct introduction of these stages into complex medium without proper preparation and exsheathment inhibits development of the parasitic stages.

Of all the numerous physico-chemical factors which have been investigated, the gas phase is the most neglected or least controlled. The importance of CO_2 as a parasite stimulant has been well established, yet it has been often overlooked. It is significant that all successful reports of parasitic helminth cultivation have indicated that CO_2 was introduced with the media. Workers with the same species and with apparently similar media who have reported negative or only slightly encouraging results seem not to have given any attention to the gas phase. Gassing with a 5% CO_2 in air mixture is a standard procedure for tissue culture systems and should be adopted for parasitic helminth work.

D. FUTURE DEVELOPMENTS

The field of *in vitro* parasitic helminth cultivation has benefitted and should continue to benefit from developments in tissue culture techniques and other allied areas. The immediate goal is the development or adaptation of chemically defined media for use under axenic conditions.

The need to culture under axenic conditions is underlined by the reports of the adverse effects of antibiotics on certain helminths. Also, the determination of the value of various media constituents is complicated by the role that bacteria (even in a bacteriostatic state) play in altering media constituents and in providing an uncontrolled source of bacterial nutrient.

Nutritional tests for essential and non-essential components can only be carried out in defined or partially defined media. The difficulties and problems of nutritional imbalance under artificial culture conditions have been discussed by Sayre *et al.* (1963) who point out the need to consider limiting as well as absolute dietary requirements. These considerations should be borne in mind in any media evaluation studies. It must also be borne in mind that the developing parasite may very well be undergoing metabolic as well as metamorphic changes and transfer to new conditions at critical times might be necessary to successful cultivation.

The ultimate hope is that an understanding of the nutritional and environmental conditions which support growth and development *in vitro* might yield a clearer insight into the nature of the host–parasite relationship. In spite of the pessimistic conclusions of the microbiologists (Smith and Taylor, 1964), it is to be hoped that work with Metazoa may lead to more meaningful results because these organisms appear to be phylogenetically more committed and less plastic in metabolism than many micro-organisms.

REFERENCES

Ackert, J. E., Todd, A. C. and Tanner, W. A. (1938). *Trans. Amer. micr. Soc.* **57**, 292–296.
Anantaraman, M. (1942). *Indian J. vet. Sci.* **12**, 187–32.
Baer, J. G. (1952). "Ecology of Animal Parasites." University of Illinois Press, Urbana.
Baker, J. A. and Ferguson, M. S. (1942). *Proc. Soc. exp. Biol., N.Y.* **51**, 116–119.
Bell, E. J. and Hopkins, C. A. (1956). *Ann. trop. Med. Parasit.* **50**, 275–282.
Bell, E. J. and Smyth, J. D. (1958). *Parasitology* **48**, 131–148.
Berntzen, A. K. (1960). *J. Parasit.* **46**, (Suppl.), 47.
Berntzen, A. K. (1961). *J. Parasit.* **47**, 351–355.
Berntzen, A. K. (1962). *J. Parasit.* **48**, 786–797.
Berntzen, A. K. and Mueller, J. F. (1963). *J. Parasit.* **49** (Suppl.), 60.
Brooks, M. A. (1963). *In* "Symbiotic Associations." Cambridge University Press, London.
Cavier, R. and Savel, J. (1953). *Ann. Nat. Zool.* **15**, 57–70.
Cheever, A. W. and Weller, T. H. (1958). *Amer. J. Hyg.* **68**, 322–339.
Chernin, E. (1963). *J. Parasit.* **49** (Suppl.), 60.

Chu, H. J. (1938). *Chin. med. J.* Suppl. 2, 411–417.
Cleeland, R. (1963). *J. Parasit.* **49**, 64–68.
Cleeland, R. and Laurence, K. A. (1962). *J. Parasit.* **48**, 35–38.
Clegg, J. A. (1959). *Bull. Res. Counc., Israel* **8E**, 1–6.
Clegg, J. A. (1965). *Exp. Parasit.* **16**, 133–147.
Dawes, B. (1954). *Nature, Lond.* **174**, 654–655.
Dawes, B. and Muller, R. (1957). *Nature, Lond.* **180**, 1217.
Diamond, L. S. and Douvres, F. W. (1960). *J. Parasit.* **46** (Suppl.), 25.
Diamond, L. S. and Douvres, F. W. (1962). *J. Parasit.* **48**, 39–42.
Dougherty, E. C. (1953). *Parasitology* **42**, 259–261.
Dougherty, E. C. (1959). *Ann. N.Y. Acad. Sci.* **77** (Art. 2), 25–54.
Douvres, F. W. (1960a). *J. Parasit.* **46** (Suppl.), 25.
Douvres, F. W. (1960b). *J. Parasit.* **46** (Suppl.), 25–26.
Douvres, F. W. (1962a). *J. Parasit.* **48**, 314–320.
Douvres, F. W. (1962b). *J. Parasit.* **48**, 852–864.
Douvres, F. W. and Alicata, J. E. (1961). *J. Parasit.* **47** (Suppl.), 35.
Douvres, F. W. and Tromba, F. G. (1962). *J. Parasit.* **48**, 269.
Dunagan, T. T. (1962). *Proc. helm. Soc. Wash.* **29**, 131–135.
Earl, P. R. (1959). *Ann. N.Y. Acad. Sci.* **77** (Art. 2), 163–175.
Ellison, T., Thomson, W. A. B. and Strong, F. M. (1960). *Arch. Biochem. Biophys.* **91**, 247–254.
Fairbairn, D. (1960). *In* "Host Influence on Parasite Physiology" (L. A. Stauber, ed.). Rutgers University Press, New Brunswick, New Jersey.
Fairbairn, D. and Reesal, M. R. (1950). *Science* **112**, 792–793.
Ferguson, M. S. (1940). *J. Parasit.* **26**, 359–372.
Ferguson, M. S. (1943a). *J. Parasit.* **29**, 136–142.
Ferguson, M. S. (1943b). *J. Parasit.* **29**, 319–323.
Florsheim, H. A., Makineni, S. and Shankman, S. (1962). *Arch. Biochem. Biophys.* **97**, 243–249.
Fried, B. (1962). *J. Parasit.* **48**, 510.
Friedl, F. E. (1961a). *J. Parasit.* **47**, 71–75.
Friedl, F. E. (1961b). *J. Parasit.* **47**, 244–247.
Fulleborn, F. (1912). *Zbl. Bakt.* **66**, 255–267.
Gilmour, D. (1961). "The Biochemistry of Insects." Academic Press, New York and London.
Glaser, R. W. (1940). *Proc. Soc. exp. Biol., N.Y.* **43**, 512–514.
Glaser, R. W. and Copia, N. A. (1935). *Amer. J. Hyg.* **21**, 111–120.
Glaser, R. W. and Stoll, N. R. (1938). *Parasitology* **30**, 324–332.
Glaser, R. W. and Stoll, N. R. (1940). *J. Parasit.* **26**, 87–94.
Glaser, R. W., McCoy, E. E. and Girth, H. B. (1942). *J. Parasit.* **28**, 123–126.
Hansen, E., Yarwood, E. A., Buecher, E. and Sayre, F. W. (1964). *J. Parasit.* **50** (Suppl.), 26.
Harpur, R. P. (1962). *Canad. J. Zool.* **40**, 991–1011.
Haskins, W. T. and Weinstein, P. P. (1957). *J. Parasit.* **43**, 28–32.
Hobson, A. D. (1948). *Parasitology* **38**, 183–227.
Hobson, A. D., Stephenson, W. and Beadle, L. C. (1952a). *J. exp. Biol.* **29**, 1–21.
Hobson, A. D., Stephenson, W. and Eden, A. (1952b). *J. exp. Biol.* **29**, 22–29.
Ingersoll, E. M. (1956). *Exp. Parasit.* **5**, 231–237.
Ito, J. and Komiya, Y. (1955). *Jap. J. Parasit.* **4**, 258–261.
Ito, J., Yasuraoka, K. and Komiya, Y. (1955). *Jap. J. Parasit.* **4**, 12–18.
Jackson, G. J. (1961). *Exp. Parasit.* **11**, 241–247.
Jackson, G. J. (1962). *Exp. Parasit.* **11**, 25–32.

Jensen, D. V. and Stirewalt, M. A. (1963). *J. Parasit.* **49** (Suppl.), 61.
Johns, F. M. and Querens, P. L. (1914). *Amer. J. trop. Dis.* **1**, 620–624.
Kim, C. W. (1961). *Amer. J. trop. Med. Hyg.* **10**, 742–747.
Kim, C. W. (1962). *Amer. J. trop. Med. Hyg.* **11**, 491–496.
Komiya, Y., Yasuraoka, K. and Sato, A. (1956). *Jap. J. med. Sci. Biol.* **9**, 283–292.
Kovalevsky, A. and Kurlov, A. (1927). *Sibirsk. arkhiv. teoret. i Klinich. medito* **2**, 27–41. Cited in Krotov (1958).
Krotov, A. I. (1958). *Uspekhi sovremennoy biologii* **46**, 2, (5) 230–239.
Lapage, G. (1933a). *Rep. Inst. Anim. Path. Univ. Camb.* **3**, 237–271.
Lapage, G. (1933b), *Nature, Lond.* **131**, 583–584.
Lapage, G. (1935). *J. Helminth.* **13**, 115–128.
Lawrence, J. J. (1948). *Aust. J. exp. Biol. med. Sci.* **26**, 1–8.
Lee, C. U. and Chu, H. J. (1935). *Proc. Soc. exp. Biol., N.Y.* **32**, 1397–1400.
Leland, S. E., Jr. (1961a). *J. Parasit.* **47**, 623–624.
Leland, S. E., Jr. (1961b). *J. Parasit.* **47** (Suppl.), 21.
Leland, S. E., Jr. (1962). *J. Parasit.* **48** (Suppl.), 35.
Leland, S. E., Jr. (1963). *J. Parasit.* **49**, 600–611.
Levin, A. J. (1940). *J. Parasit.* **26** (Suppl.), 31.
McCoy, O. R. (1929a). *Amer. J. Hyg.* **10**, 140–156.
McCoy, O. R. (1929b). *Science* **26**, 74–75.
McCoy, O. R. (1936). *J. Parasit.* **22**, 54–59.
Mendelsohn, W. (1935). *J. Parasit.* **21**, 417.
Morgan, J. F., Campbell, M. E. and Morton, H. J. (1955). *J. nat. Cancer Inst.* **16**, 557–567.
Mueller, J. F. (1958). *J. Parasit.* **44** (Suppl.), 14–15.
Mueller, J. F. (1959a). *J. Parasit.* **45** (Suppl.), 27.
Mueller, J. F. (1959b). *J. Parasit.* **45**, 561–573.
Newsome, J. and Robinson, D. L. H. (1954). *Ann. trop. Med. Hyg.* **48**, 194–200.
Parker, R. C. (1961). "Methods of Tissue Culture," 3rd ed. Harper, New York.
Penso, G. and Balducci, D. (1963). "Tissue Cultures in Biological Research." Elsevier, Amsterdam.
Phillips, A. W. and Gibbs, P. A. (1961). *Biochem. J.* **81**, 551–556.
Pitts, T. D. (1948). *Proc. Soc. exp. Biol., N.Y.* **69**, 348.
Pitts, T. D. (1960). *J. Parasit.* **46** (Suppl.), 24.
Pitts, T. D. (1962). *J. Parasit.* **48** (Suppl.), 37.
Pitts, T. D. and Ball, G. H. (1953). *J. Parasit.* **39** (Suppl.), 42.
Pitts, T. D. and Ball, G. H. (1955). *J. Parasit.* **41** (Suppl.), 47–48.
Pollack, J. K. and Fairbairn, D. (1955). *Canad. J. Biochem. Physiol.* **33**, 297–306.
Rausch, R. L. and Jentoft, V. L. (1957). *J. Parasit.* **43**, 1–8.
Read, C. P. (1950). *Rice Inst. Pamphl.* **37** (2), 1–94.
Read, C. P. (1955). *In* "Some Physiological Aspects and Consequences of Parasitism" (W. H. Cole, ed.). Rutgers University Press, New Brunswick, New Jersey.
Robinson, D. L. H. (1956). *J. Helminth.* **29**, 193–202.
Robinson, D. L. H. (1957). *Trans. R. Soc. trop. Med. Hyg.* **51**, 300.
Robinson, D. L. H. (1958). *Trans. R. Soc. trop. Med. Hyg.* **52**, 24.
Robinson, D. L. H. (1960). *Ann. trop. Med. Parasit.* **54**, 112–117.
Robinson, D. L. H., Silverman, P. H. and Pearce, A. R. (1963). *Trans. R. Soc. trop. Med. Hyg.* **57**, 238.
Roche, M. and Torres, C. M. (1960). *Exp. Parasit.* **9**, 250–256.
Roeder, K. D. (1953). "Insect Physiology." Wiley, New York and London.
Rogers, W. P. (1958). *Nature, Lond.* **181**, 1410–1411.

Rogers, W. P. (1962). "The Nature of Parasitism: the Relationship of some Metazoan Parasites to their Hosts." Academic Press, London and New York.

Rohrbacher, G. H., Jr. (1957). *J. Parasit.* **43**, 9–18.

Ross, O. A. and Bueding, E. (1950). *Proc. Soc. exp. Biol.*, *N.Y.* **73**, 179–182.

Rothman, A. H. (1959). *Exp. Parasit.* **8**, 336–364.

Sawyer, T. K. and Weinstein, P. P. (1962). *J. Parasit.* **48** (Suppl.), 35–36.

Sawyer, T. K. and Weinstein, P. P. (1963). *J. Parasit.* **49**, 218–224.

Sayre, F. W., Hansen, E., Starr, T. J. and Yarwood, E. A. (1961). *Nature, Lond.* **190**, 116–117.

Sayre, F. W., Hansen, E. L. and Yarwood, E. A. (1963). *Exp. Parasit.* **13**, 98–107.

Schiller, E. L., Read, C. P. and Rothman, A. H. (1959). *J. Parasit.* **45** (Suppl.), 29.

Senft, A. W. and Senft, D. B. (1962). *J. Parasit.* **48**, 551–554.

Senft, A. W. and Weller, T. H. (1956). *Proc. Soc. exp. Biol.*, *N.Y.* **93**, 16–19.

Silverman, P. H. (1959). *Nature, Lond.* **183**, 197.

Silverman, P. H. (1963a). *In* "Techniques in Parasitology" (A. E. Taylor, ed.). Blackwell, Oxford.

Silverman, P. H. (1963b). *J. Parasit.* **48** (Suppl.), 50.

Silverman, P. H. and Podger, K. R. (1962). *J. Parasit.* **48** (Suppl.), 15.

Silverman, P. H. and Podger, K. R. (1964). *Exp. Parasit.* **15**, 314–324.

Silverman, P. H., Poynter, D. and Podger, K. R. (1962). *J. Parasit.* **48**, 562–571.

Smith, H. and Taylor, J. (1964). "Microbial Behavior 'in vivo' and 'in vitro'." Cambridge University Press, London.

Smyth, J. D. (1946). *J. exp. Biol.* **23**, 47–70.

Smyth, J. D. (1947a). *Biol. Rev.* **22**, 214–238.

Smyth, J. D. (1947b). *Parasitology* **38**, 173–181.

Smyth, J. D. (1955). *Rev. ibér. Parasit.* Tomo extraordinar. pp. 65–86.

Smyth, J. D. (1958). *Nature, Lond.* **181**, 1119–1122.

Smyth, J. D. (1959). *Ann. N.Y. Acad. Sci.* **77** (Art. 2), 102–125.

Smyth, J. D. (1962a). "Introduction to Animal Parasitology." English Universities Press, London.

Smyth, J. D. (1962b). *Parasitology* **52**, 441–457.

Smyth, J. D. (1964). *In* "Advances in Parasitology" (B. Dawes, ed.), Vol. 2 pp. 169–219. Academic Press, London and New York.

Sommerville, R. I. (1957). *Exp. Parasit.* **6**, 18–30.

Stephenson, W. (1947). *Parasitology* **38**, 116–144.

Stoll, N. R. (1940). *Growth* **4**, 383–406.

Stoll, N. R. (1953a). *J. Parasit.* **39**, 422–444.

Stoll, N. R. (1953b). Thaper Commemoration Volume, Lucknow, pp. 259–268.

Stoll, N. R. (1954). *J. Parasit.* **40** (Sect. 2), 14.

Stoll, N. R. (1959). *Ann. N.Y. Acad. Sci.* **77** (Art. 2), 126–136.

Stoll, N. R. (1961). *J. Helminth*, R. T. Leiper Suppl., 169–174.

Stunkard, H. W. (1932). *J. Parasit.* **19**, 163.

Taylor, A. and Whitlock, J. H. (1960). *Cornell Vet.* **50**, 339–344.

Taylor, A. E. R. (1960). *Exp. Parasit.* **9**, 113–120.

Taylor, A. E. R. (1961). *Exp. Parasit.* **11**, 176–187.

Taylor, A. E. R. (1963). *Exp. Parasit.* **14**, 304–310.

Trager, W. (1957). *J. Protozool.* **4**, 269–276.

Voge, M. (1963). *J. Parasit.* **49** (Suppl.), 59–60.

Wardle, R. A. and McLeod, J. A. (1952). "The Zoology of Tapeworms." University of Minnesota Press, Minneapolis.

Webster, G. A. and Cameron, T. W. M. (1963). *Canad. J. Zool.* **41**, 185–195.

Weinstein, P. P. (1949). *J. Parasit.* **35** (Sect. 2), 14.

Weinstein, P. P. (1953). *Amer. J. Hyg.* **58**, 352–376.

Weinstein, P. P. (1954). *J. Parasit.* **40** (Sect. 2), 14–15.

Weinstein, P. P. (1958). *Amer. J. trop. Med. Hyg.* **7**, 1–3.

Weinstein, P. P. and Jones, M. F. (1956a). *J. Parasit.* **42**, 215–236.

Weinstein, P. P. and Jones, M. F. (1956b). *J. Parasit.* **42** (Sect. 2), 14.

Weinstein, P. P. and Jones, M. F. (1957a). *Amer. J. trop. Med. Hyg.* **6**, 480–484.

Weinstein, P. P. and Jones, M. F. (1957b). *J. Parasit.* **43** (Suppl.), 45–46.

Weinstein, P. P. and Jones, M. F. (1959). *Ann. N.Y. Acad. Sci.* **77** (Art. 2), 137–162.

Weinstein, P. P. and Sawyer, T. K. (1961). *J. Parasit.* **47** (Suppl.), 23–24.

Weller, T. H. (1943). *Amer. J. Path.* **19**, 503–512.

White, G. F. (1932). *J. Parasit.* **18**, 133.

Williams, M. O., Hopkins, C. A. and Wyllie, M. R. (1961). *Exp. Parasit.* **11**, 121–127.

Wilmoth, J. H. (1945). *Physiol. Zool.* **18**, 60–80.

Wyllie, R. M., Williams, M. O. and Hopkins, C. A. (1960). *Exp. Parasit.* **10**, 51–57.

Yamashita, J., Ohbayashi, M., Sakamoto, T. and Orihara, M. (1962). *Jap. J. vet. Res.* **10**, 85–96.

Yokagawa, M., Oshima, T. and Kihato, M. (1955). *Jap. J. Parasit.* **4**, 388–393.

Yokogawa, M., Oshima, T. and Kihato, M. (1958). *Jap. J. Parasit.* **7**, 51–55.

Biology and Distribution of the Rat Lungworm, *Angiostrongylus cantonensis,* and its Relationship to Eosinophilic Meningoencephalitis and other Neurological Disorders of Man and Animals*

JOSEPH E. ALICATA

*Department of Parasitology, University of Hawaii
Agricultural Experiment Station, Honolulu, Hawaii, U.S.A.*

I. INTRODUCTION

One of the important recent developments in parasitology has been the awareness that cerebral angiostrongylosis is most likely responsible for the eosinophilic syndrome frequent in man in some areas of the Pacific islands and south-east Asia. This syndrome consists of more or less distinct meningeal symptoms associated with eosinophilia of the cerebrospinal fluid. The interest in this field originated with the theory proposed in 1961 (Alicata, 1962, 1963d; Alicata and Brown, 1963) that *Angiostrongylus cantonensis* might be the etiological agent of eosinophilic meningoencephalitis of man in Tahiti. This parasite was first recovered in Formosa in 1944 from the cerebrospinal fluid of a young man who had shown meningeal symptoms and eosinophils in the cerebrospinal fluid (Nomura and Lin, 1945). A second human infection with this parasite was found in Hawaii in 1961 (Rosen *et al.,* 1962). Clinical, laboratory, and field evidences which support the above indicated theory are the following: (a) recovery of *A. cantonensis* from man in two cases of eosinophilic meningoencephalitis as cited above; (b) ability of the larvae of *A. cantonensis* to travel to the central nervous system of simian primates and

---

*Paper presented at the First International Congress of Parasitology, Rome, Italy, 19–26 September 1964.

M* 223

to produce eosinophilic meningoencephalitis (Alicata, 1962; Alicata *et al.*, 1963; Weinstein *et al.*, 1963); (c) report of two human cases of eosinophilic meningoencephalitis following the wilful ingestion of raw slugs from endemic areas (Horio and Alicata, 1961; Alicata, 1963a); (d) presence of the rat lungworm in all the Pacific islands in which cases of eosinophilic meningoencephalitis have been reported, namely Guam, Hawaii, New Caledonia, New Hebrides, Ponape, Rarotonga, Saipan, and Tahiti (Alicata and McCarthy, 1964), and absence of the disease in areas where the parasite does not occur, namely Fiji, Samoa, Tonga, and Wallis (Loison, 1963); (e) high incidence of eosinophilic meningoencephalitis in Tahiti correlated with the common consumption of raw prawns, 4% of which have been found infected with the larvae of *A. cantonensis* (Alicata and Brown, 1962); and (f) widespread incidence of the disease in certain areas of Thailand correlated with the common consumption of insufficiently cooked or preserved amphibious snails, *Pila ampullacea* (S. Punyagupta, personal communication, 1964).

II. LIFE CYCLE

A. cantonensis is a heteroxenous nematode which utilizes mollusks as intermediate hosts (Figs. 1 and 2). The complete life cycle of the parasite in the mollusk and rat hosts was elucidated by Mackerras and Sandars (1955). The adult male and female worms are usually found in the two main branches of the pulmonary artery of the rat. In heavy infection, they are occasionally found in the right ventricle of the heart. The gravid female worms lay unsegmented eggs into the blood stream, and these are carried by the blood into the smaller vessels of the lungs where they lodge as emboli. The eggs become embryonated in about 6 days (Weinstein *et al.*, 1963). The first stage larvae, which hatch from the eggs, break through the respiratory tract and migrate up to the trachea. After being swallowed, they are eventually eliminated with

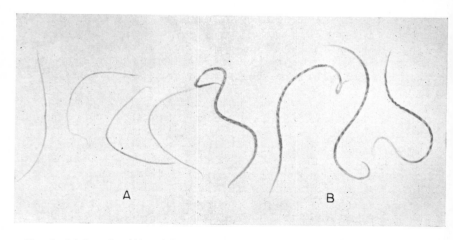

FIG. 1. Adult males (A) and females (B) of *Angiostrongylus cantonensis* from the pulmonary artery of rats. × 2.

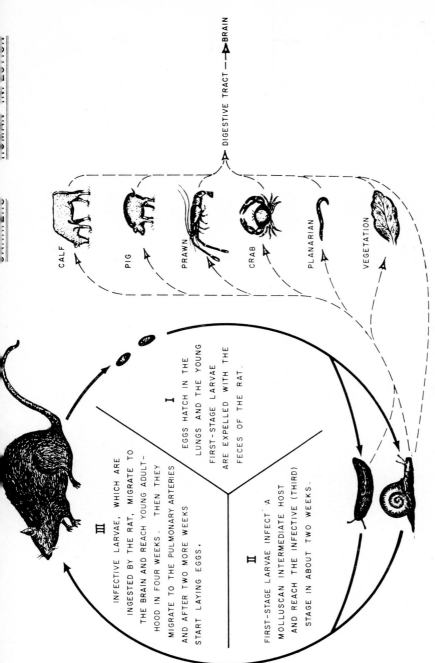

DIGESTIVE TRACT ⟶ BRAIN

CALF

PIG

PRAWN

CRAB

PLANARIAN

VEGETATION

I

EGGS HATCH IN THE
LUNGS AND THE YOUNG
FIRST-STAGE LARVAE
ARE EXPELLED WITH THE
FECES OF THE RAT.

II

FIRST-STAGE LARVAE INFECT A
MOLLUSCAN INTERMEDIATE HOST
AND REACH THE INFECTIVE (THIRD)
STAGE IN ABOUT TWO WEEKS.

III

INFECTIVE LARVAE, WHICH ARE
INGESTED BY THE RAT, MIGRATE TO
THE BRAIN AND REACH YOUNG ADULT-
HOOD IN FOUR WEEKS. THEN THEY
MIGRATE TO THE PULMONARY ARTERIES
AND AFTER TWO MORE WEEKS
START LAYING EGGS.

FIG. 2. Life cycle of *Angiostrongylus cantonensis* and possible avenues of human infection. After Alicata (1964c).

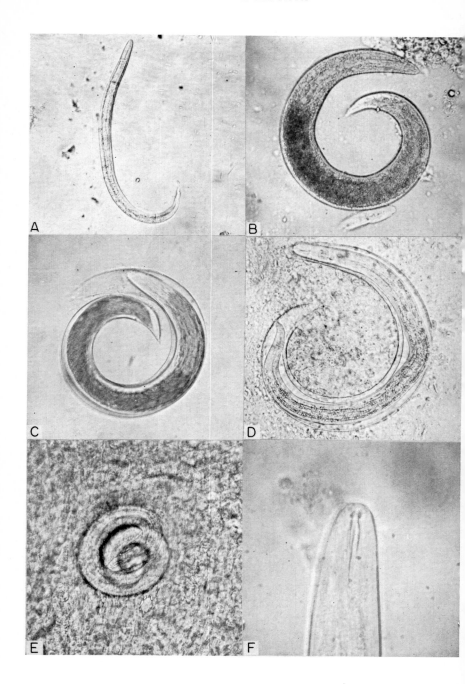

the feces of the host. These larvae measure about 0·27–0·30 mm in length and 0·015–0·016 mm in breadth and possess a distinct dorsal minute notch near the tip of the tail (Fig. 3A). In fresh water or sea water (% salinity unspecified), these larvae are able to live for about 6 days and 3 days, respectively, but are rapidly killed by drying (Richards, 1963).

A. DEVELOPMENT IN THE MOLLUSCAN HOST

Under natural conditions, several species of terrestrial mollusks (snails and slugs) serve as intermediate hosts (see below). The first stage larvae may enter the body of the mollusk equally effectively either through the digestive tract or by active penetration of its cuticle (Mackerras and Sandars, 1955; Cheng and Alicata, 1965). Within the mollusk, the larvae undergo two molts and become third stage or infective larvae (Fig. 3D). The period of development within the various species of mollusks varies. In *Subulina octona*, at room temperature (26° C), the first and second molts take place, respectively, about 7 and 12 days following infection. In *Bradybaena similaris*, the two molts take place, respectively, about 8 and 16 days following infection. In the body of the mollusk, the first and second stage larvae usually take the shape of a figure 6, whereas in the third stage the larvae are more tightly coiled (Fig. 3E). The newly formed third stage larvae are usually enclosed within the two sheaths which are cast during molting. However, within several days the larvae emerge from the sheaths, as evinced in cross sections of infected mollusks, and remain loosely embedded in the host's musculature. The infective larvae measure 0·46–0·51 mm in length and 0·26 mm in breadth. Just below the buccal cavity, the larvae possess two well-developed chitinous rods with expanded knob-like tips at the anterior end (Fig. 3F). These larvae resemble those of the cat lungworm, *Anafilaroides rostratus*, but can be differentiated by their shorter body length and esophagus (Alicata, 1963b).

Infective larvae of *A. cantonensis* have survived in the body of freshwater snails up to 12 months after infection (Richards, 1963). Outside the host tissue these larvae have been found viable and infectious to rats when kept for 4 days in distilled water or in moist soil or sphagnum moss. They were infectious to rats after being kept in *taioro* for 2 days but were not infectious on the 3rd day (Alicata and Brown, unpublished data). Snails and slugs infected with larvae of *A. cantonensis* have been found to shed some of the larvae when kept immersed in water (Cheng and Alicata, 1964).

B. DEVELOPMENT IN THE RAT HOST

Infection of rats with *A. cantonensis* probably takes place as a result of eating mollusks infected with the third stage larvae of the parasite or, possibly, by drinking water contaminated with such larvae. Experimentally, rats have

---

FIG. 3. First three larval stages of *Angiostrongylus cantonensis*. A, First stage from feces of rat, × 300; B, first stage, 6 days after molluscan infection, × 300; C, second stage in first larval molt, 8 days after molluscan infection, × 300; D, third stage enclosed by first and second molts, 12 days after molluscan infection, × 300; E, third stage in the musculature of a mollusk, × 300; F, anterior end of third stage larva, × 640. F, After Alicata (1962).

been infected by placing the third stage larvae on the scarified skin (Alicata and Brown, 1962).

When the infective larvae are ingested by rats, they quickly pass from the stomach to the small intestine and soon afterwards enter the circulatory system. They are then carried by the blood to the central nervous system, for which they have a strong affinity. Experimentally, following infection of adult rats, the infective larvae have been known to reach various organs of the body within the following periods of time: small intestine, 2 h; mesenteric venules, 2–3 h; mesenteric lymph gland, portal vein and posterior vena cava, $3\frac{1}{2}$–$5\frac{1}{2}$ h; right ventricle, 4 h; lungs, $5\frac{1}{2}$ h; cerebral hemisphere and spinal cord, 17 h (Mackerras and Sandars, 1955). In a 1-day-old rat, infective larvae have been found in the cerebral hemisphere 7 h after oral administration (Alicata, unpublished data).

While in the brain, and within the period of about 13 days following infection, the larvae undergo two additional molts and become young adults. They then emerge to the surface of the brain and remain in the subarachnoid space for about 2 weeks. Soon afterwards the juvenile worms, now 11–12 mm in length, enter the walls of the cranial venules and travel to the pulmonary artery via the right ventricle of the heart. The migratory juvenile worms have been recovered from the external jugular vein of rats 29 days after infection, and from the superior vena cava and right ventricle between the 29th and 32nd days (Mackerras and Sandars, 1955). After a period of about 1 week in the main branches of the pulmonary artery, the worms reach sexual maturity and start laying undeveloped eggs. These eggs appear to require about 6 days to embryonate and hatch in the lung capillaries (Weinstein et al., 1963). The first stage larvae are usually found in the feces of the rat 42–48 days after infection.

The details of the route of migration of the infective larvae of A. cantonensis to the brain of the rat host are not fully known; however, based on some experimental observations (Mackerras and Sandars, 1955), the probable migration is indicated in Fig. 4.

C. INTERMEDIATE AND PARATENIC HOST RANGE

A variety of terrestrial snails and slugs are known to serve as intermediate hosts for A. cantonensis under natural conditions. Those which have been reported from the Pacific islands (Fig. 5) are the garden snails, Bradybaena similaris, Opeas javanicum, and Subulina octona, and the slugs, Deroceras laeve, Vaginalus plebeius, and Veronicella alte. Included also is the giant African snail, Achatina fulica, which is of common occurrence in the islands of Micronesia and Hawaii, and Pupina complanata, present in Micronesia. Other molluscan hosts from south-east Asia include the slugs, Girasia peguensis, Microparmarion malayanum, and the snail, Macrochlamys resplendens, from Malaya (K. J. Lie, personal communication, 1964), and the amphibious snail, Pila ampullacea, from Thailand (Punyagupta, personal communication, 1964).

In all probability, most of the above named mollusks constitute important vectors in the transmission of the parasite to rats. However, little information

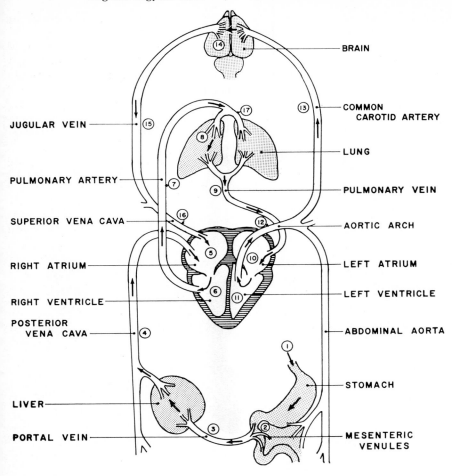

FIG. 4. Diagrammatic representation of the probable migratory route of the infective larvae of *A. cantonensis* from the intestinal tract to the brain of the rat, and the migration of the young adults from the brain to the main branches of the pulmonary artery. The route of the infective larvae is believed to be as follows: lumen of stomach (1)→ to lumen of small intestine→ to venules of intestinal wall and mesentery (2) (see below)→ to hepatic portal system (3)→ to hepatic vein→ to posterior vena cava (4)→ to right atrium of heart→ (5) to right ventricle of heart→ (6) to pulmonary artery (7)→ to lung capillaries (8)→ to pulmonary vein (9)→ to left atrium of heart (10)→ to left ventricle of heart (11)→ to aortic arch (12)→ to common carotid artery (13)→ to brain capillaries and brain proper. The route followed by the young adults from the brain is probably as follows: subarachnoid space→ to brain venules (14)→ to jugular vein (15)→ to superior vena cava (16)→ to right atrium of heart (5)→ to right ventricle of heart (6)→ to pulmonary artery (7)→ and final destination to the two main branches of the pulmonary artery (17).

In addition to reaching the right atrium of the heart (5) via the hepatic circulation as indicated above, it is likely that some of the larvae enter the lymphatics of the digestive tract and reach the heart via the thoracic duct. The route of migration of the infective larvae to the spinal cord is not known, but it has been suggested that they reach there via anastomoses between the abdominal and spinal veins (Mackerras and Sandars, 1955).

is available on the preferred species of mollusks in the diet of rodents. *Achatina* snails do not appear to be a preferred item (Strecker and Jackson, 1962).

Under experimental conditions, it has been possible to infect a variety of land snails, freshwater snails, and terrestrial slugs. (Certain clams and oysters have been found suitable experimental intermediate hosts by Cheng and Burton (1965).) The land snails include *Euglandina rosea, Helicina orbiculata*

FIG. 5. Natural intermediate and paratenic hosts for the larvae of *Angiostrongylus cantonensis* in the Pacific islands. A, *Bradybaena similaris*; B, *Subulina octona*; C, *Opeas javanicum*; D, *Pupina complanata*; E, *Achatina fulica*; F, *Deroceras laeve*; G, *Veronicella alte*; H, *Vaginalus plebeius*; I, *Macrobrachium* sp., reduced × ½; J, *Geoplana septemlineat*. All natural size except I.

I, After Alicata and Brown (1962); J, after Alicata (1963a).

and *Mesodon thyroidus* (see Ash, 1962b). The freshwater snails include the lymnaeid snails *Fossaria ollula* (see Alicata and Brown, 1962) and sixteen other species including *Ferrissia tenuis* and *Australorbis glabratus* (see Richards, 1963). It is likely that most of these freshwater snails have little opportunity to become naturally infected. However, lymnaeid snails are amphibious, and it is therefore possible for them to become exposed to the feces of infected rats. Slugs that have been experimentally infected but not found naturally infected include *Deroceras reticulatum, Limax arborum, L. flavus, L. maximus* and *Onchidium* sp. (Table I).

TABLE I

Molluscan Intermediate Hosts for A. cantonensis

(N = Natural infection; E = Experimental infection.)

Type of mollusk	Locality where infection has been reported	Reference
Snails (terrestrial)		
Achatina fulica (N)	Hawaiian Is., Ponape, Saipan	Alicata (1962); Alicata and McCarthy (1964)
Bradybaena similaris (N)	Cook Is., Hawaiian Is., Loyalty Is., New Caledonia, New Hebrides Is., Ponape, Saipan, Tahiti	Alicata and Brown (1962); Alicata (1963a); Alicata and McCarthy (1964)
Euglandina rosea (E)	Lousiana (U.S.A.)	Ash (1962b)
Helicina orbiculata (E)	Louisiana (U.S.A.)	Ash (1962b)
Macrochlamys resplendens (N)	Malaya	Lie (personal communication, 1964)
Mesodon thyroidus (E)	Louisiana (U.S.A.)	Ash (1962b)
Opeas javanicum (N)	Hawaiian Is.	Alicata (unpublished)
Pupina complanata (N)	Ponape	Alicata (unpublished)
Subulina octona (N)	(Same as *B. similaris*)	(Same as *B. similaris*)
Snails (aquatic)		
Australorbis glabratus (E)	Maryland (U.S.A.)	Richards (1963)
Ferrissia tenuis (E)	Maryland (U.S.A.)	Richards (1963)
Fossaria ollula (E)	Hawaiian Is.	Alicata and Brown (1962)
Pila ampullacea (N)	Thailand	Punyagupta (personal communication, 1964)
Slugs (terrestrial)		
Deroceras laeve (N)	Australia, Cook Is., Hawaiian Is., New Caledonia, Tahiti	Alicata (1963a); Alicata and Brown (1962); Alicata and McCarthy (1964); Mackerras and Sandars (1955)
Deroceras reticulatum (E)	Maryland (U.S.A.)	Weinstein *et al.* (1963)

TABLE I *contd.*

Type of mollusk	Locality where infection has been reported	Reference
Girasia peguensis (N)	Malaya	Lie (personal communication, 1964)
Limax arborum (E)	Australia	Mackerras and Sandars (1955)
Limax flavus (E)	Louisiana (U.S.A.)	Ash (1962b)
Limax maximus (E)	Maryland (U.S.A.)	Weinstein *et al.* (1963)
Microparmarion malayanum (N)	Malaya	Lie (personal communication, 1964)
Onchidium sp. (E)	Australia	Mackerras and Sandars (1955)
Vaginalus plebeius (N)	Cook Is., Loyalty Is., New Caledonia, New Hebrides Is., Ponape, Saipan, Tahiti	Alicata (1963a and present report); Alicata and Brown (1962); Alicata and McCarthy (1964)
Veronicella alte (N)	Hawaiian Is., New Caledonia	Alicata (1962, 1963a)

According to experimental observations (Alicata and Brown, 1962), the following snails have been found unsuitable intermediate hosts of *A. cantonensis*: (aquatic snails) *Melanoides newcombi, Physa compacta, Thiara granifera*; (terrestrial snail) *Helix aspersa*. In the last-named snail, a few larvae of *A. cantonensis* have been observed to reach the third stage, but the larvae showed degenerate internal organs and they were not able to infect rats (Alicata, unpublished data). No natural infection with larvae of *A. cantonensis* was noted in the body of marine slugs, *Steilocheilus longicaudus*, collected in brackish water on the island of Rarotonga, Cook Islands (Alicata and McCarthy, 1964), or in sand clams *(Arca scapha)* from Ponape (Alicata, unpublished).

Animals that serve as paratenic host for the infective larvae of *A. cantonensis* under natural conditions include the land planarian, *Geoplana septemlineata* (Fig. 5J), the freshwater prawn, *Macrobrachium* sp. (Fig. 5I) (Alicata, 1962; Alicata and Brown, 1962), and land crabs (Alicata, 1964a). Under experimental conditions, calves and pigs have been shown to serve as paratenic hosts (Alicata, 1964b). In the planarians, the larvae are loosely coiled in the musculature, whereas in the prawns and crabs the larvae have been found free in the stomach. The land planarian, *G. septemlineata*, is predaceous and actively attacks and feeds on snails. As a result it ingests and becomes infected with larvae which may be present in a snail host. Prawns are believed to acquire the infection by feeding on naturally infected land slugs or snails which are present on the banks of streams or are carried to streams by heavy rainfall. No larvae of *A. cantonensis* were found in the digestive tract of the freshwater fish, *Tilapia* sp., collected on the island of Rarotonga (Alicata and McCarthy, 1964). In the experimentally infected calves and pigs, the infective living larvae have been recovered from the stomach wall, liver, lungs, and spleen 2 weeks after experimental infection (Fig. 6B). In the pig, however, the larvae were found encapsulated and dead (Fig. 6C, D) in the above mentioned organs 5 weeks after infection. The comparatively early death of the larvae, therefore, appears to minimize the importance of swine as carrier hosts. Experimentally, these larvae have not been found to migrate to the voluntary muscles of pigs and calves (Alicata, 1963c, 1964b). The extent to which calves and pigs are infected under natural conditions with larvae of *A. cantonensis* and serve as source of human infection has not been determined.

The percentage and numbers of infective larvae of *A. cantonensis* found among various intermediate and carrier hosts in the Pacific islands vary in the various hosts and localities. Doubtlessly, this is correlated with the size and the migratory habit of the vector, as well as with the incidence of infection in the rat population. The larger species of snails and slugs appear to be the most commonly infected and harbor the greatest number of parasites

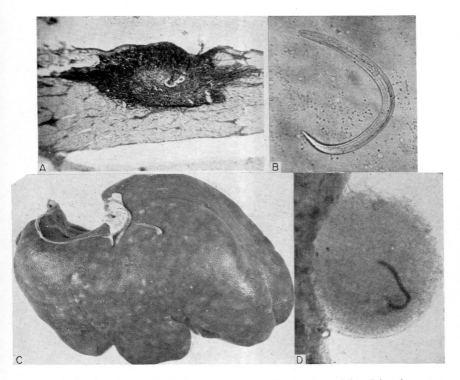

FIG. 6. A, Section of a nodule in the outer portion of a pig stomach involving the serous and muscular layers, and enclosing a section of a third stage larvae of *A. cantonensis*, 15 days after infection; B, third stage larva of *A. cantonensis* recovered from the liver of a pig 15 days after infection; C, liver of a pig showing small white nodular lesions and areas of discoloration, 35 days after infection; D, elevated cyst on the surface of the spleen of a pig containing a dead larva of *A. cantonensis*, 35 days after infection.

(Table II). *Achatina* contained 208–1 054 larvae; *Vaginalus*, 5–472; and *Veronicella*, 152–502. The number of larvae found in the small garden slug, *Deroceras*, was 5–75, and in juvenile *Vaginalus* (about 10 mm long) 5–25. Among the small garden snails *Bradybaena* and *Subulina*, the number of larvae varied from 2 to 50.

TABLE II

Incidence of Infective Larvae of A. cantonensis *among Various Intermediate and Carrier Hosts Found under Field Conditions in the Pacific Islands*

Name of host	Locality	No. examined	% Infected	Approx. no. of larvae found in each	Reference
Coconut crabs	Saipan	25	12·0	(Undetermined)	1
Land snails					
Achatina fulica	Hawaiian Is.	10	100	208–1 054	1
	Ponape	25	100	(Undetermined)	1
	Saipan	25	100	(Undetermined)	1
Bradybaena similaris	Cook Is.	25	52·0	2–25	2
	New Caledonia	75	—	30 (1 snail)	3
Pupina complanata	Ponape	25	12·0	1–5	1
Subulina octona	Cook Is.	25	74·0	5–50	2
	New Caledonia	25	4·5	3 (1 snail)	3
Land slugs					
Deroceras laeve	Cook Is.	25	100	5–75	2
	New Caledonia	56	69·6	74 (1 slug)	3
Vaginalus plebeius	Cook Is.	25	100	10–150	2
(juvenile)	Cook Is.	20	100	5–25	2
Vaginalus plebeius	New Caledonia	46	—	472 (1 slug)	3
Veronicella alte	Hawaiian Is.	10	100	152–502	1
Freshwater prawns					
Macrobrachium sp.	Cook Is.	60	3·3	2–3	2
	Ponape	50	6·0	3–3,720	1
	Saipan	50	10·0	(Undetermined)	1
	Tahiti	300	4·0	3–114	4
Land crabs	Saipan	40	5·0	(Undetermined)	5
Land planarian					
(Undetermined)	Cook Is.	25	12·0	5–15	2
Geoplana septemlineata	Hawaiian Is.	25	80·0	(Numerous)	1
(Undetermined)	New Caledonia	66	69·6	(Undetermined)	3
(Undetermined)	Tahiti	25	100	(Numerous)	1

[1] Alicata (unpublished); [2] Alicata and McCarthy (1964); [3] Alicata (1963a); [4] Alicata and Brown (1962); [5] Alicata (1964a).

The larval infection among freshwater prawns from several of the Pacific islands has been found to vary from 3 to 10% and the number of larvae found varied from 2 to about 3 720 (Fig. 7). Among the land planarians, of which there are several species present in the various islands of the Pacific, the incidence of larval infection was found to vary from 12 to 100%. This difference may also be due partly to the difference in the predaceous habits which may exist among various species of land planarians.

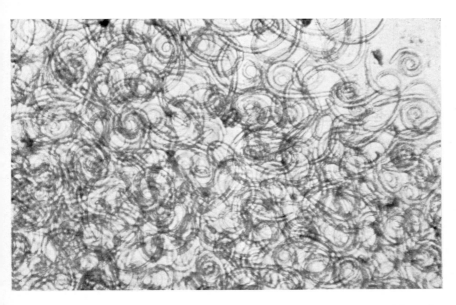

Fig. 7. A portion of about 3 720 infective larvae of *A. cantonensis* recovered from the stomach of a natural infected freshwater prawn on the island of Ponape. × 180.

D. FINAL HOST RANGE

A. cantonensis reaches sexual maturity only in the two main branches of the pulmonary artery and sometimes in the heart of various species of rats. The known species of wild rats include the following: the Norway rat, *Rattus norvegicus*, and the black rat, *R. rattus*, reported from Australia and Pacific islands (Mackerras and Sandars, 1955; Alicata, 1963a); the field rat, *R. exulans*, reported from Malaya and the Pacific islands (Lim *et al.*, 1962; Alicata, 1963a); *R. argentiventer*, *R. bowersi*, *R. jalorensis*, *R. mulleri*, and *R. rattus diardi*, reported from Malaya (Lim *et al.*, 1962). In addition, the parasite can develop to the young adult stage in the central nervous system of a variety of mammals including cat, man, monkey, mouse, and possibly others. No parasites were found in the brains of two calves each of which had been fed approximately 50 000 *Angiostrongylus* larvae and killed 15 days later (Alicata, 1963c). Similarly, no parasites were found in the brain of two young pigs each of which had been fed approximately 10 000 larvae and killed 35 days later (Alicata, unpublished data); the failure to find the parasites might have been due to the difficulty in locating them in such large organs. The parasite does not migrate to or develop in the central nervous system of chickens (Alicata, 1963c).

The incidence of lungworm infection in the various species of wild rats in the Pacific shows considerable variation (Table III). In endemic areas, the Norway and Polynesian rats usually show a high and approximately equal rate of infection, whereas the incidence among the black rats is usually lower and about one-half that of the other two species of rats (Table III). In all probability, the difference is not due to species susceptibility but rather to feeding habits and quantity of mollusks generally consumed by the different species of rats. The percentage of infection with lungworms among rats captured in Malaya was as follows: *Rattus argentiventer*, 23; *R. bowersi*, 16; *R. exulans*, 20; *R. jalorensis*, 50; *R. mulleri*, 4; *R. rattus*, 8 (Lim et al., 1962).

The bandicoot rat (*Bandicota indica memorivaga*) has been found to be a final host in the rat lungworm in Taiwan (Kuntz and Myers, 1964).

TABLE III

Incidence of A. cantonensis *among Rats in Various Pacific Islands*

Locality	Species of rat (No. examined/No. infected/% infected)			Total	Reference
	R. norvegicus	R. rattus	R. exulans		
Caroline Is.					
Pingelap	0/0/0·0	21/3/14·0	9/3/33·0	30/6/20·0	1
Ponape	0/0/0·0	460/92/20·0	766/345/45·0	1 226/437/35·6	1
Ponape	0/0/0·0	81/19/23·4	15/12/80·0	96/31/32·9	2
Moen	0/0/0·0	26/16/61·0	11/8/73·0	37/24/64·8	1
Cook Is.					
Rarotonga	126/121/96·0	57/34/61·9	57/49/85·9	240/204/85·0	3
Formosa	(Not recorded)	(Not recorded)	(Not recorded)	(Not recorded)	4
Guam	0/0/0·0	45/11/24·4	0/0/0·0	45/11/24·4	5
Hawaiian Is.					
Oahu	(Not recorded)	(Not recorded)	(Not recorded)	75/9/12·0	6
Loyalty Is.					
Lifou	4/4/100	14/5/35·7	23/23/100	41/32/78·1	7
Mariana Is.					
Saipan	10/9/90·0	99/12/12·1	1/1/100	110/22/20·0	2
Marshall Is.					
Majuro	0/0/0·0	3/0/0·0	44/1/2·3	47/1/2·2	1
New Caledonia	41/38/92·6	48/25/52·1	15/15/100	104/78/75·0	7
New Hebrides Is.					
Espiritu Santo	8/7/87·5	9/4/44·4	43/43/100	60/54/90·0	7
Tahiti	(Not recorded)	(Not recorded)	(Not recorded)	70/62/88·5	8

[1] Jackson (1962); [2] Alicata (unpublished); [3] Alicata and McCarthy (1964); [4] Yokogawa (1937); [5] Lindquist and Li (1955); [6] Ash (1962a); [7] Alicata (1963a); [8] Alicata (1962).

III. Geographical Distribution and Incidence of Infection

As far as is known, the lungworm, *A. cantonensis*, has been found among rats only in eastern Asia (Canton, China (Chen, 1935); Malaysia (Schacher and Chee-Hock, 1960); Thailand (Punyagupta, personal communication, 1964)), Australia (Mackerras and Sandars, 1955), and many islands of the Pacific (Table III). The parasite possibly occurs among rats in Sumatra, Indonesia, where clinical cases of eosinophilic meningoencephalitis similar to those occurring in the Pacific islands have been reported (Smit, 1962). The young adult worms have been reported from man in Formosa (Nomura and Lin, 1945), Hawaii (Rosen *et al.*, 1962), and Thailand (Prommindaroj *et al.*, 1962); they probably occur also in Viet Nam (see p. 240).

The location and percentage incidence of infection (in parentheses) of the lungworm among rats in the various Pacific islands investigated are as follows (Table III): Espiritu Santo, New Hebrides (90); Formosa (percent unrecorded); Guam (24·4); Lifou, Loyalty Islands (78·1); Oahu, Hawaiian Islands (12·0); Majuro, Marshall Islands (2·2); Moen, Caroline Islands (64·8); New Caledonia (75·0); Pingelap, Caroline Islands (20·0); Ponape (29·2–35·6); Rarotonga, Cook Islands (85·0); Saipan, Mariana Islands (20·0); Tahiti (88·5). Areas in the Pacific which have been studied and where the lungworm has not been found among rats include New Zealand, Samoa (Alicata and McCarthy, 1964), Fiji, Tonga, Wallis (Loison, 1963), Philippines (Z. de Jesus, personal communication, 1964), Japan and Amami Islands (K. Nishimura, personal communication, 1964).

The geographical area in which *A. cantonensis* is at present known to occur is limited to the narrow tropical belt which extends from approximately 23° S. (Tropic of Capricorn) to 23° N. latitude (Tropic of Cancer) (Fig. 8), and from Thailand (100° E. longitude) to the island of Tahiti (150° W. longitude). This area is characterized by a tropical or subtropical climate, moderate to heavy rainfall and luxurious vegetation. All these factors are ideal for the propagation and spread of rodents and mollusks.

As indicated above, the rat lungworm has not been found in Japan or in New Zealand, which are located, respectively, somewhat north and south of the above mentioned endemic belt. The cool or freezing climatic conditions during a part of the year in these areas may not be favourable for the propagation and spread of the parasite.

Of special interest is the apparent absence of the lungworms from rats in Fiji, the Philippines, Samoa, Tonga, and Wallis Islands, where climate and animal life are in general similar to those of other Pacific islands in which the parasite occurs. In all probability, this observation indicates that *A. cantonensis* is a somewhat recent immigrant to the Pacific islands, and has not had time to become more widely distributed. The place of origin of *A. cantonensis* appears to be eastern Asia. It was first recorded from Canton, China, by Chen in 1935, and in 1937 it was reported from Formosa by both Matsumoto and Yokogawa. It appears to have gradually spread eastward to various Pacific islands through importation of either infected rats or infected mollusks. This has probably been brought about by recent, increased commercial

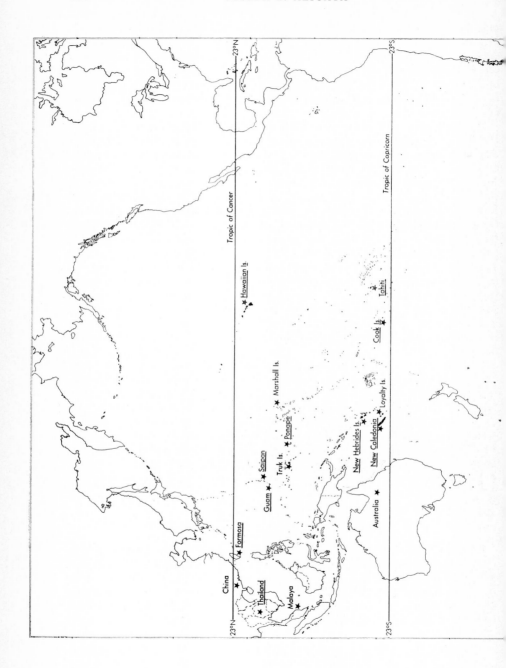

and military shipping operations, especially during World War II, from the Far East to various Pacific ports. Further evidence of the possible recent dispersal of rat lungworm in the Pacific is the contemporary occurrence of eosinophilic meningoencephalitis in the Pacific islands. This was first noted in Formosa in 1944 (Nomura and Lin, 1945), Ponape in 1947 (Bailey, 1948), in New Caledonia in 1951 (Trubert, 1952), and in Tahiti in 1958 (Franco *et al.*, 1960).

In connection with the introduction and spread of *A. cantonensis* in the Pacific, some consideration should be given to the possible role of the giant African snail, *Achatina fulica*. This snail is very susceptible to infection with larvae of *A. cantonensis* (Table II). During the 19th century, according to Mead (1961), the *Achatina* snails moved from their East African origin to south-east Asia, and from there to east Asia and the Pacific islands. They were found in Malaya in 1911, China in 1931, Formosa in 1932, the Marianas and the Hawaiian Islands in 1936. It appears likely, therefore, that *A. fulica* might have assisted in the spread of the rat lungworm in some of these islands. It should be pointed out, however, that *A. fulica* is not known to occur in either Tahiti or New Caledonia where the parasite is endemic. Furthermore, the parasite does not appear to be present in the Philippines where *A. fulica* is present. In connection with the importation of *A. fulica* from East Africa to south-east Asia and the Pacific areas, and its possible role in the spread of murine angiostrongylosis in these areas, observations appear to be necessary to determine the presence of *A. cantonensis* in East Africa or surrounding territories.

The examination of the pulmonary arteries of rats in the countries listed below has yielded negative findings for *A. cantonensis* (the information in most instances has been obtained through personal communication. The name of the investigator is shown in parentheses): Brazil, dozens of rats (J. F. Teixeria de Freitas); Great Britain (Cambridge, Cardiff, Liverpool, London, Nottingham, St. Albans and Wolverhampton), 191 rats (Sandars, 1957); the Netherlands, 13 rats (D. J. B. Wijers); Israel, about 500 rats (G. Wertheim); Puerto Rico, 120 rats (D. D. de Leon); Germany, 50 rats (H. J. Stammer).

IV. Relationship to Human and Animal Diseases

A. EOSINOPHILIC MENINGOENCEPHALITIS

Eosinophilic meningoencephalitis is a syndrome characterized by the presence of eosinophils in the cerebrospinal fluid of mammals. In man, this syndrome has been observed in connection with some of the cases of non-helminthic and helminthic infections involving the central nervous system. Of the former, it has been observed in cases of purulent meningitis, cerebral tumors, tubercular meningitis, epidemic cerebrospinal meningitis, and

←—————

FIG. 8. Presently known geographical distribution (★) of *Angiostrongylus cantonensis* among rats in south-east Asia and the islands of the Pacific. Areas in which eosinophilic meningoencephalitis have been reported are underscored. After Alicata (1964c).

neurosyphilis (Kaczynski, 1936). Of the helminthic infections, it includes trichinosis (Terplan *et al.*, 1957), cerebral cysticercosis (Kulkav, 1931), cerebral echinococcosis (Applebaum and Wexberg, 1944), cerebral schistosomiasis (Castaigne *et al.*, 1959), cerebral paragonimiasis (Uematsu and Shiozaki, 1935; Nonomura, 1941), and cerebral angiostrongylosis. Of the latter, at least four cases have been reported as follows. In case 1, young adult *A. cantonensis* were found in the brain of a patient in Hawaii (Rosen *et al.*, 1962). In case 2, foreign material and cellular reaction were found in the brain of the patient which were similar to those in case 1 (Rosen *et al.*, 1962). In cases 3 and 4, the diagnosis was based on the history of the patients, which indicated that they had ingested raw slugs. One of these patients was from Hawaii (Horio and Alicata, 1961) and the other from New Caledonia (Alicata, 1963a).

In the Pacific basin, cases of eosinophilic meningoencephalitis have been reported from various islands of Micronesia, Polynesia, and Melanesia. These include Cook Islands (Alicata and McCarthy, 1964), Guam (Loison, 1963), Hawaiian islands (Rosen *et al.*, 1962), New Caledonia (Trubert, 1952), New Hebrides (Loison, 1963), Ponape (Bailey, 1948), Saipan (Allison, 1962), and Tahiti (Franco *et al.*, 1960). In addition, human infections have also been reported from Formosa (Nomura and Lin, 1945), Japan (Nonomura, 1941), the Philippines (Sison *et al.*, 1951), Sumatra (Smit, 1963). Thailand (Punyagupta, personal communication, 1964), and possibly Viet Nam (K. Jindrak, personal communication, 1962); in the case from Viet Nam sections of young adult nematodes resembling *A. cantonensis* were found in the brain tissue.

The clinical, laboratory, and epidemiological findings in cases of eosinophilic meningoencephalitis in Micronesia, Polynesia and Melanesia indicate that the disease is not caused by bacteria, fungi, Protozoa, spirochaetes, tumors, or viruses (Allison, 1962; Bailey, 1948; Rosen *et al.*, 1962; Trubert, 1952). Furthermore, it is not caused by parasitic diseases such as cysticercosis, echinococcosis, paragonimiasis, trichinosis, and schistosomiasis, since these are not known to occur endemically in these areas. The findings, however, indicate that instances of the disease in these areas, as well as in Sumatra (Smit, 1962), are generally similar in character and most likely are caused by the same etiological agent. The presence of an eosinophilic response in these cases led some investigators to theorize that the agent is a helminthic parasite, probably acquired by eating certain raw fish (Rosen *et al.*, 1961). Other workers (Vaillant *et al.*, 1961) in New Caledonia theorized that the eosinophilic syndrome in man is produced by a thermostable toxin similar to that occurring in fish poisoning, acquired by eating certain species of toxic fish. This theory, however, fails to take into account the absence of eosinophilic meningoencephalitis in other islands of the Pacific such as Samoa and Fiji, where cases of fish poisoning are known to occur (Loison, 1955). More recent observations, however, outlined in the introduction of this paper, strongly suggest that the eosinophilic syndrome reported in many areas of the Pacific and south-east Asia is due to cerebral angiostrongylosis.

The eosinophilic meningoencephalitis reported from Japan and, possibly, from the Philippines, where *A. cantonensis* has not been recorded, in all probability is due to cerebral paragonimiasis. In Japan, Uematsu and Shio-zaki (1935) reported a pleocytosis of 1 441 cells/mm³, consisting practically all of eosinophils, in the cerebrospinal fluid of a patient who showed menin-geal irritations, cloudiness of both lungs in the X-ray examination, and numerous *Paragonimus* eggs in the sputum. Similarly, Nonomura (1941) re-ported a pleocytosis with 98% eosinophils in the cerebrospinal fluid of another patient in Japan. Although no parasite eggs were found in the sputum of this patient, Nonomura concluded that the pleocytosis was most likely produced by cerebral paragonimiasis. Furthermore, the sporadic cases of eosinophilic meningoencephalitis which have also been reported from Europe, North and South America, where *A. cantonensis* is not known to be present, are possibly caused by one or more species of helminths which occasionally invade the central nervous system (Smit, 1962). Of special importance in this connection is the finding of eosinophilic infiltration of the meninges resulting from *Toxocara canis* larvae infection which has been observed in man (Dent *et al.*, 1956). Etiologically, however, infection with larvae of this parasite occurs most commonly in young children (Beaver, 1962), whereas eosinophilic meningoencephalitis in the Pacific and south-east Asia areas occurs largely among adults (Franco *et al.*, 1960; Rosen *et al.*, 1961; Smit, 1962, 1963).

The eosinophilic response noted in the cerebrospinal fluid of human and simian cases of angiostrongylosis has been suggested as being due to meta-bolic products left behind by the parasite or resulting from the death of the parasite in the central nervous system (Weinstein *et al.*, 1963). This opinion is in accord with related observations by Done *et al.* (1960) in pigs experi-mentally infected with larvae of *Toxocara canis*. It was found that eosinophilic infiltration of the brain was quite spectacular in proximity to static or en-capsulated larvae, many of which were apparently dead.

B. NEUROLOGICAL AND RELATED DISORDERS

Various forms of neurological disorders have been noted in connection with cerebral angiostrongylosis among various animals and man. It appears likely that the severity of nervous symptoms may be correlated with the number of developing parasites present.

Rats which have been given up to about 150 infective *A. cantonensis* larvae have not as a rule shown evidence of cerebral derangement. One of such rats, however, which had been experimentally infected for a period of about 1 year developed a form of neurological symptom demonstrated by keeping its head bent to one side (Alicata, unpublished data). Two rats which had received a large number of larvae exhibited circling movements 5 days after infection (Mackerras and Sandars, 1955). Complete paralysis of the hind quarters was reported in a rat which had received only 23 larvae. The micro-scopic examination of the spinal cord of this rat revealed severe destruction of the dorsal and lateral funiculi throughout the cervical and portions of the thoracic cord, and focal lesions of the ventral funiculus (Weinstein *et al.*, 1963).

According to observations by Mackerras and Sandars (1955), mice which received 20–30 infective larvae showed no ill effects. Of five mice, however,

N

which had been fed from 70–100 larvae, all but one showed cerebral irritation consisting of incoordination of gait, circling movements, and twitching when handled. Four of these mice died or were killed in a moribund condition between the 2nd and 5th days, and one died on the 18th day.

In guinea-pigs, doses of 100–200 infective larvae failed to produce any signs of cerebral derangement (Mackerras and Sandars, 1955).

Observations carried out with rabbits also indicate a degree of relationship between neurological symptoms and size of the infection. This was evinced in four groups of rabbits (groups 1–3, four rabbits each, and group 4, two rabbits) in which 100, 200, 500 and 1 000 larvae were fed to the animals in groups 1–4, respectively. The two rabbits that received 1 000 larvae developed paralysis of the hind quarters 24 h after infection and died 2 days later. All the other rabbits showed no neurological symptoms, except one that received 100 larvae. This rabbit developed posterior paralysis 9 days after infection and died the following day (Alicata, unpublished data).

In monkeys, no neurological disorders were recorded among four rhesus monkeys infected with 335–1 700 larvae (Weinstein et al., 1963). No such symptoms were noted in two calves that were fed approximately 50 000 larvae each and killed 15 days later (Alicata, 1963c), or in two 3-month-old pigs fed approximately 10 000 larvae each and killed 35 days later (Alicata, unpublished data).

In man, partial loss of vision and presence of a species of *Angiostrongylus* in the anterior chamber of one eye has been recorded from Thailand (Prommindaroj et al., 1962). Localized paresthetic skin areas in various parts of the body, characterized by a burning sensation, pain, and exaggerated sensitivity to touch, have been found to be a common symptom among patients with eosinophilic meningoencephalitis in the Pacific islands (Bailey, 1948; Franco et al., 1960; Rosen et al., 1961). In Tahiti, approximately 5% of persons with the disease have shown facial paralysis of the lower motor neuron type. Although such a symptom has been found to last only a few weeks, a case was reported where paralysis of the external rectus muscle of the eye persisted for about a year (Rosen et al., 1961). A case showing facial paralysis and vertigo was reported from Sumatra (Smit, 1963). No information is available on whether or not facial paralysis in man is correlated with high intake of larval parasites.

C. METHODS OF HUMAN INFECTION

Based on field observations, the ingestion of uncooked food containing infective larvae of *A. cantonensis*, or of food containing an infected intermediate or a carrier host, appears to be the chief source of human infection. Other less likely methods consist of drinking water contaminated with the infective larvae, or through contact of the broken skin with soil containing such larvae. These methods are discussed below.

1. *Food*

The method by which contaminated food may serve as a vehicle for human angiostrongylosis appears to vary in different areas depending on the local eating habits and beliefs of the people. In some areas of Thailand, the infection in man is believed to be acquired through the common consumption of improperly prepared snails, *Pila ampullacea*. These are large amphibious and nocturnal animals commonly found in creeks, ponds, and muddy areas. The fleshy, head-foot parts of the snails are cut out and then either dipped in boiling water or stored in an icebox to keep fresh. They are then eaten after being chopped in small pieces, seasoned with lime juice, salt, and hot pepper, and mixed with vegetables (Punyagupta, personal communication, 1964). Studies carried out in Tahiti have indicated that freshwater prawns, *Macrobrachium* sp., are the main source of infection in that area. The infective larvae of the parasite have been found in 4% of the prawns examined (Alicata and Brown, 1962). These crustaceans are customarily eaten raw by most Tahitians. Records indicate that in 1961, approximately 12 000 lb of prawns were sold in the food markets in the town of Papeete. This large consumption of prawns is believed to be responsible for the many cases of eosinophilic meningoencephalitis which have occurred in recent years in Tahiti. Another possible source of food infection in Tahiti is *taioro*. This product consists of grated coconut to which is added prawn juice, prepared by grinding the stomach and surrounding portion of the prawns in fresh water. Experimentally, larvae of *A. cantonensis* have been found infective to rats after being kept in *taioro* for a period of 2 days.

Although prawns and *taioro* are eaten in Tahiti throughout the year, the largest amounts are consumed during social parties and annual feasts. This accounts for the frequent occurrence of the illness within a relatively short time among groups of persons who had eaten a common meal (Rosen *et al.*, 1961; Alicata and Brown, 1962). Of thirty cases of the illness which occurred in recent years, twenty-eight stated that they had eaten raw prawns and/or *taioro*, and two admitted having frequently consumed raw salad greens (Alicata and Brown, 1962). Most Tahitians, however, do not customarily eat raw salad greens.

In other areas of the Pacific, where eosinophilic meningoencephalitis is less common or is sporadic, and prawns are not ordinarily consumed raw, the illness is believed to be brought about by other eating habits. In New Caledonia the annual number of cases from 1956 to 1962 has been found to vary from four to twenty-two. It has been theorized that some of these cases are due to the accidental ingestion of a small intermediate or carrier host harboring the infective larvae of *A. cantonensis* (Alicata, 1963a). The basis for this theory is the occurrence of most of these cases among Europeans of French extraction, who customarily eat large amounts of raw salad greens, and the uncommon occurrence of the illness among the local Melanesians who ordinarily do not consume salad greens (Loison, 1963). On two occasions in Noumea, small slugs have been noted on lettuce served at restaurants. Land planarians and small slugs have been seen coiled in broken ripe strawberries and in fallen ripe figs and mangoes. Moreover, the illness in New Caledonia appears to be more prevalent in the cooler months of the year. This coincides with the period when vegetation such as lettuce is grown and consumed more abundantly and mollusks are most active (Alicata, 1963a).

Another possible, but as yet unproved, source of infection in New Caledonia, is the customary habit of some of the local Europeans of eating raw calf and pig livers. As already indicated, pigs and calves have been shown experimentally to serve as paratenic hosts for the infective larvae of *A. cantonensis*. In the Hawaiian islands, where a total of eight cases of eosinophilic meningoencephalitis has been recorded, one case which occurred in a Japanese patient was traced to the eating of raw land slugs (Horio and Alicata, 1961). This action was motivated by the belief among some Japanese that mollusks have great medicinal properties (Mead, 1961). It is likely that some of the other cases have resulted from accidental ingestion of one of the intermediate hosts of the rat lungworm.

At present the source of *Angiostrongylus* infection in the Micronesian islands is not clearly known. It appears likely that some cases, at least, occur as a result of eating raw crabs. During 1947 and 1948, approximately 250 cases of eosinophilic meningoencephalitis were reported from Ponape (Bailey, 1948). Although the medical records appear to be incomplete, recent information indicates that this illness has occurred less frequently in this area. Seven cases were observed in Saipan in 1958 (Allison, 1962) and four cases occurred in Ponape in 1963 (C. Barbosa, personal communication, 1964). Although the Micronesians do not habitually eat raw prawns, they are known to consume a variety of raw fruits, such as ripe bananas, duriens, papayas, soursops, etc., which frequently fall to the ground and may become contaminated with small snails or slugs. Furthermore, they frequently eat raw scavenger animals such as land and mangrove crabs, and occasionally some do eat raw freshwater prawns. In the islands of Ponape and Saipan, 6 and 10% respectively, of the prawns examined have been found infected with larvae of *A. cantonensis*. Furthermore, the stomachs of two out of forty land crabs (*Cardisoma hirtipes*) from Saipan which were examined, harbored infective larvae morphologically identical to those of *A. cantonensis* (see Alicata, 1964a).

During a visit to Micronesia by the writer in 1964, two sisters who had shown symptoms of eosinophilic meningoencephalitis in Saipan in 1958, both reported having eaten raw land crabs shortly before the onset of illness. Of nine similar cases in Ponape, seven gave a history of having eaten mangrove crabs, and two had eaten mangrove crabs and raw freshwater prawns.

During the above indicated visit, the giant African snail, *Achatina fulica*, was found to be very common in Saipan and less common in Ponape. Moreover, the examination of twenty-five snails from each of these localities revealed that all of them harbored larvae of *A. cantonensis* (Alicata, unpublished data). It appears that land crabs do occasionally attack and feed on *Achatina* snails, as has been observed by Williams (1951) in Kenya. Furthermore, it appears possible for mangrove crabs to feed on *Achatina* snails which are washed from the mountainous areas into the mangrove swamps following torrential rainfalls. Of importance in this connection is that in a visit to Ponape by the writer in 1948, the *Achatina* snail population was found to be much higher than in 1964. As a result, it appears likely that around 1948 infection with *A. cantonensis* among the mangrove crabs might have been more common, and this could account for the higher incidence of eosinophilic meningoencephalitis in Ponape during that period. Furthermore, it is likely that cases of the disease which were believed to have occurred among Japanese troops in Ponape during 1944 and 1945 (Bailey, 1948) might have been due to eating imperfectly cooked *Achatina* snails. These snails were eaten not only because they were supposed by the Japanese to possess curative powers, but because the exigency of war made the eating of the snails a necessity (Mead, 1961). The extent to which eosinophilic meningoencephalitis in Micronesia is transmitted through the ingestion of improperly cooked liver or other visceral organs of pigs is as yet unknown. In Micronesia, pigs are allowed to roam freely in the fields, and it is likely that they feed on mollusks, especially on *Achatina fulica*, which are ubiquitous. Furthermore, farmers frequently feed *Achatina* snails to pigs; although the snails are usually boiled, it is likely that sometimes they are not adequately cooked.

2. *Water and Soil*

Although human infection with larvae of *A. cantonensis* through water or soil is questionable, such a possibility does exist. Third stage larvae of this parasite are known to escape from molluscan hosts in water, especially from those that are injured. This suggests that open bodies of water may become contaminated. Infection may, therefore, result from drinking from such water, a habit that is often practised by some native people in the Pacific (Cheng and Alicata, 1964).

The escape of larvae from injured mollusks or land planarians also may contaminate soil. It appears possible, therefore, that the habit of going barefoot in the tropics may occasionally lead to infection through broken skin areas. Experimentally, it has been possible to infect rats by placing the infective larvae on scarified skin but not on intact skin (Alicata and Brown, 1962).

V. CONCLUSION

Studies carried out during the past few years have indicated the importance of the rat lungworm as the most likely etiological agent of cerebral angio-strongylosis of man in several areas, including south-east Asia and the Pacific islands. Because of the fact that up to 1961 this parasite was hardly known, its recognition now as an important parasite of man has opened up a new chapter in the field of human parasitology. It should be pointed out, however, that the studies of Mackerras and Sandars (1955) on the life cycle of the parasite in the rat host paved the way for this new finding.

The more important information which has been obtained concerning *A. cantonensis* since 1961 includes: (1) ability of the parasite to migrate, develop and produce eosinophilic meningoencephalitis in man and simian hosts; (2) the existence of a parallel relationship between the geographical distribution of human cases of eosinophilic meningoencephalitis and distribution of the parasite in the rodent host; (3) ability of the parasite to utilize, under natural conditions, a variety of land mollusks as intermediate hosts, and to utilize freshwater prawns, land planarians, land crabs, pigs, and calves as carrier hosts; and (4) the apparent transmission of the parasite to man by ingestion of uncooked carrier hosts and molluscan intermediate hosts.

The information which has thus far been obtained in connection with the relationship of *A. cantonensis* to human disease can only be regarded as basic preliminary information. There are many gaps which remain to be investigated in the fields of biology, epidemiology, immunology, pathology, chemotherapy, and others. Some of the more urgent research needs include: (1) determination of a simple technique for the diagnosis of human angiostrongylosis, which includes the possible use of purified worm antigen suitable for cutaneous testing; (2) more information on animals which serve as carrier hosts for the infective larval parasite, and the methods of human infection; (3) more information on the effects of the parasite in the primate and other mammalian hosts, with special reference to neurological and related disorders. Much of the knowledge gained from these and related studies will assist in the better diagnosis, understanding, and control of this newly recognized disease-producing agent.

ACKNOWLEDGEMENT

Part of the work reported here has been supported by Research Grant NB-04965 of the Institute of Neurological Diseases and Blindness, Institutes of Health, U.S. Public Health Service.

Published with the approval of the Director of Hawaii Agricultural Experiment Station as Miscellaneous Paper No. 165.

REFERENCES

Alicata, J. E. (1962). *Angiostrongylus cantonensis* (Nematoda: Metastrongylidae) as a causative agent of eosinophilic meningitis of man in Hawaii and Tahiti. *Canad. J. Zool.* **40**, 5–8.

Alicata, J. E. (1963a). The incidence of *Angiostrongylus cantonensis* (Chen) among rats and mollusks in New Caledonia and surrounding islands and its relationship to eosinophilic meningitis. *S. Pac. Comm. Tech. Pap.* **139**, 1–9.

Alicata, J. E. (1963b). Morphological and biological differences between the infective larvae of *Angiostrongylus cantonensis* and those of *Anafilaroides rostratus. Canad. J. Zool.* **41**, 1179–1183.

Alicata, J. E. (1963c). Incapability of vertebrates to serve as paratenic host for the infective larvae of *Angiostrongylus cantonensis. J. Parasit.* **49** (5, Sect. 2), 48.

Alicata, J. E. (1963d). Experimental work on eosinophilic meningitis. *Plant. Hlth* **18**, 17–23.

Alicata, J. E. (1964a). Land crabs as probable parentenic hosts for the infective larvae of *Angiostrongylus cantonensis. J. Parasit.* **50** (3, Sect. 2), 39.

Alicata, J. E. (1964b). Pigs and calves as carrier hosts for the infective larvae of *Angiostrongylus cantonensis. J. Parasit.* **50**, (3, Sect. 2), 39.

Alicata, J. E. (1964c). Parasitic infections of man and animals in Hawaii. *Tech. Bull. Hawaii Agric. Exp. Sta.* **61**, 1–139.

Alicata, J. E. and Brown, R. W. (1962). Observations on the method of human infection with *Angiostrongylus cantonensis* in Tahiti. *Canad. J. Zool.* **40**, 755–760.

Alicata, J. E. and Brown, R. W. (1963). Observations on the cause and transmission of eosinophilic meningitis in Hawaii and the South Pacific. *Proc. Hawaii. Acad. Sci.* 1962–63, 14–15.

Alicata, J. E. and McCarthy, D. D. (1964). On the incidence and distribution of the rat lungworm, *Angiostrongylus cantonensis*, in the Cook Islands, with observations made in New Zealand and Western Samoa. *Canad. J. Zool.* **42**, 605–11.

Alicata, J. E., Loison, G. and Cavallo, A. (1963). Parasitic meningoencephalitis experimentally produced in a monkey with larvae of *Angiostrongylus cantonensis. J. Parasit.* **49**, 156–157.

Allison, M. E. (1962). A meningoencephalitis syndrome characterized by eosinophilia of cerebrospinal fluid. *Amer. J. trop. Med.* **11**, 238–240.

Applebaum, I. L. and Wexberg, L. E. (1944). Eosinophilia in cerebrospinal fluid. *J. Amer. med. Ass.* **124**, 830–831.

Ash, L. R. (1962a). Observations on the helminth parasites of rats in Hawaii. *J. Parasit.* **48**, 66–68.

Ash, L. R. (1962b). Quoted by Malek, E. A. (1962). "Laboratory Guides and Notes for Medical Malacology." 154 pp. Burgess Publishing Co., Minneapolis.

Bailey, C. A. (1948). Epidemic of eosinophilic meningitis, previously undescribed disease, occurring on Ponape, Eastern Caroline. *U.S. Nav. Med. Res. Inst.* Oct. 14, Project NM 005 007, Rept. No. 7, 1–32.

Beaver, P. C. (1962). Toxocarosis (visceral larva migrans) in relation to tropical eosinophilia. *Bull. Soc. Path. exot.* **55**, 555–576.

Castaigne, P., Buge, A., Escourolle, R. and des Lauriers, A. (1959). Manifestations nerveuses de bilharzioses. *Bull. Soc. Med. Paris* **75**, 749.

Chen, H. T. (1935). Un nouveau nematode pulmonaire, *Pulmonema cantonensis* n. g., n. sp., des rats de Canton. *Ann. Parasit. hum. comp.* **13**, 312–317.

Cheng, T. C. and Alicata, J. E. (1964). The possible role of water in the transmission of *Angiostrongylus cantonensis* (Nematoda: Metastrongylidae). *J. Parasit.* **50**, (3 Sect. 2), 39–40.

Cheng, T. C. and Alicata, J. E. (1965). *Malacologia* **2**, 267–274.

Cheng, T. C. and Burton, R. W. (1965). *J. Parasit.* **51**, 29.

Dent, J. H., Nochols, R. L., Beaver, P. C., Carrera, G. M. and Staggers, R. J. (1956). Visceral larva migrans with a case report. *Amer. J. Path.* **32**, 777–803.

Done, J. T., Richardson, M. D. and Gibson, T. E. (1960). Experimental visceral larva migrans in the pig. *Res. Vet. Sci.* **1**, 133–151.

Franco, R., Bories, S. and Couzin, B. (1960). A propos de 142 cas de meningite à eosinophiles observés à Tahiti et Nouvelle-Calédonie. *Med. trop. Marseille* **20**, 41–55.

Horio, S. R. and Alicata, J. E. (1961). Parasitic meningoencephalitis in Hawaii—A new parasitic disease of man. *Hawaii med. J.* **21**, 139–140.

Jackson, W. B. (1962). *In* "Pacific Islands Rat Ecology," 274 pp. B. P. Bishop Museum, Bull. 225, Honolulu.

Kaczynski, M. (1936). Cytologie de liquide cephalo-rachidien. *J. belge Neurol. Psychiat.* **36**, 94–105.

Kulkav, A. E. (1931). The diagnosis of racemose cysticercus during life. *Arch. Neurol. Psychiat.* **24**, 135.

Kuntz, R. E. and Myers, B. J. (1964). *Amer. J. trop. Med Hyg.* **13**, 686–692.

Lim, B. L., Ow Yang, C. K. and Lie, K. J. (1962). Prevalence of *Angiostrongylus cantonensis* in Malayan rats and some possible intermediate hosts. *Med. J. Malaya* **17**, 89.

Lindquist, W. D. and Li, S. Y. (1955). Some nematodes of rats from Guam, M. I., and notes on species of *Rictularia. J. Parasit.* **41**, 194–197.

Loison, G. (1955). Poisonous fish of the South Pacific. *S. Pac. Quart. Bull.* **5**, 28–31.

Loison, G. (1963). *S. Pac. Comm. Tech. Pap.* **139**, 1–9.

Mackerras, M. J. and Sandars, D. F. (1955). The life history of the rat lungworm, *Angiostrongylus cantonensis* (Chen) (Nematoda: Metastrongylidae). *Aust. J. Zool.* **3**, 1–25.

Marshall, J. T. (1962). *In* "Pacific Island Rat Ecology." 274 pp. B. P. Bishop Museum, Honolulu, Hawaii, Bull. 225, Honolulu.

Matsumoto, T. (1927). On a nematode found in the lung, especially the pulmonary artery of the wild rat. *J. med. Ass. Formosa* **36**, 2620–2623.

Mead, A. R. (1961). "The Giant African Snail." 257 pp. University of Chicago Press.

Nomura, S. and Lin, H. (1945). First clinical case of *Hemostrongylus ratti*. Yokogawa in man. *Taiwan No Ikai* **3**, 589–592. (In Japanese; for English translation see *Amer. J. trop. Med. Hyg.* **13**, 589–590, 1964.)

Nonomura, T. (1941). Ein Fall von parasitärer Meningitis, hervorgerufen durch *Distomum pulmonum* mit besonderer Beruchsichtigung des Auxtretens der eosinophilen Leukozyten im Liquor cerebrospinalis. *Okayama Igakkai Zasshi* **53**, 54–68.

Prommindaroj, K., Leelawongs, N. and Pradatsundarasar, A. (1962). Human angiostrongyliasis of the eye in Bangkok. *Amer. J. trop. Med. Hyg.* **11**, 759–761.

Richards, C. S. (1963). *Angiostrongylus cantonensis*: Intermediate host studies. *J. Parasit* **49** (5, Sect. 2), 46–47.

Rosen, L., Laigret, J. and Bories, S. (1961). Observations on an outbreak of eosinophilic meningitis on Tahiti, French Polynesia. *Amer. J. Hyg.* **74**, 26–41.

Rosen, L., Chappell, R., Laqueur, G. L., Wallace, G. D. and Weinstein, P. P. (1962). Eosinophilic meningitis caused by a metastrongylid lungworm of rats. *J. Amer. med. Ass.* **179**, 620–624.

Sandars, D. F. (1957). Lungworm from rats captured in Britain. *Nature, Lond.* **179**, 109–110.

Schacher, J. F. and Chee-Hock, C. (1960). Malaysian Parasites. XLVII. Nematode parasites of three common house rat species in Malaya, with notes on *Rictularia tani* Hoeppli, 1929. *Stud. Inst. med. Res. Malaya* **29**, 209–216.

Sison, A. G., Campos, P. C. and Apostol, R. (1951). Eosinophilia in spinal fluid (4 cases). *Acta med. philipp.* **8**, 95–107.

Smit, A. M. (1962). "Over eosinofilie bij worminfecties en eosinofiele meningites" Doctoral thesis in Public Health, University of Amsterdam, 125 pp.

Smit, A. M. (1963). Eosinophilic meningitis. *Trop. geogr. Med.* **15**, 225–232.

Stammer, H. J. (1956). Die parasiten deutscher Kleinsauger. *Zool. Anz. Suppl.*, **19**, 362–390.

Strecker, R. L. and Jackson, W. B. (1962). *In* "Pacific Islands Rat Ecology," 274 pp. B. P. Bishop Museum, Bull. 225, Honolulu.

Terplan, K., Kraus, R. and Barnes, G. (1957). Eosinophilic meningoencephalitis with predominantly cerebellar changes caused by *Trichinella* infection. *J. Mt. Sinai Hosp.* **24**, 1293.

Trubert, E. (1952). Meningites aigues, benigne, de nature indeterminée observées sous forme épidémique en Nouvelle-Calédonie. *Bull. Ass. med. N.-Calédonie* **4**, 1–23.

Uematsu, S. and Shiozaki, S. (1935). Cerebral paragonimiasis accompanied by meningitis. *Zikken Iho* **21**, 1491–1497. (In Japanese.)

Vaillant, A., Peyrin, A., Cavallo, A. and Bordes, F. P. (1961). Reflexions sur les rapports possibles entre les eosinophilies rachidiennes et l'ichtyotoxisme en Nouvelle-Calédonie. *Bull. Soc. Path. exot.* **54**, 1075–1090.

Weinstein, P. P., Rosen, L., Laqueur, G. L. and Sawyer, T. K. (1963). *Angiostrongylus cantonensis* infection in rats and rhesus monkeys, and observations on the survival of the parasite in vitro. *Amer. J. trop. Med. Hyg.* **12**, 358–377.

Williams, F. X. (1951). Life-history studies of East African *Achatina* snails. *Bull. Mus. comp. Zool. Harv.* **105**, 295–317.

Yokogawa, S. (1937). A new species of nematode found in the lungs of rats *Haemostrongylus ratti* sp. nov. *Trans. nat. Hist. Soc. Formosa* **27**, 247–250.

Feeding in Ectoparasitic Acari with Special Reference to Ticks

DON. R. ARTHUR

*Department of Zoology and Animal Biology, King's College,
University of London, England*

I. INTRODUCTION

A classification of the feeding mechanisms of invertebrate animals proposed by Yonge (1928) included arthropods feeding on vertebrate body fluids *in toto* under the heading of suctorial feeders. Since that time considerable advances have been made in our knowledge of the feeding habits of ectoparasitic arthropods. Among the significant papers which have established that certain groups of insects, for example, feed on blood are: mosquitoes (Gordon and Lumsden, 1939; Griffiths and Gordon, 1952; O'Rourke, 1956); tsetse flies (Gordon *et al.*, 1956); triatomine bugs (Lavoipierre *et al.*, 1959); *Haematopota pluvialis* (Dickerson and Lavoipierre, 1959); *Chrysops* (Gordon and Crewe, 1948, 1953; Lavoipierre, 1958) and *Culicoides* (Gordon and Duke, 1955), and others. Gorirossi (1950) has postulated that a mite, *Bdellonyssus bacoti*, feeds on blood.

In other cases of arthropod feeding it has been reported that the blood is not the sole nutritive product, e.g. Shortt and Swaminath (1928) noted that the sandfly *Phlebotomus argentipes* occasionally imbibed a pale yellow fluid thought to be a serous fluid from the wound, instead of blood, whilst in larval trombiculid mites (Jones, 1950; Wharton and Fuller, 1952) we have no evidence of blood feeding.

All the aforementioned arthropods are vectors, to a greater or lesser degree, of various organisms pathogenic to man and his stock, and the need for knowledge of their feeding mechanisms in relation to transmission of disease has been summarized thus by Gordon and Willett (1958): "For a proper understanding of the early stages of an arthropod-borne parasite while in the mammalian host it is necessary not only to study its movements and morphology while in the vertebrate host but also to have some knowledge of the site and its manner of introduction by the vector".

Very little attention has been directed to the constituents of the food ingested by ectoparasites when feeding on vertebrate tissues, mainly because it has been generally assumed, and it is largely true, that blood is the sole food imbibed. However, Gordon (1958) affirmed that "for all practical purposes the parasitic type of (arthropod) bite is adapted to the obtaining of the blood meals, although it is true that, in a few instances, as in the case of trombiculids, it is not blood but lymph which is taken up, nor should it be forgotten that all blood sucking arthropods *take up fluids other than blood*, from their host, an important point when we remember that by this type of feeding, organisms . . . which are not usually present in the circulation, may be taken up by the feeding insect".

Our present interest is in the feeding of ticks and we have referred to the feeding of larval trombiculids because of their possible evolutionary implications in tick feeding. Otherwise the approach adopted in the present contribution involves (1) the feeding mechanism, but without details of the functional morphology of ticks which can be obtained elsewhere; (2) the sites of saliva deposition in the tissues as a means of establishing the possible extent and distribution of any inoculated pathogens; (3) the histopathology of (a) trauma produced by the mouth parts in the skin, and (b) skin reactions due to the salivary secretions. The questions of how pathogens reach the blood circulation, whether the pathogens undergo a tissue stage before reaching the circulation and how and when pathogens are taken up by vectors from blood and/or extravascular tissue still remain fields for active research.

The methods involved in elucidating 1–3 above are based on studies of the functional morphology of the mouth parts of ticks, on histological studies of the bitten area of the host, on studies of the constituents and functions of salivary secretions and histological investigations of the skin at varying time intervals from the injection of pathogens, both by the bite of infected arthropods and by syringe inoculation of infected salivary gland emulsions. The technique of direct observations on the mouth parts of arthropods while feeding in the host's skin (Gordon and Lumsden, 1939; Griffiths and Gordon, 1952) has now been used for studying feeding in soft ticks by Lavoipierre and Riek (1955) and in hard ticks by Gregson (1960a) and promises to be a fruitful development.

II. Feeding in Larval Trombiculid Mites

Larval trombiculids attack a variety of animals, and some are important pests of sheep in Australia, whilst *Trombicula akamushi* and *T. deliensis* are vectors of tsutsugamushi disease. They are included in this review because they illustrate a possible step in the evolution of blood sucking by ticks.

The initial penetration of the skin is effected by the minute cheliceral claws, whose movement and fixation are controlled by the cheliceral muscles. The bases of these claws can rotate. In free-living larvae, when viewed dorsally, the claws lie either with their broad lateral borders in the horizontal plane and the convex or concave edges facing inwards, or with the convex edge of one facing the concave margin of the other, depending on the action of the cheliceral muscles. The bases of the chelicerae rotate preparatory to piercing, so that their inner lateral borders are more or less contiguous, with the pointed apices directed dorsally. The claws are maintained rigidly in this position by the contraction of two sets of muscles when they puncture the skin. Initial puncturing is facilitated by the inclination of the body at about an angle of 45°, whereby the mouth parts obtain an additional thrust, after which the body is lowered as the claws make their curving penetration under the surface.

In dorsal view the cheliceral claws give the appearance of a spearhead since the space between them widens towards their bases, and as the claws become more deeply embedded the puncture increases in width. Jones' (1950) observations show the claws, *in situ*, are parted anteriorly, suggesting that after entry they rotate slightly, enlarging the puncture and facilitating the passage of saliva into the wound. The mechanical action of the chelicerae allows penetration to a depth of 20–25 μ in *Trombicula autumnalis* (Jones, 1950) and attachment to the skin is accomplished by these claws (Schumacher and Hoeppli, 1963). When the oral aperture is applied to the orifice of the puncture intimate association of the mouth parts and the integument is completed by the product resulting from the action of saliva upon the surrounding tissue (Jones, 1950). The view taken by Schumacher and Hoeppli (1963) is that the gap between the mouth parts and the skin is sealed off by a hyaline mass which rapidly coagulates into a solid gel, and that this secretion is produced from the salivary glands of the mite and is forced out under pressure. It moulds itself around the mouth parts and the epidermis, and insinuates itself into the intercellular spaces of the adjacent Malpighian layer.

Compression, rupture and displacement of the epidermal cells around the laceration are the first observable effects of penetration by the mite (Schumacher and Hoeppli, 1963), although cells adjacent to the secretion frequently show disorganized cytoplasm and pyknotic nuclei. No structure resembling the tissue canal (= the "stylostome" or "histosiphon" of some authors) can be detected when the mouth parts are first inserted. Earlier authors (Gudden, 1871; Brandis, 1897; Brandes, 1908) considered the stylostome as a retractile organ, and others (Toldt, 1923; Vitzhum, 1930; Winkler, 1953) that the central canal contained a tongue-like organ. The investigations of Jourdain (1899), André (1927), Jones (1950), Hoeppli and Feng (1931), Hoeppli and Schumacher (1962) and Schumacher and Hoeppli (1963) have, however, indicated that the stylostome is a secretory derivative from the salivary glands of the mite.

According to Jones (1950) the saliva secreted by the mite, after preliminary attachment by the cheliceral claws, exerts a histolytic action on the Malpighian cells, in response to which the host lays down protective tissue around them. The disorganized liquefied tissue is then sucked into the alimentary canal as a result of pharyngeal peristalsis, and on exhaustion of the supply the sucking action ceases, to be followed by further alternating salivary injections and imbibitions of digested tissue. By a repetition of these processes the saliva, pumped under pressure, is forced through the newly deposited protective tissue producing a fountain-like effect and affecting the Malpighian cells within a relatively wide arc. The conclusions to be drawn from Jones' studies are that in the harvest mite (*T. autumnalis*) the hyaline mass of the "stylostome" is composed principally of superimposed layers of keratinized epithelial cells deposited to counteract the inimical effects of the mite secretion and that the salivary secretion is of one type only. Jourdain (1899) and André (1927) contended that the walls of the stylostome were formed from solidified secretion probably produced by the larval salivary glands. André, too, stated that the stylostome produced an alteration of the host tissue peripherally, and he deduced from this that its function was to transform host tissue into nutritive material suitable for ingestion by the mite. The recent work of Schumacher and Hoeppli (1963) agrees with these authors in considering the stylostome as being of salivary origin, but they recognize that the secretions are of two types. The first secretion, to which we have already referred, is inoculated after penetration by the cheliceral claws, and this solidifies rapidly into a rather solid gel. Comparable changes in the physical state of the saliva of living mites are given by Jones (1950), Willman (1955) and Cross (1962). Histochemical tests on the hyaline mass produced in the host tissue as a result of the feeding of the mite show the presence of substantial quantities of acid mucopolysaccharides and are indicative of salivary origin (Schumacher and Hoeppli, 1963). The general shape of the mass and its physical structure, as revealed in polarized light, suggest that it is inoculated in batches at successive stages of feeding. The birefringence noted in certain areas of the mass has been attributed by these authors to the specific orientation of molecules as a result of mechanical strain. Further, they note that the birefringence is confined to areas of increased opacity at the periphery of the mass and of its individual portions. The increase in opacity indicates a more rapid solidification of these areas which possibly is responsible for the strain exerted on the molecules. The direction of flow in the central canal may possibly be another factor responsible for the orientation of molecules in the inner wall of the feeding tube. There is also an increased opacity where the hyaline mass is in apposition to the host tissues and this may assist in the solidification of these areas.

André (1927) and Jones (1950) have assumed that the purpose of mite salivary secretion is to liquefy host tissue for nutriment, but Schumacher and Hoeppli (1963) have indicated that rapid gelation of the secretion would hardly have this effect, and there is no evidence that this secretion has a histolytic effect. Moreover, if histolysis were effected—as suggested by André and Jones—this would lead to liquefaction of tissue around the wound and the detachment of the mite.

The ejection of this first secretion is followed by the ejection of another secretion (Schumacher and Hoeppli, 1963), which is forced out from the salivary glands under pressure and forms a central canal through the more solid hyaline mass. This connects the buccal cavity of the mite with the intercellular tissue of the host. The suggestion for the existence of two types of salivary secretions is not surprising in view of the complexity of the cellular organization of the gland as shown by Thor (1904) and Jones (1950) in mites and Till (1959, 1961) in ticks. But until more information is available concerning their biochemical action their biological role is speculative. Moreover, it has been established that ticks likewise produce dual secretions (Gregson, 1960b; Arthur, 1962). The second secretion differs physicochemically from the first in that it remains fluid and does not gelate (Schumacher and Hoeppli, 1963). Its histolytic properties are also indicated by varying degrees of vacuolation, intercellular oedema and even vesiculation, particularly at the apex of the stylostome (Hoeppli and Schumacher, 1962). Here a sinus is formed and this frequently contains eosinophilic leucocytes undergoing necrosis and liquefaction. The surrounding epithelium is oedematous with considerable infiltration of leucocytes. Acanthosis and parakeratosis may occur beyond the inflammatory area, but a dermal reaction is almost invariably present as a fairly dense and widespread accumulation of inflammatory cells. The reaction is dominated by numerous eosinophilic leucocytes and large numbers of plasma cells, and the dermis bordering the sinus shows cellular infiltration and interstitial oedema. During the actual process of feeding these two secretions are deposited alternately in the host tissue, and after inoculation of the second secretion the mite sucks in liquids. By this means the feeding tube or stylostome becomes more massive and is longer, and it is completed either within the epidermis in *T. autumnalis* (Jones, 1950) or in the dermis (Brandis, 1897; Vitzhum, 1930; Ewing, 1944; Wharton and Fuller, 1952; Winkler, 1953; Hoeppli and Schumacher, 1962; Schumacher and Hoeppli, 1963). Jones (1950) assumed that the histosiphon is derived from keratinized epithelial cells, but there is no evidence of epidermal cells being involved in its formation within the dermis (Wharton and Fuller, 1952). The possibility that the stylostome is formed by the reaction of the host tissues to the salivary secretion has been suggested by Brethes (1909), André (1927), Talice (1929), Feng and Hoeppli (1933), but hitherto no investigation appears to have been made on this problem, or to determine how and to what extent the two reactants participate in its formation

Previous to 1962 it was assumed that the nutrient source was derived from liquefied tissue elements (see, for example, André, 1927; Jones, 1950) and there is no evidence that solids are introduced into the alimentary canal at any time (Jones, 1950). The recent work of Hoeppli and Schumacher indicates that it consists of tissue fluid. This is accessible to the mite once initial penetration has been effected and the feeding tube has gained access to the intercellular spaces of the Malpighian layer and even to those of the dermis. Preservation of the connexion with intercellular spaces, presumably by the anticoagulant action of the salivary secretion, implies replenishment of free fluid by its increased effusion towards the source of irritation. Schumacher and Hoeppli (1963) do not consider digestion of cellular material adequate to maintain a significant flow of nutritive material, although they do recognize, as already indicated, that histolysis of tissue does occur around the apex of the stylostome. The preservation of enzyme activity in tissue cells depends on the structural and functional integrity of these cells and according to Schumacher and Hoeppli (1963) changes in the structure or the function of cells or cell components are indicative of metabolic upsets. The application of appropriate enzyme tests to the stylostome does not show activity of alkaline and acid phosphatase, non-specific esterase, succinic dehydrogenase and DPN and TPN-diaphosphorase, and any changes in enzyme activity are closely limited to those areas of the skin which are mechanically affected by the action of the parasite. This applies particularly to the epithelial cells in close association with the stylostome and the region at its apex, and rather supports the claims of these authors that tissue fluid is the main source of food.

Trombiculid mites occur in many parts of the world, and the tropics are particularly rich in species. Of the 400 or so species described, ten are known to attack man occasionally, fourteen are regular feeders on him in certain areas and two of these, viz. *Trombicula akamushi* and *T. deliensis*, are vectors of rat typhus (Audy, 1952). Their natural hosts are rats to which they cause no local reaction. "Scrub itch", causing an intense delayed action in man, results from the bite of the other twelve species, and on this basis Audy (1951) suggested that reptiles or birds are their "natural" hosts and that the reaction in mammalian skin to mite bite is due to feeding on incidental or "unnatural" hosts. To test the validity of Audy's supposition the skin reaction of 100 wild rats of various species, two tree squirrels (*Callosciurus nigrovittatus*), four skinks (*Mabina multifasciata*), all naturally infected with different species of *Trombicula* mites, and two chickens experimentally infected with *T. akamushi* and *T. deliensis* were investigated histologically by Hoeppli and Schumacher (1962). Their conclusions indicated that skin reactions due to infestation by various mite species followed an essentially similar pattern, irrespective of whether the stylostome was confined to the Malpighian layer or extended into the dermis. The changes included local necrosis, oedema, inflammatory infiltration and proliferation of epidermal tissue. An "early and rather diffuse inflammatory infiltration with rapidly increasing numbers of eosinophilic leucocytes, plasma cells and later histocytes in the affected area" occurred in the dermis. This reaction was comparable to that produced by any foreign body within the skin and primarily of the exudative or proliferative type. The results as a whole showed a basic similarity in the type of reaction produced, but were very different in degree. It was not found possible to correlate the intensity of the skin reaction with either different host or mite species. Audy's supposition on "natural" or "unnatural" hosts for different mite species requires further investigation under controlled experimental conditions.

This discussion on the feeding of trombiculid mites has been introduced at this stage as an evolutionary background to understanding the feeding of ticks, which do utilize free tissue fluids, tissue fluids resulting from digestion of cellular elements and blood.

III. Feeding in Ticks

Details of the functional anatomy of the feeding mechanisms of various genera and species of ticks have been given by Bertram (1939), Douglas

(1943), Arthur (1951, 1953a, b, 1957, 1960, 1962, and unpublished 1964) and Gregson (1960a, b).

The feeding period for all stages of hard ticks (Ixodidae) is measured in days, whereas in nymphs and adults of soft ticks (Argasidae) it is a question of minutes and hours, as shown in Table I, compiled from various sources by Arthur (1962).

TABLE I

Feeding Times for the Nymphs and Adults of some Argasid Ticks

Species	Stage	Time for each feed	Wt. when unfed (mg)	Wt. of blood meal (mg)
Argas reflexus	Nymph	½–2 h	—	—
A. reflexus	Adult	5 min–2 h	—	—
A. persicus	As for *A. reflexus*			
A. boueti	Nymph	30–60 min (feeds in last instar, but only if 3 instars occur)		
A. boueti	Adult	30–35 min	—	—
A. (Chiropterargas) confusus	Adult	40 min–2 h	—	—
A. (Carios) vespertilionis	Nymph	30–40 min	—	—
A. (Carios) vespertilionis	Adult	30–40 min	—	—
Ornithodoros moubata	Nymph	30 min	28·5	68·3
O. moubata	Adult	30 min	33·4	88·5
O. savignyi	Nymph	15–30 min	—	—
O. savignyi	Adult	15–30 min	—	—

A notable exception to this rapid feeding rate among argasids is afforded by nymphs and adults of *Argas brumpti*, which require 90 days and 8–21 days respectively to become replete. Here we may have an analogous situation to that observed in hard ticks, where the cuticle may not be preformed. The argasid larvae require longer feeding periods to become replete; thus larvae of *Argas persicus* and *A. reflexus* feed for 5–10 days, *A. boueti* for 6–25 days, *A. brumpti* for 6–15 days, *A. confusus* for 5–30 days, *A. vespertilionis* for 17–19 days and *Ornithodoros delanoe acinus* for 7–14 days (Arthur, 1962). The work of Lees (1952) and Balashov (1957) suggests that the slow feeding of ixodid ticks and of the larvae of argasid ticks is correlated with the formation of the cuticle and only on its abrupt cessation towards the end of the feeding period is the rapid distension of the body possible. On the other hand, the cuticle of nymphs and adults of argasid ticks is preformed before feeding commences (Lees, 1952) and the body is immediately capable of passive swelling after ingesting nutrient material. The larvae of certain species of *Ornithodoros* do not feed and have become devices for allowing ticks to leave the eggs. Thus those of *O. moubata* remain quiescent after they leave the egg, do not feed and moult to nymphs. In some individuals of *O. savignyi* this process has evolved further and moulting to nymphs is completed within the egg (Arthur, 1962).

The number of occasions on which argasid nymphs feed is variable; the nymphs of *A. persicus* and *A.* (*Carios*) *vespertilionis* feed twice, those of *A.* (*Chiropterargas*) *confusus* and *A. brumpti* feed three times. A fourth feeding period may, however, occur in the latter. *A. boueti* is of interest, for if two nymphal instars occur no feeding takes place, but if three nymphal instars develop feeding occurs in the third one (Hoogstraal, 1956). Feeding periods in the nymphs of *Ornithodoros* species are also variable; e.g. in *O. moubata* 4–5 feeds are taken and in *O. savignyi* 4–7 feeds. Adults of soft ticks are capable of feeding several times and this is in contrast to the hard ticks which feed only once.

As in mites, the feeding process in ticks is initiated by the chelicerae, which are forced out anteriorly by the contraction of the dorso-ventral muscles of the idiosoma. By this means the digits at the tips of the chelicerae press against the skin of the host and its laceration is effected by the alternate shearing motions of the digits, which are produced when the abductor muscles (inserted on the base of the digit) pull strongly and the digits move outwards. This action in some hard ticks may be of long duration, but in soft ticks the penetration of the skin is usually very active and rapid. Penetration of such a tough medium as skin requires a rigid structure and this property is conferred on the chelicerae by the sclerotization of their walls and pressure exerted by the contained haemolymph (Arthur, 1962). The hypostome enters the wound either passively in the wake of the chelicerae or it may be slightly elevated by the action of its basal elevator muscles. The first movements of the chelicerae are accompanied by the straightening of the hindermost pair of legs of the tick, whereby the body at first tilts at an angle of 45° to the skin. With the deeper penetration of the mouth parts into the skin, this angle increases quite considerably. The depth to which mechanical penetration can be achieved by the chelicerae is a function of their length and of the degree of protraction of the cheliceral shafts. Within the limits of any one species this will show a graded series which increases from the larva to the nymph, and the nymph to the adult feeding stage. Thus in larval forms, with short cheliceral shafts, mechanical penetration may be superficial, reaching beyond the Malpighian layer (Arthur, 1962), whereas in females deep blood capillaries may be ruptured by the cheliceral digits as shown by Gregson (1960a) working with *Dermacentor andersoni*. Saito *et al.* (1960) and Saito and Ohara (1961) reported that the depth of penetration into the host tissue by the trophi of ticks showed considerable variation. Thus, in *Ixodes* ticks the hypostome was deeply embedded in the dermis, whereas in *Haemaphysalis* and *Boophilus* insertion was superficial. After insertion of the mouth parts all active movements of the extra basis components cease except for occasional movements of the cheliceral digits.

As in trombiculid mites the mechanical action of the chelicerae is reinforced by secretory activity, the source of which is the paired salivary glands. Till (1959, 1961) stated that in *Rhipicephalus appendiculatus* each gland consists of a mass of spherical alveoli approximately 0·02–0·04 mm in diameter. The alveoli are of two types, one being located at the anterior end of the gland, the other forming its bulk. The cells of the anterior part of the gland have an indefinite peripheral structure with fibrils radiating in the direction of the ductules, where they end freely. The nuclei of these cells are small and located near to the lumen. In the remainder of the gland the cells are relatively large, having large basal nuclei and containing either ferment granules or pale, reticulate cytoplasm lacking such granules. Nordenskiöld (1908) further recognized two types of cells within these multicellular alveoli of *I. ricinus*, viz. those having coarse secretory granules (= *Mundungszellen*) and those with fine secretory granules (= *Funduszellen*). These granular alveoli have been further investigated in *R. appendiculatus* by Till (1959), who showed structural differences in the glands of males and females of this species. Two types of granular alveoli are recognized in the female (Till's types II and III), and three in the male (Till's types II, III and IV). The type II alveoli in both sexes occupy the anterior two-thirds of the gland and open into the main duct or into its larger branches. Within this type of alveolus Till distinguishes two different kinds of cells in the female and an additional kind in the male. The two kinds of cells common to both male and female contain either coarse, deep red-staining granules (with Mallory's stain) or reticular cytoplasm with a varying number of coarse, blue-staining granules. The cells, which occur only in the male, contain bright yellow-staining granules. These are difficult to identify in unfed ticks, but are readily evinced in those which have imbibed blood.

The second type of granular alveoli (= Till's type III) predominate in the posterior part and on the terminal branches of the anterior third of the salivary glands. The cells comprising these alveoli are divisible into those containing coarse, orange-red-staining granules, those with large (5 μ) orange-staining globules and those either devoid of secretory granules or else with blue-staining granules of varying sizes. The transient nature of this last group of cells depends on the stage of development of the tick, for in feeding females, nymphs and larvae they become very large, but remain inconspicuous in males. Till considers that this type of cell corresponds to Nordenskiöld's *Funduszellen* and the remainder to his *Mundungszellen*.

A third type of granular alveolus is found scattered amongst the preceding granular type in males only. They are composed of a number of similar cells which become filled with purple-staining granules after the tick begins to engorge. Despite recognition of these different cell types, the role their contents play in the life of ticks awaits elucidation.

Gregson (1955) demonstrated the conditions under which ticks extrude saliva, and the quantities extruded. This he did by immobilizing ticks on a wad of Plasticine and then counter-sinking the hypostome and chelicerae in a hole of 1 mm diameter cut in a thin sheet of tin. A capillary tube of 1 mm bore, previously drawn out to an 0·44 mm orifice and calibrated in μg was then inserted over the hypostome. By this means the palpi were pushed apart and the soft cheliceral sheath pushed back in much the same way as happens when a tick is normally attached to the host. About 7 μg of secretion was produced within a few minutes of stimulation, even after keeping the tick at room temperature for 1 h or on ice for 3 h subsequent to removal from the host. No secretion appeared to be produced after 30 min when the tick may withdraw some or all of its exudation. Having reached maximum secretory activity no tick could be induced to secrete further, even several hours later, without further feeding on a host. Gregson's results also indicate that as the female continues to feed the secretion increases to a maximum of 34 μg. This is produced by fast feeding, mated females (weight 150–650 mg) between the 5th and 6th days of feeding, but is delayed for a day or two by slow feeding, unmated ticks (weight 150–250 mg). The average quantities of secretion are similar in mated or unmated females whose weights are up to 200 mg, but heavier, mated female ticks occasionally secrete more than unmated females. Rapid diminution of secretions follows on the 8th day of attachment even though the tick is still feeding (Table II).

TABLE II

Tick Secretion Data: Ranked Analysis of Mean Secretion (after Gregson, 1955)

No. of ticks	Wt. range of ticks (mg)	Mean wt. of ticks (mg)	Total secretion (μg)	Range of secretion (μg)	Mean secretion (μg)
11	1–50	25	12·5	0–3·0	1·1 ± 1·0
40	51–100	74	86·0	0–9·0	2·3 ± 2·3
67	101–150	125	243·0	0–17·5	3·6 ± 3·7
63	151–200	175	376·0	0–18·0	6·0 ± 4·7
52	201–250	225	375·0	0–20·0	6·1 ± 5·5
34	251–300	275	282·0	0–22·0	8·3 ± 6·7
22	301–350	325	192·0	0–20·0	8·7 ± 6·3
22	351–400	375	187·0	0–34·0	8·5 ± 9·0
17	401–450	425	141·5	0–24·0	8·3 ± 7·5
7	451–500	475	45·0	2·0–14·0	6·4 ± 4·4
10	501–550	525	90·0	0–22·0	9·0 ± 7·6
6	551–600	575	34·0	2·0–12·0	5·7 ± 4·0
20	601–650	625	153·0	0–19·0	7·6 ± 7·4
9	651–700	675	42·0	0–15·0	4·7 ± 5·5
10	701–750	725	55·0	0–11·0	5·5 ± 4·3
9	751–800	775	35·5	0–10·0	3·9 ± 4·2
1	801–850	825	7·0	7·0	7·0

In these experiments partially fed female ticks were removed from the host and variation in the quantity of exudation may be attributed to the secretion of saliva by the tick immediately before being tested, or to abnormal increase due to lack of blood or to the formation of a clot within the feeding apparatus.

In other experiments Gregson (1955) offered the following forms of blood to the ticks (*D. andersoni*):

(a) Heparinized blood: 2 ml blood plus 1 ml saline containing 4 μg heparin;

(b) Heparinized blood: as above, plasma only;

(c) Heparinized blood: 1 ml blood plus 4 μg heparin;

(d) Fresh blood.

Feeding females accept heparinized blood *in vitro* when the intake may be continuous for periods of more than 1 h. Generally whole blood plus heparin is preferred to diluted blood or only plasma, but a greater secretory response occurs when given plasma alone. Gregson reports that one tick, when given a column of heparinized blood beneath pure clotted blood, drank the serum from around the clot hesitantly. When this was exhausted, she secreted repeatedly, continuously teasing at the clot by an alternate slashing motion of the cheliceral teeth. The clot was finally assimilated, but did not appear to be dissolved by the secretion. Following this the heparinized blood was reached and drunk continuously and quickly. Various functions have been attributed to the salivary secretions and the first to be demonstrated was that of the coagulation of blood (Sabbatani, 1898). Subsequently, Nuttall and Strickland (1908) reported that the quantity of anticoagulant in the glands of a single tick may delay coagulation of 0·02 ml of human blood for 45–95 min. More recent quantitative measurements show that 1 ml of tick (*I. ricinus*) salivary extract of one-quarter dilution delayed clotting in 2 ml of sheep's blood for at least 12 h (Foggie, 1959).

Weak and slow-acting haemolysins have also been detected in tick saliva, exercising their effects some little time after the imbibition of blood (Pavlovsky and Chodukin, 1928, 1929). Lavoipierre and Riek (1955) also report a delay of 2 h before haemolysis takes place in the gut of females of *O. turicata*.

Stained sections of the mouth parts of the ixodid ticks *in situ* in the host tissue reveal that they penetrate into the corium (Fig. 1), where they are surrounded by a somewhat homogeneous zone, the "cement layer" of Cowdry and Danks (1933). The nature of this layer is a matter of dispute, much as is the analogous stylostome of trombiculid mites. Both Cowdry and Danks (1933) and Hoeppli and Feng (1931) considered it to be a secretory product derived from the tick. Foggie (1959) indicated that the "cement substance" is a host-tissue reaction and suggests that the "foreign body" type of reaction surrounding it is, in part at least, exogenous in origin. He supports his claim by experimental evidence of inoculation of salivary gland extracts into host tissues which failed to produce a "cement" reaction.

In fixed preparations the "cement" substance appears as superimposed layers in skin tissue on which adults of *I. hexagonus* had fed (Arthur, 1953b), but with no indications of finely granular layers alternating with the lamellae as described by Cowdry and Danks (1933). This is superficially reminiscent of the hyaline mass of the stylostome of mites, as shown by Jones (1950). Again, as in trombiculid mites, the arrangement of the material as well as its physical structure, as revealed by polarized light, is suggestive of local and intermittent waves of deposition of fluid material (Arthur, unpublished) as the mouth parts of the tick penetrate the tissue. In sections stained with a specific collagen stain the "cement" zone gives a positive reaction, but its significance as yet eludes us (Arthur and Sutton, unpublished). The direct observational studies of Gregson (1960b) show that mechanical laceration of the host tissue is followed by the exudation of white free-flowing fluid which bathes the mouth parts and flows into the puncture. The fluid gelates rapidly

to a latex-like consistency and moulds itself around the trophi, and is function-
ally comparable to the primary secretion of trombiculids. During removal of
ticks from their hosts this solidified secretion is often found around the
mouth parts, and in the past it has been interpreted frequently as forcibly
removed host tissue. Its primary function is to hold the ectoparasite in
position, and recent work (Arthur, unpublished) indicates that it has no
histolytic properties.

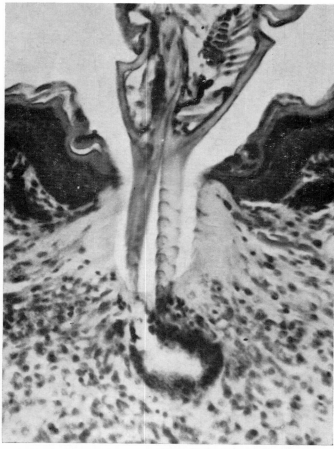

Fig. 1. Tick trophi embedded in rat skin to show the "cement" zone and host tissue
reaction.

A second type of salivary secretion does not appear to gelate as does the
first, and succeeds the first in time. Its more fluid consistency is shown by its
lines of flow between the cellular components producing widespread effects.
The area involved is, however, subject to the intensity of the packing of the
skin components (Arthur, 1962). In lizard skin, where this "packing" is fairly

loose the lines of flow are well dispersed, but in tissue, such as in mouse ear, with much closer "packing", the strand-like effects are more circumscribed. Gregson (1960b) describes this second secretion as a clear fluid. It seems incontrovertible that this secretion contains lytic agents for at the distal extremity of the hypostome in actively feeding *Ixodes* ticks the laminated "cement" material is replaced by a pale, opaque, coagulated mass indicative of coagulation necrosis, resulting from the destruction of local tissue cells by lysins. This mass frequently contains dispersed melanin granules, small chromatin granules and any nuclei remaining are frequently pyknotic. Cytolysins destroy only local tissue cells without affecting blood cells, which are ingested whole by the tick (Cowdry and Danks, 1933). The histolytic potency of the secretion of some ticks at least (which at the time of feeding contains both eosinophilic and basophilic material) is demonstrated by the liquefaction of the cartilage of the pinna of mouse ear by nymphs of *I. trianguliceps* and of the ear tissues of a rhinoceros by a female of *Dermacentor rhinocerinus* (Arthur, 1962). Partial penetration of the cartilage of the pinna of a guinea-pig as a result of infestation of the ear by *Dermacentor sinicus* is also reported by Hoeppli and Feng (1931). The cartilage surrounding the penetrating trophi is misshapen, suggestive of an initial liquefaction process and having passed through the cartilage the effects of the secretion are manifest as an outward flow into the dermal tissue. The cytoplasm of these cells is disorganized and the nuclei are reduced to chromatin granules. The tip of the hypostome eventually comes to lie near the epidermis of the inner surface of the ear and here again the nuclei frequently show pyknosis and karyorhexis. Occasionally the homogeneous exudate extends deeply into the subcutaneous layers and exercises a solvent action on the muscles.

Thus far it would appear that feeding in ticks is similar to that observed in Trombiculid larva, and it would seem that originally the two forms originated from a stock which fed on extravascular tissue fluids, and only with the acquisition of lengthened chelicerae, and probably with more potent secretions, was feeding on more deeply situated tissues possible. The resemblance goes further than this, for a blood meal does not appear to be essential for the development of the immature stages of ticks. On occasions, all stages have been observed to become fully engorged and to remain quite white in colour. The gut contents, under these circumstances, have always yielded negative results for haem (Sutton and Arthur, 1962). Presumably these "white ticks" have fed on tissue fluid only (Foggie, 1959), and this seems to be a normal occurrence in the larvae of some species. On heavily infested animals in poor health, Riek (1957) has reported that many engorging adult females may be translucent and filled with clear fluid in contrast to the dark colour resulting from ingested blood.

Apart from laceration of capillaries by the chelicerae of *D. andersoni* and the formation of the blood pool (Gregson, 1960b), it has been noted that the effect of the secondarily produced secretion is to cause distension of the endothelial cells of the capillaries resulting in their eventual rupture and the production of a haemorrhagic area (Gregson, 1937).

Red blood cells are strikingly absent from the homogeneous layer which surrounds the extra-basis region except at its tip, whilst polymorphonuclear leucocytes, present in some numbers within the capillaries, also occur extra-vascularly. Groups of red blood cells have also been encountered between muscle fibres of the corium into which the homogeneous exudate has pene-trated. Only red blood cells appear to be undamaged, the remaining cells being either completely broken down or represented by granular fragments (Arthur, 1962). These observations support the suggestion of Cowdry and Danks (1933) that cytolysins destroy local tissue cells, without affecting the blood cells which are ingested by the tick (Hughes, 1954; Tatchell, 1964), by way of the hypostomal groove and gutter.

By use of transillumination techniques Lavoipierre and Riek (1955) demonstrated that the secretion in soft ticks is forced into the tissues and that, unlike hard ticks, no rapidly hardening secretion is produced. All active movements of the extra-basis components cease when penetration is complete except for occasional movements of the cheliceral digits. The salivary secretion then appears in the host tissues as a puff of clear liquid against the dark background, to be succeeded by a sucking action until the area is clear once more. These alternating secretory and suctorial activities occur inter-mittently throughout the feeding cycle, with the resting periods between them becoming increasingly longer.

Such alternating activities of salivary secretion in soft and hard ticks is under the influence of a controlling mechanism as shown in *Dermacentor andersoni* by Gregson (1960b) and in *Ornithodoros moubata* by Bertram (1939), who suggested that the "tongue-like" process or labrum is responsible. The dorsal conical prolongation of the basis capituli in living *Ornithodoros* ticks is pressed against the upper surface of the fused hypostome and the palps, so that the opening into the salivarium is reduced to a slit-like aperture. During the contraction of the pharynx it is suggested that the mesial mem-brane is dilated and so closes off the salivarium, whereby the salivary glands and the salivarium form a closed system. The ducts themselves are lined with a chitinous intima, and if the duct walls react to increasing pressures in a manner analogous to the tracheal tubes in insects, then during pharyngeal expansion Bertram suggests that the ducts would be compressed and their lumen reduced or obliterated. Conversely, contraction of the pharynx would, by reducing the pressure transmitted to the walls by the haemocoele fluids cause them to assume an almost circular section. The lumen of each duct, therefore, would increase as the pharynx constricted and since the buccal cavity would be closed anteriorly in this phase, salivary fluid would be drawn from the alveoli of the glands into the lumen of the ducts. Dilation of the pharynx would result in the collapse of the tongue-like process and the slot-like opening above the mesial membrane would communicate with the preoral food cavity. The opening of the aperture would coincide with the commencement of the suggested compression of the salivary ducts, caused by the dilation of the pharynx within the relatively confined space of the basis capituli, and salivary fluid would therefore be passed from the ducts into the preoral food cavity.

The acquisition of a blood meal very soon after the mouth parts of argasid ticks have penetrated the host tissue is suggested by the work of Lavoipierre and Riek (1955). On the basis of the rates of feeding and the macroscopic and microscopic lesions produced they divided the ornithodorid ticks into the following groups: (a) *O. moubata* group, including *O. moubata*, *O. moubata normandi*, *O. arenicolus*, *O. brasiliensis*, *O. dugesi*, *O. gurneyi*, *O. graingeri*, *O. hermsi*, *O. parkeri*, *O. puertoricensis*, *O. rostratus*, *O. rudis*, *O. salahi*, *O. turicata* and small adults of *O. savignyi*; (b) *O. erraticus* group, including *O. erraticus*, *O. canestrinii*, *O. coriaceus*, *O. delanoei* var. *delanoei erraticus*, *O. lahorensis*, *O. talaje*, *O. tholozani* var. *crossi*, *O. tholozani* var. *typicus*; (c) *O. savignyi* large adults. Members of the *O. moubata* group require about 1½ h to become completely engorged, but occasionally some may feed for a shorter time and certain strains may be fully fed within 15 min. The haemorrhage produced by these ticks is widespread, superficial and diffuse and infiltrates the dermal tissues in which a few invading neutrophils are found. Members of the *O. erraticus* group feed more rapidly, becoming fully fed within 1 h. That the blood is acquired rapidly is indicated by the occurrence of a small haemorrhage around the mouth parts when they first become embedded in the skin. This progressively increases to about 3 mm, when the tick is fully fed and drops off, subsequent to which the haemorrhagic area may quadruple its area. Pathologically, this haemorrhage is more extensive than that produced by members of the *O. moubata* group and extends into the deeper regions of the dermis and to the outer muscular layers. The area is, however, more circumscribed than that produced by members of the *O. moubata* group. The lesion produced looks "angry" and is oedematous.

The third group, viz. the large individuals of *O. savignyi*, produce a less extensive haemorrhage and there is no swelling around the puncture. Histopathologically, the changes induced in the tissues are similar to those resulting from the bites of the *O. erraticus* group, but are more restricted. Bearing in mind the short interval of time required for feeding, the rapid production of haemorrhages is suggestive of a very rapid lytic action by the salivary secretion. Further investigation on the gut contents of argasid ticks in all developmental stages is, however, urgently required.

The ixodid ticks pose rather a different problem, for as Foggie (1959) states, red blood cells are not essential for the development of the various instars. Moreover, they remain attached to their hosts for days, and appear to require some days to produce a haemorrhage.

Most authors have noted in histological studies involving penetration of host tissue by the trophi of hard ticks, appearances indicative of breakdown of host tissue in addition to cellular reactions and haemorrhages. Even so, these changes in the skin have not usually been considered in relation to the diet of the tick, and it has more often than not been stated or implied that only blood feeding occurs.

Relevant histopathological features of the skin around the inserted mouth parts which are of significance in feeding are (1) the "cement" zone of Cowdry and Danks (1933) (= "homogeneous eosinophilic zone" of Hoeppli and Feng, 1931); (2) the oedematous tissue produced as a result of the second or more fluid salivary secretion, and (3) the formation of haemorrhages.

Talice (1930) did not record the presence of any material resembling the "homogeneous eosinophilic zone" in skin infested by *Dermacentor reticulatus*. Hoeppli and Feng (1931, 1933), who made the first extensive study of histopathological effects of the bites of hard ticks on the mammalian host, maintained that hard ticks are blood feeders; this was despite the fact that they saw similarities between the "homogeneous eosinophilic zone" and the effects of some nematodes (1931) and mites (1933) on their hosts which probably feed on tissue fluid, and that they also found that cartilage could be destroyed during tick feeding. "In cases of ticks there can be no doubt that they feed on blood, and there seems no reason to assume an extra-intestinal digestion, although it is somewhat indicated by the homogeneous area" (1933).

The available evidence from both hard ticks (Gregson, 1960a, b; Arthur, 1962) and trombiculid larvae (Schumacher and Hoeppli, 1963) is that the primary secretion (p. 252) responsible for production of the cement zone is essentially concerned with fixing the parasite to the host, and there is no substantiated evidence that the cement layer is disorganized host tissue, or that it represents a nutrient source for ticks.

Oedema in the skin around the mouth parts of engorging hard ticks has been observed as a normal response to feeding. Talice (1930) reported oedema as a feature of the intense skin reaction around the puncture produced by *Dermacentor reticulatus*. Gregson (1937), working with females of *Dermacentor andersoni*, noted oedema throughout the tissues, filling the lymph spaces with a thick transudate. He also stated that "as the tick does not penetrate deeply enough to obtain blood from the capillary bed, it is entirely dependent on the production of oedema and haemorrhage for its access to the blood fluid". Cases of *Ixodes hexagonus* encysted within overgrowths of the skin of some hosts reported by Nuttall (1914) and Arthur (1951) and of *Hyalomma excavatum* by Hoogstraal (1956) are probably attributable to increasing oedema and inflammatory swelling of the hosts' skin, the surface of which rises above the subjacent tissue in which the hypostome is buried. Foggie (1959) described oedematous tissue in the wound area caused by *I. ricinus*, but he did not discuss the possibility of the oedematous fluid forming a significant component of the diet. The formation of oedematous tissue is not specifically mentioned by Hoeppli and Feng (1931, 1933) in their detailed descriptions of the histopathology of skin infested by various species of ticks, although in a review of their own and other work they mention oedema as being a feature. Cowdry and Danks (1933) suggested that tissue fluid or serum may contribute to the "cement substance" but made no reference to oedematous tissue apart from this.

Mironov and Baldina (1942), Volodina (1942) and Olsuf'ev and Kagramanov (1947) also studied changes in the skin and underlying tissues induced by the bite of hard ticks.

The earlier works of Hoeppli and Feng (1931, 1933) and of Talice (1930) both indicate that there is no doubt that ticks feed almost exclusively on blood and that there is "no reason to assume an extra-intestinal digestion although it is somewhat indicated by the homogeneous area". Haemorrhages were recorded in the skin around the mouth parts of hard ticks in the histological investigations of Talice (1930), Hoeppli and Feng (1931, 1933), Cowdry and Danks (1933), Gregson (1937), Arthur (1951, 1953a) and Foggie (1959). Talice found a haemorrhagic core surrounded by leucocytes in the dermis beneath the tip of the hypostome. Cowdry and Danks (1933), working with *Rhipicephalus appendiculatus*, and Gregson (1937), with *Dermacentor andersoni*, believed that the tick obtained its blood meal by secreting saliva which resulted in a swelling and breakdown of capillaries and the establishment of a haemorrhage.

Arthur (1951, 1953a) noted haemorrhages between the dermal fibres of the skin and also commented on the occurrence of destroyed tissue at the tip of the hypostome suggestive of coagulation necrosis. Pavlovsky and Alfeeva (1949) found a complete absence of haemorrhages or hyperaemia in sections of the skin of various species infested with *Hyalomma*, although the gut of engorging ticks contained blood. They concluded that ixodid ticks feed on a pathological exudate produced by an interaction of the tick's saliva and the skin tissue of the host, together with blood elements which become admixed with this tissue in some undetermined way. Foggie (1959), working with *I. ricinus*, also deduced that tissue other than blood formed a significant component of the diet. "As digestion proceeds, capillary walls become damaged and blood cells as well as tissue cells are taken in by the ticks." Foggie also furnished evidence that red blood cells are not essential for the development of the various instars.

In all other studies related to the feeding of hard ticks the basic assumption has been that they are purely blood feeders. Thus, Hughes (1954), who also reviewed earlier work, and Lees (1946, 1952) studied the histology of the gut and digestion of the blood meal, whilst Jellison and Kohls (1938) determined the actual amount of blood withdrawn by females of *Dermacentor andersoni* from rabbits, as did Kitaoka (1961b) for females of *Boophilus microplus* and *Haemaphysalis bispinosa*. When Lees (1946) investigated the water balance of hard ticks he determined the loss of water colorimetrically from their blood meals by evaporation. Lees (1952) and Kitaoka and Yajima (1958) studied the increase in size of ticks and in the weight of the cuticles in relation to the process of feeding, but there is no indication in these three papers that anything other than blood is digested. Wigglesworth (1943), using spectroscopic, colorimetric and other methods, studied the fate of haemoglobin in a number of blood-sucking arthropods, including *I. ricinus*, but did not discuss any other component of the food.

The presence of an anticoagulant in the salivary secretion of *I. ricinus* found by earlier workers and recently confirmed by Foggie (1959) implies blood feeding, although it is of interest to note that Schumacher and Hoeppli (1963) refer to the "irritant" (i.e. secondarily produced secretion) as part of another secretion which is injected by trombiculud mites, possibly in order to prevent clotting of the fluid nutrient (i.e. free tissue fluid *but not blood*). A suggestion that a hard tick may feed on tissue other than blood was made by Gregson (1935) when he recorded the immature stages of *Ixodes ricinus californicus* feeding on the skin of the lateral pouch of a lizard (*Gerrhonotus multicarinatus* Blainville). Sections of the skin showed that it was very poor in blood vessels, and the suggestion was made that the larvae and nymph fed on lymph. A real understanding of the dietary constituents of the tick' meal can be appreciated only against the background of imbibition of the meal and the associated metabolic processes involved. Most of the work on this aspect has been investigated in *Ixodes ricinus*.

The sequence of events during feeding consists of a long period of slow feeding followed by a short period of rapid feeding (Lees, 1946). Sutton and Arthur (1962) found that the majority of females of *I. ricinus* feeding on cattle reached the end of the period of slow feeding (weight about 50 mg in about 5–6 days in contrast to Lees' figure of about 7 days. They then fed very rapidly, reaching full engorgement in the next half day or so, i.e. in $5\frac{1}{2}$–7 days. Moreover, the growth curve shows that there is a slight acceleration in the "growth rate" during the period of slow feeding prior to the onset of the period of rapid feeding (Fig. 2).

The weight of females of *I. ricinus* increases from about 2 mg (unfed) to an average of 250 mg (fully fed), although the highest weight recorded by Sutton and Arthur (1962) was 450 mg, i.e. an increase of the order of 100–200%. The increased distension of the gut caeca of engorging ticks suggests that the increase in weight is primarily due to food intake. Losses of nitrogenous excretory materials during feeding form a negligible proportion of the material lost from the tick. White pasty masses of guanine and small quantities of dilute urine are lost during engorgement (Lees, 1946), whilst guanine in the faeces is excreted during feeding and droplets of straw-coloured fluid are eliminated towards the end of engorgement (Hughes, 1954). Schulze (1943) recorded two cases of engorging females of *I. ricinus* in which faeces, including effete gut cells loaded with excretory granules and guanine bodies, were excreted. Faeces were observed to be periodically voided at all stages of feeding, but not after detachment (Sutton and Arthur, 1962). On voidance the excreta was fluid and became solid on drying. It varied in colour from yellow through red to nearly black and this paralleled the colour of the tick. Sutton and Arthur (1962) did not analyse the composition of this excreta, but since Lees (1946) stated that, apart from the white guanine, the excreta consists of undigested blood, they postulated that the faecal colour was a reflection of the composition of the food ingested. The voidance of large quantities of red, undigested blood during feeding by *I. ricinus* is reported by Lees (1946), but the quantitative information on the withdrawal of blood from the host by ticks is given by Jellison and Kohls (1938) and by Kitaoka (1961b). By determining total nitrogen, iron and sterols, Kitaoka showed that individuals of *B. microplus* with a mean body weight of 253·6 mg may remove 0·707–0·805 ml of blood, this being equivalent to 2·79–3·14 times the weight of an engorged tick. Comparable results were obtained for *H. bispinosa*, but in view of the "higher degree of accumulation, concentration and excretion" in this species Kitaoka concluded that greater quantities of blood were removed from the host, than were taken by *B. microplus*.

The results of Jellison and Kohls were based on the feeding of *D. andersoni* on rabbits, the quantities being calculated either from the dry weight of the

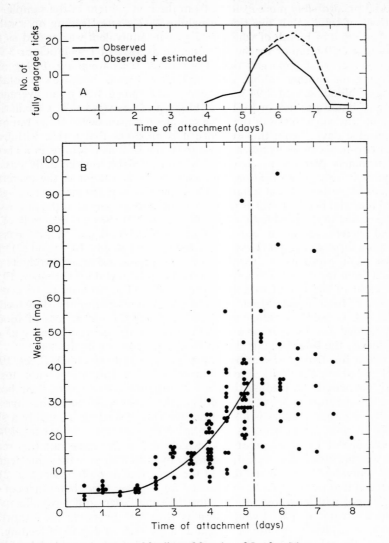

FIG. 2. The rate and pattern of feeding of females of *Ixodes ricinus*.

A. The continuous line shows the number of ticks which become fully engorged at the stated number of days. Observations never exceeded 9 days. Estimations were therefore made of the time which would have been required by ticks, which were still attached at the end of the period of observation and which had been attached for 5½ or more days, to become fully engorged. These were added to the "observed" times and together are indicated by the discontinuous line. Six ticks required more than 8½ days to become fully engorged.

B. Dots represent individual ticks; the vertical broken line shows the approximate point of transition between the long period of slow feeding and the short period of rapid feeding; the curve shows the trend for weight increase during the period of slow feeding. (Courtesy of the Zoological Society of London.)

material or, probably more exactly, from the iron content of the sample. On the basis of total solids five ticks weighing 2·42 g after feeding on a rabbit removed 9·6 g of blood, of which 7·17 g or its equivalent was passed as tick faeces and 2·50 retained by the ticks, i.e. an average of 1·93 g/tick or 3·99 g of blood per g of engorged tick. Four other ticks weighing 0·99 g after engorging on another rabbit, and similarly analysed, withdrew a total of 9·45 g of blood, passed 7·94 g as faeces and retained 1·57 g; an average of 2·36 g of blood per tick or 9·51 g of blood/g of engorged tick. Calculations based on the iron analysis of the same samples gave somewhat lower but quite comparable data. From this evidence it is apparent that a tick withdraws about two-to-six times as much blood from the host as it retains in its body. Unfortunately there is no quantitative data available on the daily passage of faeces in relation to feeding, but since the iron content of the excreta is comparable to total faecal weights, it is suggestive that the greater passage of faecal material occurs towards the end of the feeding period, if the discussion on the nature of the food imbibed is valid (see p. 270). Since (1) the bulk of the voided excreta appears to consist of undigested blood (i.e. "food" passing unaltered through the gut (Lees, 1946; Jellison and Kohls, 1938) and (2) most of the waste products of digestion (i.e. nitrogenous excretory products and excreta from the digestive tract) accumulate in the rectal sac (Hughes, 1954), the weight of the tick at different periods of feeding appears to be a valid measure of food intake. Much of the ingested fluids during the slow feeding of the tick is used for cuticle synthesis (Lees, 1952) and as loss of food is compensated for by this process and other synthetic processes, e.g. egg production, the total weights due to food ingestion are unaffected.

Water is lost from *I. ricinus* by evaporation through the cuticle (Lees, 1946, 1947) and above the "critical temperature" of 32° C the rate of water loss is greatly increased. As feeding ticks are in intimate contact with their hosts, whose temperature is 37° C, two-thirds of the water from the blood ingested by fully engorged females is lost before the end of feeding, probably a substantial fraction of this being by evaporation through the cuticle (Lees, 1946). It is reasonable to assume that ticks which feed at the same rate (i.e. reach given weights in the same times), lose water by evaporation to the same degree, but as individual ticks do not feed at the same rate as each other (Fig. 2), it is deduced that ticks which have attached for a longer time than others of the same weight will have lost more water than the latter, and have effectively fed to a greater extent. Evaporation is therefore probably an important factor in considering the use of weight as a measure of degree of feeding. If, however, the minority of ticks which have not become engorged by $5\frac{1}{2}$–$6\frac{1}{2}$ days (30%) is ignored, the variation is much reduced, i.e. ticks reach a given weight within a range of ± 1–$1\frac{1}{4}$ days. Therefore, the error caused by the variation in loss by evaporation is reduced. Results based on ticks where the time of attachment and weight were known are similar to those based on the greater number of ticks where the weights only were known. It is therefore concluded that error introduced by different rates of evaporation may be ignored (Sutton and Arthur, 1962).

The histopathological effects on the skin of hosts induced by feeding ticks

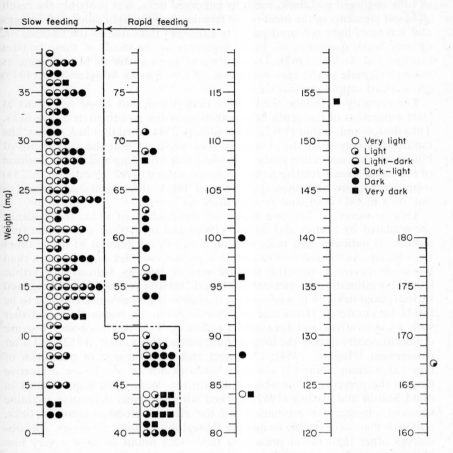

FIG. 3. Correlation between the weights of ticks and the colour of caecal contents. Symbols represent individual ticks (arranged in ascending order of weight), the colour of whose caecal contents is indicated by the black:white ratio. The approximate transition point, between the long period of slow feeding and the short period of rapid feeding, is indicated by the vertical chain-dotted line. (By permission of the Zoological Society of London.)

are indicative of extra-oral digestion (see earlier references, p. 265; Arthur and Sutton, unpublished). The marked variation in the colour of the caecal contents of engorging females led Sutton and Arthur (1962) to postulate that these differences were a reflection of the composition of the diet imbibed by ticks. Ticks with lighter coloured caecal contents fed on a predominance of tissue other than "blood", while those with darker caecal contents had fed primarily on blood. Observations of colour differences of undigested excreta and of eggs and larvae support these views. The colour of the eggs and larvae of fully engorged and dark, partially engorged ticks, was probably the result of blood pigments in the meal of the females, and the light colour of the eggs and larvae of light coloured partially engorged ticks due to the absence of, or only small quantities of, blood pigments in the meals of these females (Sutton and Arthur, 1962). The findings of the transfer of blood pigments from the female to the eggs and larvae of *I. ricinus* by Wigglesworth (1943) gives added support to this view.

The capacity to imbibe fluids other than blood, and blood, is in part at least a function of the depth of penetration by the mouth parts of the ticks. Thus Sutton and Arthur (1962: discussion, p. 254) stated that in *I. ricinus* "the mouthparts may enter the skin at various angles so that the availability of blood will vary according to the individual that is feeding and on the position of the blood vessels relative to the surface". Foggie (1962: discussion, p. 254) supports this view and states that "you get 'black' ticks when one happens to 'hit' on a blood vessel, and another does not".

This, however, is but one aspect of the feeding of ticks, for evidence accumulated by Sutton and Arthur (1962) and by Arthur and Sutton (unpublished) indicates that ticks feed on a significant amount of tissue other than blood. As "non-blood" tissue is a greater complex of substances than blood, a spectrophotometric method was devised by Sutton and Arthur (1962) for estimating the amount of "blood" relative to "non-blood" ingested by individual ticks. In this connexion the following three objectives had to be fulfilled accurately: (1) estimate total haemoglobin, i.e. haemoglobin together with its derivatives and breakdown products. This was necessary because digestion occurs during the long feeding period (Lees, 1946, 1952) and after detachment (Hughes, 1954); (2) detect and estimate minute quantities of ingested haemoglobin; (3) estimate haemoglobin or its chosen derivative despite the presence of non-blood derivatives. With these requirements in mind Sutton and Arthur (1962) worked with the haem derivative pyridine haemochromogen for estimations of the relative blood content of ticks, although they were unable to include choleglobin in their estimates. All substances other than blood present in ticks were found to have a very low absorption at the α-absorption maximum of pyridine-haemochromogen, so that the estimation of haemoglobin and its derivatives could be made in their presence.

The characteristic absorption of spectra of pyridine-haemochromogen solutions made from a number of ticks of closely similar weight is illustrated in Fig. 4, together with a control curve for pure haemin. The caecal contents represented by curves A, B, C and D were very dark in colour; the curves agree very closely in shape with the control curve E, and with each other and they run very nearly parallel with one another. This indicates that pyridine-haemochromogen was consistently formed and that absorption due to "other substances" present was insignificant. The absorption spectra due to ticks of similar weight and caecal colour are also of the same order of magnitude, as evidenced by a comparison of curves A–D with curves F and G, the latter being those for ticks having "light" and "very light" coloured caecal contents respectively; accordingly the optical density readings are very much lower.

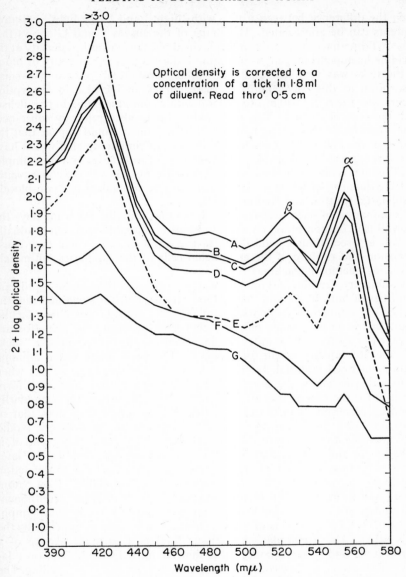

FIG. 4. The characteristic absorption curves of pyridine-haemochromogen solutions made from the contents of five ticks of similar weight but of different caecal colour, together with a control for haemin. (Courtesy of the Zoological Society of London.)

Optical density is corrected to a concentration of a tick in 1·8 ml of diluent. Read through 0·5 cm.

Key: A, Gut very dark, wt. 44 mg; B, gut very dark, wt. 41 mg; C, gut very dark, wt. 42 mg; D, gut very dark, wt. 42 mg; E, haemin, concentration 0·03 mg/ml; F, gut light, wt. 43 mg; G, gut very light, wt. 43 mg.

Even the difference between a tick with "light" and "very light" coloured contents can be appreciated. The shape of the curves F and G shows that *some* pyridine-haemochromogen was formed but the *low* optical density at the pyridine haemochromogem α-maximum indicates that the quantity of blood in the ticks was very low and that "other substances" present had small absorption at this wavelength. In these curves an increase in absorption occurs over the range 440 mμ to 520 mμ with a consequent loss in parallelism with the control curve E. This is probably due to absorption by substances other than blood (Sutton and Arthur, 1962). Thus it would appear that the nature of the diet varies considerably in ticks of similar weights which have therefore ingested comparable total quantities of food (Fig. 3). For example, tick D contains about ten times as much blood as tick G, with the consequence that the quantity of blood in the former must be equivalent to "non-blood" in the latter (Sutton and Arthur, 1962).

Examination of fixed preparations shows that initially, for some days the tick will feed on non-blood (Arthur and Sutton, unpublished), but gradually the salivary secretions extend down to the capillary bed, where they cause distension and rupture of the endothelial cells of the capillaries, ultimately producing haemorrhagic areas.

In summary, females and immature stages of ixodid ticks ingest significant quantities of both blood and "non-blood" tissue, but it is suggested that the method of feeding is fundamentally similar to that of the larvae of trombiculid mites. In the smaller mites only the chelicerae penetrate the skin (for anchorage purposes) and the mites are dependent on the formation of a "sucking tube" of salivary origin for access to free tissue fluids and a minimal quantity of lysed material. In ticks, which are relatively large in size when compared with mites, the deeply inserted hypostome and chelicerae form channels for the conveyance of food and saliva. Moreover, the secondarily produced secretion of ticks exerts a greater lytic action than does that of mites and results in greater digestion of tissue elements. Accordingly, ixodid ticks are able to feed more deeply and extensively than mites, and it is probably for this reason that blood is included in their diet. In the later stages of feeding, when haemorrhages have been produced due to the action of salivary secretion, blood is presumably more "available" than "non-blood" and forms the main food constituent. This "non-blood" component may consist of (1) host tissue which is already fluid (e.g. tissue fluid, lymph) and/or (2) solid components of the skin tissue which could be liquefied by the tick's saliva. The accumulation of tissue fluid is a constant feature of a microtrauma and it seems conceivable that ixodid ticks could feed on relatively substantial quantities of this during the long period of slow feeding. The extensive liberation and breakdown of mast cell granules, which accompanies the accumulation of tissue fluid in a microtrauma, is amongst evidences that have been amassed to suggest that fluid other than blood may form a component of the food of *I. ricinus* (Arthur and Sutton, unpublished). From experimental data the course of feeding may be constituted of the three following phases: (1) ticks up to 8–10 mg weight have mainly blood in their gut and this could be attributed to (a) the carry-over of blood from the previous instar and/or (b) the imbibition of small quantities of blood released from superficial capillaries ruptured during the act of penetration by the mouth parts; (2) "non-blood" then usually forms a major component of the food for varying lengths of time even up to half a day from full engorgement. "Non-blood" feeding occurs until such time as a sufficiently extensive haemorrhage has been induced; (3) blood is then predominantly ingested, presumably because this fluid tissue, derived from the circulatory system under pressure, is a more readily available source of food than "non-blood".

IV. DIGESTION IN TICKS

The process of digestion in ticks has received relatively scant attention when compared with that of insects, and in all cases the emphasis has been on the digestion of blood (Christophers, 1906; Roesler, 1934; Hughes, 1954; Weitz and Buxton, 1953; Balashov, 1961; Kitaoka, 1961b; Tatchell, 1964). The gross anatomy of the gut of a number of genera has been reviewed by Arthur (1962) and detailed histological changes during the process of feeding by Hughes (1954), Till (1961), Balashov (1961) and Tatchell (1964).

During feeding in both ixodid and argasid ticks excess plasma water is eliminated either through the cuticle (Lees, 1952) or by ultrafiltration through the coxal glands (Lees, 1946). This allows a greater amount of haemoglobin and serum protein to be stored in the available volume of the gut. It also allows a proportion of the blood meal to be retained unchanged as a food reserve and avoids its transformation into fat or other reserve material.

Digestion in argasid ticks occurs after the tick has detached itself from the host and, according to Balashov and Tatchell, it proceeeds in three stages. From a study of the curves for the concentration of haemoglobin digestion does not take place during the first few days after feeding while the gut epithelium is developing. Haemolysis, absorption and digestion follow with the formation of an active epithelium and lasts about 14 days at 28° C. This is referred to as the rapid stage of digestion. The third or slow stage of digestion persists until either further feeding or death occurs (Tatchell, 1964). These three stages are also recognized by Balashov (1961) but there is considerable variation in timing when compared with Tatchell's observations. Thus the first stage lasts from 10 to 15 days during which blood agglutination and haemolysis take place. The second phase persists for several weeks or months, whilst the third stage may be a period of long starvation during which the tick survives on half digested residue in the gut lumen. Tatchell's criticisms of Balashov's timing of the various stages is that they are based on histological findings and not on critical haemoglobin concentration, and the suggestion is put forward that the ticks were maintained at sub-optimal temperatures.

Ixodid ticks feed on the host for several days and in *I. ricinus*, at least, digestion commences once blood enters the intestinal caeca (Hughes, 1954). Initially the qualitative and quantitative rates of digestion while the tick is on the host are relatively slow when compared with the continuation of the process after the tick has become fully engorged and dropped off from the host.

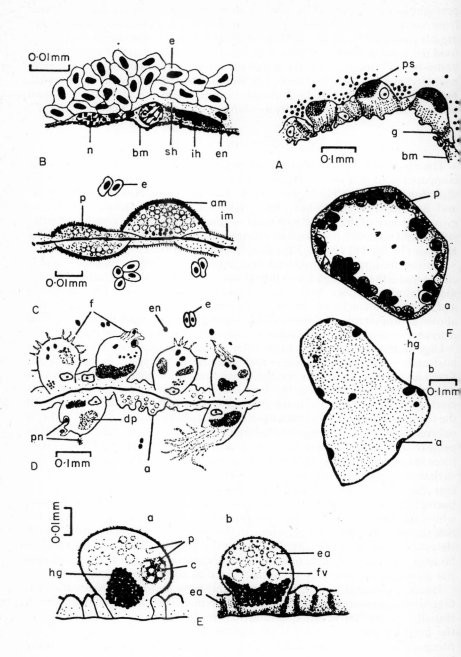

V. Preliminary Conditions prior to Haemolysis and Digestion

Histologically the walls of the mid-gut and its caeca of the unfed *I. ricinus* consist of a basement membrane which is covered externally by a loose meshwork of large, simple muscle fibres arranged both circularly and longitudinally, which is thought to be responsible for the pulsating movements of the mid-gut during the early stages of feeding, for distributing the blood and non-blood fluids along the tract and for assisting in the admixture of the ingested nutrients with the digestive enzymes. The epithelium at this stage consists of small cells with basal nuclei, uniform non-vacuolated cytoplasm and long, club-shaped highly vacuolated cells with central or distal nuclei. The latter project far into the lumen and among the larger cells some have the cytoplasm crowded with eosinophil granules (Hughes, 1954). These are the so-called "secretory cells" of Roesler (1934).

Between the projecting cells and in the lumen of the caeca there is a colloidal eosinophilic material, which constitutionally is similar to the granules noted in the secretory cells. Similarly in starved argasid ticks Tatchell (1964) noted empty-looking columnar or cuboidal cells (Fig. 5), comparable to the large vacuolated cells of *I. ricinus*, and a few small undifferentiated cells, comparable to the small non-vacuolated cells reported by Hughes (1954). Two types of periodic acid–Schiff (PAS)-positive granules occur in the columnar cells of *A. persicus* (Tatchell, 1964); those at the base of the cell and adjacent to the lateral walls are removed by saliva digestion and are presumably glycogen, whereas the more distal granules are generally saliva-fast. Hughes and Tatchell agree that these large cells disintegrate, are shed into the lumen during the early stages of feeding, and have no digestive function. Hughes considered these to be exhausted cells without any digestive function which have been carried over from the previous instar, their vacuoles originally containing absorbed food which has been utilized during development. The origin of the columnar type cells in *A. persicus* is unknown, and Tatchell (1964)

FIG. 5.

A. Section through gut epithelium of starved *Argas persicus*.

B. Developing epithelium, 24 h after feeding.

C. Developing epithelium, 48^-72 h after feeding, showing alkaline phosphatase activity in the microvilli of the absorbing cell.

D. Drawing showing the changes in form of the filaments of the phagocytic cells.

E. (a) Non-specific esterase in normal digesting cell; (b) esterase activity in digesting cell after inhibition in 10^{-5}M E 600 and subsequent activation with 10^{-3}M cysteine.

F. Sections through a gut caecum of *Argas*. (a) During rapid phase of digestion; (b) after the rapid phase (from Tatchell, 1964).

Key: a, Absorbing cell; am, alkaline phosphatase activity in microvilli of absorbing cells; bm, basement membrane; c, cysteine-activated esterases; dp, nucleoprotein degradation products;, e, erythrocyte; ea, esterase activity; en, nucleus of erythrocyte; f, filaments; fv, fat vacuole with "cap" of esterase activity; g, glycogen; hg, masses of haematin granules; ih, intracellular accumulation of haemolysin; im, inactive microvilli; n, nucleus; p, protein vacuole; pn, nucleus being phagocytosed; ps, PAS-positive saliva-fast material; sh, secreted haemolysin.

o

suggests that they may have developed from the basal remnants of digestive cells after the discharge of the final undigested granular products or they may have been produced in "numbers inversely proportional to the remaining food material".

The removal of these cells leaves the gut epithelium as a thin sheet of cells in *I. ricinus* (Hughes, 1954) and in *A. persicus* (Fig. 2, Tatchell, 1964). In *I. ricinus* this is brought about by the spreading of the small cells, which previously had been "heaped up in places to a depth of three cells" (Hughes, 1954) and not, as stated by Roesler (1934), by the stretching and flattening of a single layer of cells. The initial distension of the gut epithelium in all ticks is due to the ingestion of blood, and this is followed in *I. ricinus* by a proliferation of its constituent cells so that they grow up at intervals to form cone-like masses projecting slightly into the lumen. The nuclei of these cells, originally at the base, now migrate to the middle or even to the apices of their cells and the cytoplasm becomes vacuolate. Colloidal material appears within the vacuoles, and this is strongly eosinophilic. These proliferated cells are then budded into the lumen, assume a rounded form and mix freely with the blood meal. Till (1961) reported a similar release of epithelial cells in *Rhipicephalus appendiculatus*, as did Balashov (1961) in some argasids and Christophers (1906) in *Ornithodoros savignyi*. Hoogstraal (1956) believed that the process is similar in *O. moubata*, and these workers report that the epithelial cells occur as a number of reddish granules in the still partially fluid blood. Their nuclei are large, circular or oval and their cytoplasm is finely reticulate or partially vacuolated. Other large, dark staining, rounded cells with rather small nuclei are present, but their substance is markedly vacuolate. It is stated that the epithelial cells in *A. persicus* at this early stage of feeding are always attached by stalks to the basement membrane (Robinson and Davidson, 1914; Tatchell, 1964). It is possible that the wandering cells, described by other workers in other species, may be similarly attached but released into the lumen during mechanical disturbance. This, however, requires confirmation either by dissection under ice-cold saline, thus inactivating the tick, or by opening the gut under formol-saline, to fix the cells rapidly, as recommended by Tatchell (1964).

VI. HAEMOLYSIS

Although Pavlovsky and Chodukin (1928, 1929) detected haemolysins in the saliva of ticks and indicated that they became effective some time after the blood had been imbibed, there is now a considerable body of evidence that haemolysis is effected principally by products derived from the gut epithelial cells. Hughes (1954) observed that as blood enters the caeca the corpuscles are rapidly destroyed and he attributed this initially to the eosinophilic colloidal material within the lumen, and later to the cells proliferated from the gut epithelium during feeding. The point is also made that the process is not only haemolytic; it involves the digestion of the red cell envelopes, which entirely disappear leaving the blood as a homogeneous mass in the gut caeca.

In argasid ticks Lavoipierre and Riek (1955), working with *O. turicata* females, showed that there is a delay of about 2 h before haemolysis takes place in the gut. Similarly Tatchell (1964) demonstrated that the gut caeca of engorged, recently detached ticks of *A. persicus* are filled with unlysed, agglutinated blood corpuscles bounded by a thin developing epithelium, presumably derived from the original undifferentiated cells, and the basement membrane. At 28° C and 24 h after detachment from the host the epithelial cells, though not enlarged, are filling with saliva-fast PAS-positive material, which ultimately passes into the lumen, and has a colloidal appearance. After 2–3 days the PAS-positive colloid penetrates between the corpuscles and lyses and distorts the peripheral blood corpuscles; and by the 6th day after feeding lysis of the contents of the gut is almost complete (Tatchell, 1964). This author points out there is an absence of extracellular enzyme activity in the lumen and he does not refer to the digestion of the lipid membranes of the erythrocytes (cf. Hughes, 1954) although noting that the nuclei of avian red blood corpuscles remain undigested in the tract after release by haemolysis.

VII. Absorption and Digestion

Cells derived from the first proliferation of the epithelium in hard ticks, when still attached to the host, migrate through the lumen (Hughes, 1954) and having lost their eosinophil contents fill up with dark brownish-black granules, which suggests they have absorbed and metabolized some of the blood. These cells ultimately break down and the enclosed granules are freed into the gut. At this stage the tick is fully fed and drops off the host. The continuation of this process when the tick is free of the host will be considered later. These cells are not referred to in *I. ricinus* by Roesler (1934) but their existence is confirmed by Till (1961) in *R. appendiculatus*, where, it is suggested, they have absorptive and digestive properties. The mid-gut and diverticulata of *O. moubata* are greatly distended 24 h after a meal, and contain a soft coagulum from which a considerable amount of fluid blood may drain. Blood corpuscles are apparently unchanged. Intensely dark, globular granules measuring 0·5–5 μ are scattered through the mass and collect particularly at the edge of the fresh blood. The black granules are the breakdown products derived from a previous blood meal, and there is considerable admixture of these diverticular contents with newly ingested blood. After some time, a number of budded epithelial cells occur in the still partially fluid blood, and films of the contents made 24 h after a blood meal contain cells derived from the gut epithelium in addition to the host's leucocytes (Christophers, 1906).

The other large, dark-staining rounded vacuolate cells referred to earlier also occur freely in the gut lumen according to this author, and these are crowded with material which suggests phagocytosis of blood corpuscles, black granules and chromatin fragments. These cells are present 6 h after the completion of the blood meal and are believed to be wandering digestive cells. According to Hoogstraal (1956) the absorptive and digestive processes in *O. savignyi* follow this pattern. Attached cells of the mid-gut also play an active part in the digestive processes, for the swollen and vacuolated portions of the large projecting cells are crowded with products of digestion, much as in the free cells in the lumen (Christophers, 1906; Hoogstraal, 1956). Absorption of blood (haemoglobin) by attached cells has been demonstrated by Wigglesworth (1943) in *O. moubata*, in which there is a breakdown to protohaematin, and alkaline haematin is present in the haemolymph of the tick. No free iron has been detected in the gut lumen, gut cells or other tissues.

As the diverticular contents are digested, the muscle fibres, which in the fully distended organ slightly indent the surface, sink more and more into the body of the viscus. The wall between the fibres becomes ballooned and eventually forms flask-like pockets with only a narrow opening connecting with the lumen. The epithelium is present, as a rule, in the pockets, though it is generally more noticeable on the ridges formed by the contracted muscular fibres. Remains of ingested blood, in the form of black granules, are present both in the pockets and in the lumen (Hoogstraal, 1956).

Returning now to consider further digestion in *I. ricinus*, Hughes (1954) noted that the engorged female, on detachment from the host, continues to proliferate gut epithelial cells in large numbers at an increasing rate. These cells, which do not contain eosinophil colloids, remain attached to the basement membrane, absorb the blood meal and metabolize it, before finally becoming loaded with dark granules, which are liberated eventually into the gut lumen. Succeeding generations of these absorptive cells are produced and by their continued activity the gut contents are diminished and there is an accumulation of dark excretory granules. The data from these investigations have the common features that absorption and digestion are carried out by the same cells, and that these processes are effected both by wandering cells detached from the epithelium and by those remaining attached to the epithelium. This view was not entirely accepted by Balashov (1961), who described two types of epithelial cell active throughout the digestion of the blood meal in some argasids, viz. the normal digestive cells and the secretory cells. Tatchell (1964) recognizes three major types of cell in the epithelium. One type, already referred to, contains cells which secrete a saliva-fast PAS-positive colloid responsible for haemolysis. A second type contains cells whose free margins were produced into long filaments, projecting into the lumen either singly or in masses and either variously directed or concentrated in one direction. The observations suggest that the filaments may enmesh free nuclei and draw them into the cell, and the possibility of their independent activity is indicated by the variability of the surface membranes of their cells. The third type of cells are those concerned with absorption and digestion. The free border of these cells, across which proteins and lipids must be transported, show a sparse distribution of microvilli and during the absorption of protein there is increased alkaline phosphatase activity along them, and this persists for 3–14 days after feeding. Such activity ceases when absorption is completed and digestion begins. Intracellular digestion is preceded by the enlargement of the cell due to the accumulation of protein vacuoles. These vacuoles react positively to a modified benzidine test for haem groups and contain either unaltered material from the lumen or relatively undegraded substances. The enlarging cell tends to have smaller vacuoles distally "as if they were pinocytic vesicles enlarging before being pinched off" (Tatchell, 1964). At their borders there is strong aminopeptidase activity but all the vacuoles are not being digested at the same time. Tatchell's (1964) data on enzyme action, coupled with the information of Keilin and Wang (1947), adduce evidence showing that proteolytic digestion is intracellular and that the contents within the lumen are unchanged food material. As a result of increased absorption the shapes of the cells also change: in the unfed tick they are broad based and dome-like, later becoming club-shaped, and finally they consist of apical bulbs borne on slender stalks. Contrary to other findings, Tatchell's studies indicate that the cells are both absorptive and digestive, emphasize the need for further work at the cellular level, particularly biochemical studies.

According to Hughes (1954) lipids, probably ceroid-like and derived from erythrocytic envelopes, are digested in the lumen, and the tall cells of the gut are largely filled with fat, which becomes progressively depleted prior to feeding. Although Roesler (1934) stated that the fat content of all tissues is high, Tatchell (1964) failed to demonstrate fat reserves other than those in the gut, where he found large numbers of fat droplets in the basal regions of active epithelial cells, which coincides with the region showing non-specific esterase activity. During the slow phases of digestion the fat droplets are concentrated at the free edges of the cells. In *A. persicus* fat droplets first appear within 3 days of feeding, becoming very abundant at 6–7 days. Hughes (1954) suggests that the lipid may contribute to the reserve fat transferred from one instar to another; in the female the large quantities of lipids are necessary to supply the large quantities of yolk required, and it may be the source of grease excreted through the cuticle during digestion of the meal. More specific information is given for the fate of fats in *A. persicus* by Tatchell (1964). Fats persist for only short periods in the female, disappearing by the 12th day after feeding, and they are used for waterproofing the eggs. The deposition of sterols and crude fats in *Boophilus microplus* and *Haemaphysalis bispinosa* is dependent upon their concentration in the host's blood, and their presence in small amounts in the excreta suggests that they are probably essential for the development of ticks (Kitaoka, 1961a). This writer also stated that the highest lipid content was attained when *B. microplus* and *H. bispinosa* reached a body weight which indicated impending oviposition. In males and nymphs of *A. persicus*, however, the rate of disappearance of fat from the tissues may be very slow, up to several months.

Cell inclusions, other than those associated with digestive processes have been seen in engorging ticks of *Dermacentor andersoni* and *D. albipictus*. These inclusions are always confined to the epithelium of the mid-gut diverticula (Gregson, 1938) but the gut cells of larval ticks are devoid of such granules. After the tick has imbibed blood, assimilative changes in the gut are accompanied by the presence of large numbers of minute colourless non-motile globules, being most abundant in the cytoplasm at the free ends of the cells and decreasing in numbers near their bases. As assimilation continues, these globules increase in size and ultimately the epithelial cells are packed with them. The gut cells in the fully fed female become distended with globules and increase their size enormously. Eventually they become detached and float in the fluid of the gut lumen. The globular materials differ from volutin bodies in their capacity to resist heat (80° C) for over 5 min, are Gram positive and do not stain with dilute solutions of neutral red in the living cell. They are not destroyed by acid fixatives, nor do they stain with janus green, i.e. they are neither mitochondria nor rickettsiae.

VIII. REMOVAL OF UNDIGESTED RESIDUES

On completion of digestion the epithelial cells of both ixodid and argasid ticks are filled with dark granules. In *I. ricinus* these cells break down liberating their granules into the lumen (Hughes, 1954) and in *A. persicus* the granules are often deposited within the protein vacuole and by accretion in size grow up to about 3 μ in diameter (Tatchell, 1964). They generally accumulate in the cell when it has attained its apical bulb form, and as a result of the breaking of the narrow stalk the cell is set free in the lumen, where it disintegrates rapidly.

The granules in *I. ricinus* are derivatives of melanin (possibly derived from the tyrosine of protein) and of haematin (Hughes, 1954) whilst the nature of the granules in *A. persicus*, as shown by spectrophotometric analysis, is pure or almost pure haematin (Tatchell, 1964). In both species it is agreed that the large intracellular granules when released into the lumen break down into finer components.

IX. THE PROCESS OF ENGORGEMENT UNDER FIELD CONDITIONS

Lavoipierre and Riek (1955), Balashov (1961) and Tatchell (1964), amongst others, have referred to short feeding periods measured in hours or minutes in argasid ticks, by contrast with long feeding times of ixodid ticks extending over a period of days.

Most females of the Ixodidae remain attached and feeding on the host for 7–12 days, and although this period may be prolonged, it is rarely shorter than 5 days for complete engorgement. In *I. ricinus*, for example, the duration of feeding has been variously given by different authors; thus it may be from 7 to 8 days (Bertkau, 1881; Kossel *et al.*, 1903; Samson, 1909; Nuttall and Warburton, 1911; Blagoveshchensky and Pomerantzev, 1930; Edwards and Arthur, 1947; Milne, 1947; Tchij, 1949; Lees, 1946, and others), but it may extend over 10–14 days or extremely to 20–25 days (Samson, 1909; Nuttall and Warburton, 1911; Blagoveshchensky and Pomerantzev, 1930; Edwards and Arthur, 1947; Carrick and Bullough, 1940; Kheisin, 1953; and others). Carrick and Bullough (1940) also demonstrated that the feeding period of sheep ticks can be prolonged by inducing them to feed on hedgehogs in hibernation. It is difficult to ascertain the causes of these fluctuations in all cases, although changes in temperature have a marked effect on the rate of digestion in *A. persicus*, giving a Q_{10} of approximately 2 (Tatchell, 1964). However, similar effects can be demonstrated for moulting and egg laying and it is possible that, in both argasid and ixodid ticks, the temperature effect on digestion is no more than a reflection of a range of metabolic activities.

The sequence of events during feeding of *I. ricinus*, which has been dealt with more adequately than any other ixodid species, consists according to Lees (1946) of a slow period for the first 6 or 7 days during which the body weight increases from 2 to 30–50 mg, and is followed by a rapid acceleration to 250–450 mg on the last day. Sutton and Arthur (1962) found that the majority of females feeding on cattle reached the end of the period of slow feeding in about 5–6 days (Fig. 2), then reached full engorgement in the next half day or so (i.e. in 5½–7 days). They also indicated (Fig. 2) that there is a slight acceleration in the growth rate prior to the onset of the period of rapid feeding. Similar triphasic trends have been observed in the engorgement of nine species in five genera of ticks by Balashov (1958), in *Boophilus microplus* by Kitaoka and Yajima (1958) and in *Haemaphysalis bispinosa* by Kitaoka (1962).

Kheisin (1953) and Balashov (1954) observed a similar pattern of feeding in the Siberian tick, *Ixodes persulcatus* Schulze. The weight of an unfed female of the Siberian tick is 2–3 mg and its weight increases two to three times in the last 10–12 h of blood sucking, when the weight increase is from 120–180 to 300–450 mg. The diurnal changes of weight which take place during the feeding of *I. ricinus* on large-horned cattle were investigated by Kheisin and Lavrenenko (1956), who also showed that female ticks drop on the 7th to 8th day after attachment during the summer. Attachment of the majority of the ticks to the host's body occurs in the morning and proportionately fewer will attach in the afternoon and in the evening. This accounts for the fact that some ticks found in the evening weigh 5 mg, i.e. they attached in the morning, and others weigh 3 mg having attached in the evening. This difference of weight remains constant throughout the feeding period. During the first 6 days of feeding the average weight of ticks used by Kheisen and Lavrenenko (1956) increased by 55 mg with a significant speeding up of feeding between day 4 and day 6, when compared with the first 3 days. During the night between the 6th and 7th day this acceleration of ingestion becomes most

TABLE III

Changes in Weight of I. ricinus *Females when Feeding on Large Horned Cattle (from Kheisin and Lavrenenko, 1956)*

	Weight of female (mg)			Increase in weight (mg/day)
	Min.	Max.	Average	
1st evening	3	5	4·25	2·75
2nd evening	6	10	8·25	4·0
3rd evening	12	18	15·25	7·0
4th evening	23	36	28·5	13·25
5th evening	39	42	40·5	12·0
6th evening	46	66	57·0	16·5
7th morning	208	300	230·0	173·0
7th evening	65	85	73·0	16·0
8th morning	250	450	280·0	207·0

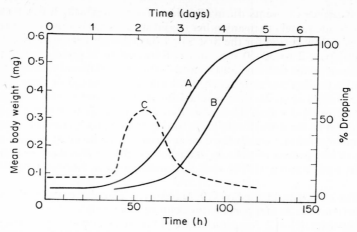

FIG. 6. Growth (A), dropping curves (B) and change of variation coefficients (C), in the larvae of *Haemaphysalis bispinosa* during feeding. (After Kitaoka and Yajima, 1958.)

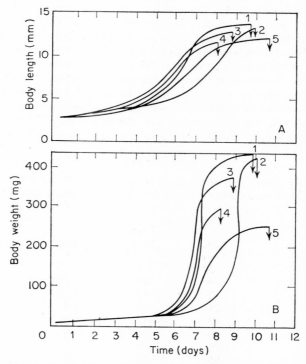

FIG. 7. Growth curve of body length (A) and weight (B) in adults of *Boophilus* during feeding (arrows indicate time of dropping off). (After Kitaoka and Yajima, 1958.)

pronounced, for on the morning of the 7th day the tick weight is 208–300 mg, i.e. in a period of 9 h (in Kheisin and Lavrenenko's experiments) 3·4 times as much blood is imbibed as in the previous 6 days. It was noted also that females which had fed for 6 days, i.e. females which attached in the second half of the day, were insufficiently replete to drop off on the morning of the 7th day. During the night from the 7th to the 8th day their average weight increased up to 200 mg, and prior to detachment on the morning of the 8th day the weight increase was 250–450 mg. These data are summarized in Table III. The general form of the graph for the weight increase in feeding females in all these cases is that of a sigmoid curve (see, for example, Figs. 6 and 7). Kitoaka and Yajima (1958) also demonstrated that the feeding process is divisible into three stages when based on the relative distension ratios of body length, body width and body thickness to body weight. These ratios for *Boophilus microplus* are given below.

Relative distension coefficient	1st stage 3–10 mg	2nd stage 10–80 mg	3rd stage 80 mg
K_1 body length:body weight	0·56	0·28	0·24
K_2 body width:body weight	0·55	0·30	0·32
K_3 body thickness:body weight	0·33	0·33	0·44

During the first stage, increases in length and width ratios of the body are distinctive and exceed that of body thickness; in the second stage, length, width and thickness ratios approach very nearly to one another and in the third stage the body thickness: body weight ratio assumes the ascendancy. These stages correspond to the unfed, flattened and engorged ticks. Similar observations on the larvae of *Haemaphysalis bispinosa* Neumann reveal that although the normal feeding period is 6 days, there is no increase in body weight for the first 38 h and most active ingestion is completed in the last 19 h.

X. RHYTHMICITY OF DETACHMENT BY REPLETED TICKS

Rhythmicity of detachment of ticks following engorgement has been studied by Russian workers (Serdyukova, 1954; Balashov, 1954; Kheisin and Lavrenenko, 1956; Pomerantzev and Alfeev 1935), and by a Japanese worker (Kitoaka, 1962). The Russian school indicates that the periods of pasturing cattle exercise a profound influence on the timing of the dropping off of engorged ticks. Thus cattle which are pastured in daylight hours and return each evening to cattle sheds bear only engorged and ready to detach ticks in the morning before the herd is driven off to pasture, even though they may not be fully engorged on the previous evening. Conversely, night pasturing of a herd results in fully engorged ticks being ready to fall off when the cattle are moved to pasture in the evening (Balashov, 1954; Kheisin and Lavrenenko, 1956). Summarized information of these results for *I. persulcatus* is given in Table IV.

Females of *B. microplus* and larvae and nymphs of *Hyalomma anatolicum* on day-pastured stock also detached themselves in daylight (Serdyukova,

TABLE IV

Rhythm of Dropping Engorged Females of Ixodes persulcatus *during Normal Day-
time and Night-time Pasturing (from Balashov, 1954)*
(Registration of 25 cows in each case.)

Time of inspection (day, month, h)	Overall no. of females	No. of females ready to consume last portion of blood	No. of engorged females	No. of dropped females
Day-time pasturing from 07.00 to 19.00 h				
25. v. 19.00	228	43	0	—
26. v. 06.00	228	2	41	0
26. v. 19.00	232	40	0	41
27. v. 06.00	231	0	40	1
27. v. 19.00	232	32	0	40
28. v. 06.00	232	1	31	0
28. v. 19.00	219	35	0	31
29. v. 06.00	219	0	35	0
29. v. 19.00	222	27	0	35
30. v. 06.00	222	3	24	0
30. v. 19.00	241	37	0	24
Night-time pasturing from 21.00 to 06.00 h				
21. vi. 20.00	81	2	14	—
22. vi. 06.00	82	16	0	14
22. vi. 20.00	82	1	15	0
23. vi. 06.00	90	22	0	15
23. vi. 20.00	89	3	19	1
24. vi. 06.00	99	17	0	19
24. vi. 20.00	99	2	15	0
25. vi. 06.00	95	15	0	15
25. vi. 20.00	95	1	14	0
26. vi. 06.00	96	18	0	14

1954). Confirmation of the day-time drop-off of the engorged *B. microplus*
comes from the investigations of Kitaoka (1962) who also demonstrated a
similar rhythm in *Haemaphysalis bispinosa*. Most larvae and nymphs of
Haemaphysalis leporispalustris drop off their hosts, hares and rabbits, in their
forms and burrows during the day (Nuttall *et al.*, 1915) and similarly females,
nymphs and larvae of *I. hexagonus* drop off during daylight in the nests of
hedgehogs (Arthur, unpublished).

This coincidence of the dropping off of ticks and the behaviour patterns
of their hosts is dependent, according to Kheisin and Lavrenenko, on the
intensification of tick feeding on the penultimate day prior to detachment and
particularly on the phase of final rapid ingestion of blood when the host is
resting. This has some substantiation from the presented data from Balashov's work where, by reference to the third column (Table IV), it is seen that

there is no consumption of the last portion of blood by ticks when the cattle are in the fields. It is also suggested by these Russian workers that whilst the rhythm of dropping may be basically dependent on feeding it may be secondarily influenced by the physiological state of the parasite and by external influences. Both Balashov (1954) and Kheisin and Lavrenenko (1956) observed that whilst cattle were resting fully engorged ticks did not drop off but did so immediately after movement took place. Kitaoka (1962) expressed the opinion that movement of the host was not a prime factor in assisting detachment, for he wrote that in an experiment involving females of *H. bispinosa* "the infested animal had no rest and chewed throughout the night but the females manifested an enhanced feeding activity around midnight, showed engorgement in the morning and dropped off a little later". Kitaoka, like Nuttall many years ago, considers light to be the predominant stimulus inducing fully satiated females of *B. microplus* and *H. bispinosa* to release themselves. The possibility of the degree of attachment afforded by the trophi for adhering to the host also merits further consideration as suggested by Arthur (1962), Sutton and Arthur (1962: discussion), Saito *et al.* (1960) and Saito and Ohara (1961). In cases where the mouth parts are deeply embedded in the host tissue, e.g. *I. persulcatus* and *I. ricinus*, body movements would undoubtedly facilitate extraction of the mouth parts from the skin, particularly where the ticks occur in the axillary regions and in the groin. In other ticks, e.g. *H. bispinosa* and *Boophilus microplus*, where the attachment is relatively superficial (Saito *et al.*, 1960; Saito and Ohara, 1961), less intense stimuli would effect the release of the tick. Despite these speculations we have as yet little positive information on the mechanics whereby such ticks release themselves from the holding "cement" and from the host tissue. It would also be of considerable interest to investigate the timing of the imbibition of the last blood meal by other ixodid ticks and to ascertain when fully replete ticks detach themselves from wild hosts and from domestic stock which do not undergo the regular rhythmicity of having specified periods of "rest" (e.g. as in a cattle shed) and a specified period of motion (e.g. as in pastures) within a 24 h period.

XI. Factors Influencing Attachment to the Host

Attachment to the host for feeding purposes by ticks is determined by the interaction of groups of sense organs, viz. Haller's organ (for structural details, see Arthur, 1956, 1962; and for physiology, see Lees, 1948; El Ziady, 1958); temperature and tactile bristles on the legs in hard ticks (Lees, 1948), temperature perception through the integument of soft ticks (El Ziady, 1958) and chemoreceptors on the apex of palpal segment IV (Lees, 1948).

Hindle and Merriman (1912) found that *A. persicus* with amputated forelegs (hence the removal of the odour-perceiving organ) attach themselves to artificial membranes made from rat diaphragm, when the latter were placed over 0·8% sodium chloride or gelatine solutions, at a temperature of 42° C. Under similar conditions, normal ticks failed to attach. Similar results are obtained for *I. ricinus*, according to Totze (1933), and are indicative of the role of odour as a prerequisite for attachment to hosts.

The attraction of ticks to membranes and hosts is also conditioned by temperature. Lees (1948) showed that below 20° C unfed females of *I. ricinus* are indifferent to the smell of sheep wool alone. The attractiveness of sheep's wool for attachment by ticks is increased by raising the temperature from 20° to 37° C, and at 37° C is highly attractive. Lees carried out experiments using living sheep, freshly prepared lambskin (i.e. having an odour stimulus) and membranes from rat diaphragm (i.e. lacking an odour stimulus) to determine the interaction of temperature and odour. Apart from the living sheep, ticks were placed on artificial membrane surfaces at alternating temperatures, so that by permutation of experiments the ticks could be subjected to both stimuli acting together, to one stimulus alone or to neither stimulus. Under the influence of temperature and odour stimuli a high percentage of ticks attach, in the presence of one or the other only 10% attach but where both are lacking there is no attachment. Absence of the thermal response elicits little response by the tick, and lack of chemical stimulation does not stimulate the tick to test the surface of the membranes. Warm (37° C) lambskin membrane was almost as attractive as the living sheep.

Further experiments showed that seven ticks out of ten, with amputated palpal organs but with intact forelegs, attached to live sheep, but some attached to warmed membranes prepared from the diaphragm of a rabbit. Amputation of both palpal and fore-limbs resulted in a failure to attach to freshly prepared lambskin membranes, diaphragm or living animals. After removal of only the forelegs, six out of ten ticks attach to living sheep but only one on rat diaphragm at 37° C. On the basis of these experiments Lees (1948) reported that the sensilla at the apex of the palps form an additional organ concerned with the chemical perception of the host skin. When on the host, and prior to attachment, the palpi are waved excitedly and the apical segments, bearing the sensilla, are protracted and retracted rapidly. Similar movements are reported by Arthur (1962) when the male endeavours to find the sexual orifice of the female preparatory to inserting the spermatophore. Wilkinson (1953) noted that the strongest questing behaviour in larvae of *Boophilus microplus* occurs in response to chemicals, but vibration, air currents, interrupted illumination, warmth and moisture all play a part in reacting to the host.

Hungry soft ticks appear to be unable to detect hosts at a distance (El Ziady, 1958) and find hosts at random, becoming aware of them only on contact. The experimental work of El Ziady also suggests that suitable temperature may be of more significance than odour in host selection by small forms of *O. erraticus*.

When ixodid ticks are on the host they require a preliminary period of stimulation before the mouth parts penetrate the skin. The longer the period of starvation, the faster do they proceed to attach, as Lees (1948) demonstrated when two batches of *I. ricinus*, which had moulted 7 months and 6 weeks previously, were placed to feed on sheep. The older ticks attached within 24 h, and of these 90% were ready to feed within 4 h. None of the younger ticks attached within 4 h, 60% after 40 h and the remainder failed to attach and succumbed to the effects of desiccation. A very high proportion of the larvae of *Boophilus microplus* insert their mouth parts into the skin of cattle within 1 h of being placed on the host (Wilkinson, 1953) as also did larvae of *I. ricinus* on day-old rats (Arthur and Sutton, unpublished). In the case of *Boophilus*, only a small percentage wandered about the body hairs for 2–3 days. The first signs of penetration are the slight withdrawing of the palps and the tick bends the body so that it appears to stand on its capitulum. The hypostome and chelicerae meanwhile are being pushed between the hairs on to the surface of the skin.

XII. Feeding Sites on Natural Hosts, with Particular Reference to the Genus *Ixodes* in Britain

Roubaud (1916) postulated that successful external parasitism of the warthog and of man by *O. moubata* was due to the attraction of their hairless skins. The occurrence of ticks among the hair of the back of the warthogs, however, limits the plausibility of this theory. Nevertheless, El Ziady (1958) suggested that hair is a hindrance to the feeding tick and hairless parts of the host's body are preferred by the small forms of *O. erraticus*. In the absence of hairless parts, the tick will feed from the slightly hairy parts of the body.

Earlier workers stated that infestations of females of *I. ricinus* on sheep are limited to the bare, or hairy areas or short-woolled regions adjoining these parts, but Milne (1947) found that an average of 16% (maximum of 38%) of the ticks feeding on sheep are found under the long wool of the lower neck, chest and shoulders. Comparable areas of the withers, back, rump and flanks are not infested. Female ticks also attach to the head, ears, legs, the axillary and inguinal regions and adjacent short-woolled areas of sheep. Proportionately the heaviest infestation is on the head, becoming progressively less in the axillae and in the inguinal region. Large numbers of females attaching to the fleece desiccate before arriving at suitable attachment sites, which is enhanced by the fairly low relative humidity of the fleece and the high temperature near the skin (Evans, 1950). Evidence of the limiting effect of the fleece on the distribution of *I. ricinus* on sheep comes from a comparison of the tick populations on the head, and in the axillary and inguinal regions of ewes and lambs (Evans, 1950). His results showed that lambs are more heavily infested in the axillary region than are ewes, and he considered that the fleece of the older sheep acts as a barrier against the movement of unfed parasites towards the axillary and inguinal regions. In contrast to this, most females of *I. rubicundus* attach in wool-covered sites and few on the bare parts of sheep. The rate of feeding in both regions is similar (Stampa, 1959).

On sheep the nymphs of *I. ricinus* are found on the distal parts of the ears, snout and chin on the head, and on the lower arm in the axillary region. Larvae of the same species occupy the tips of the ears, around the nostrils and lips on the head, round the fetlock and in the axillary region (Milne, 1949). The nymphs on cattle are most numerous immediately behind the nostrils, whilst the primary regions of the head selected for feeding by the larvae are the lips and nostrils. Larvae and nymphs are abundant below the wrist and ankle joints on the foreleg and hindleg, the larvae being most abundant around the fetlock (Evans, 1950). Experimental infestations of 1-day-old (i.e. hairless) rats with larvae of *I. ricinus* have the vast majority of the population attaching in and around the ears and beneath the head in the neck region (Arthur, unpublished). The introduction of comparable samples of larvae on to these hosts, in which hair growth has begun, select similar feeding sites, and the ticks orientate themselves in the opposite direction to that of the growth of the individual hairs (Arthur and Sutton, unpublished).

An interpretation of this zoning of different developmental stages on sheep has been suggested by Milne (1949). The majority of ticks on the fore part of the body arrive by way of the ears (distally), nose, lips, hoof and lower leg, and the larger the tick stage the farther does its attachment site recede from the region of pick-up. Milne considered that this recession bears a correlation with the gradients in friction: "thus on proceeding from lips back to cheeks, we find external friction decreasing and hair length (cover) increasing from about $\frac{1}{16}$ to 1 in. or more in blackfaced sheep; at the same time we meet first a zone of larvae, then a zone of nymphs and finally a zone of females. Lessened external friction without increase in cover may suffice, e.g. positions towards the roots of the ears or in bare parts of the axillae". There is general unanimity that more female ticks attach on the head than in the axillary or inguinal regions of sheep, and there is also a tendency for the numbers of *I. ricinus* ticks to decrease in numbers from head to tail on small mammals.

Lees (1948) accounted for the zoning of different instars on the grounds of the need for differential physiological stimulation, believing that females of *I. ricinus* may require more prolonged stimulation before attaching than do nymphs, and nymphs more than do larvae. Females accordingly tend to travel farther from their site of pick up than do nymphs, and nymphs farther than larvae before being sufficiently stimulated to insert their mouth parts into the skin. Lees also showed that recently moulted ticks require more prolonged stimulation than do older females, and consequently newly emerged ticks would tend to wander farther than older ones.

The heaviest infestations of *I. ricinus* on cattle occur on the forelegs and in the axillae, the next favourable situations appear to be groins and udder, followed in turn by the folds of the flank and the dewlap. Light infestations occur on the head and the escutcheon. On the head the feeding sites are limited to the base of the ears and to parts of the lower jaw (Edwards and Arthur, 1947; Evans, 1950). *I. ricinus* is practically never found on the back and upper sides of large animals such as the cow and sheep, but this site is frequently selected by this species on small mammals such as shrews, voles and hares (Arthur, 1953a). Milne suggests that this habit on sheep may be "associated with some limit to the distance a tick required to crawl over the body before becoming sufficiently stimulated to attach".

According to Evans (1950) the percentage of females on the fore-quarters of cattle increases during the course of tick activity, whether in the spring or in the autumn. In the early part of the season there is a greater number of ticks on the hind-quarters, but later the fore-quarters carry the heavier infestations. Applying Lees' concept of differential physiological stimulation and age, Evans expressed the opinion that at the beginning of the tick season young females of *I. ricinus* will attach themselves at a considerable distance from the points of pick up, while older females later in the season will attach nearer to the sites of pick up because they require less stimulation.

Evans (1950) also considered the possibility of migration of ticks from one part of the body to another, but disregarded this postulate because of lack of evidence. However, according to Galuzo (1943) larvae of *Hyalomma detritum* in Russia do select different sites on the same host, according to the season. In the cooler months of the year (October to November) the larvae attach themselves to parts of the body exposed to the sun, but summer-feeding larvae select the shaded undersides of the host. Variations in the movement of ticks from one part of the body of the host to another are also shown in the one host tick *Boophilus*. Larvae of *B. annulatus* show a preference for feeding on the legs, belly or dewlap whence the nymphs move to the flanks and belly, where both they and the adult females, to which they give rise, feed. The larvae of *B. decoloratus* show preference for the dewlap and neck, or else wander to the tip and outer pinna of the ear, where on moulting to nymphs they remain to feed again. On transforming to the adult they undergo a migration to the flanks and belly for feeding. Comparable movements occur in *Boophilus microplus*, where the larvae feed on the inner surface of the ear and also moult there. The nymphs and adults are, however, found only on the flanks, belly and udders (Arthur, 1962). If a stimulation period is required for *Boophilus* species, as doubtless it is, then its intensity varies from species to species. As judged by changes in their position, the nymphs of *B. annulatus* and *B. microplus* require more physiological stimulation than do nymphs of *B. decoloratus*, which occupy the same feeding sites as their larvae, but the females of the latter species require more sustained stimulation than do females of *B. annulatus* and *B. microplus*.

It has been observed commonly that when compared with large mammals, the smaller the host and the fewer are the numbers of *I. ricinus* present. Milne (1949) elaborated this observation and showed that the smaller the host and the fewer are females of this species relative to nymphs, and the fewer the nymphs relative to larvae. Also, in general, the smaller the host and the lower the average weight of female ticks (*I. ricinus*) and of nymphs and larvae. This has been interpreted in terms of the amount of ground covered in unit time: i.e. the smaller the host, the less ground generally covered and the less the opportunity for contact with *I. ricinus* ticks. These considerations, presumably, would apply to all tick species whose free living stages occur in the hunting and grazing areas of their hosts. On the contrary, there are species of ticks which, for the most part, have more restricted habitats (e.g. nests and burrows) in which all the developmental stages of the parasite exist together, and their hosts tend to use regular "runs" to and from these sites. One such species is *I. hexagonus*, which is a habitué of the nests of hedgehogs and, less frequently, of those of polecats, stoats and foxes (Arthur, 1953c). The adults of this tick feed successfully in the axillae, groin and perineal regions of these hosts, i.e. those areas which are most nearly hairless. Quite frequently nymphs occur alongside females in these situations, but most commonly they occur with larvae on the face and tips of the ears. Such hosts return to a potential source of infection on each occasion when they visit their "lairs", but this is not so with small mammals infested only with *I. ricinus* (Arthur, 1953c, 1963).

Ticks on birds are confined to the head and the upper neck, and this is attributed to active de-ticking by the host. In this respect, most workers agree that the bird's beak is a more efficient tool for de-ticking than either the teeth or claws of small mammals (Shcheglova, 1939; Milne, 1949). De-ticking also occurs in some of the primates, particularly when they live in families, and for a proper assessment of the major zones of attachment, an old "hobo" is the best subject (Arthur, 1965).

Possibly the structure of the skin may exercise some effect in the distribution of the ectoparasites on different hosts. The microstructure of the skin depends on the part of the body from which the sample is taken (Arthur, 1953b). The skin of cattle, for example, is thickest along the back (4·4–5·2 mm), has crossing fibre bundles and is therefore firm. Along the rump and flanks the thickness varies from 3·9 to 5·2 mm and the fibre bundles cross less frequently. In the axillae and the groins the skin in thinnest, ranging from 1·8 to 2·4 mm with the fibres arranged horizontally, and the underlying tissue is consequently more open and lacks firmness. Comparable variations are observed in the skins of other mammals. Habitual parasites of small mammals, such as *I. trianguliceps* and other *Ixodes* of African small mammals, occupy similar sites to those occupied by *I. ricinus* on large mammals (Arthur, 1965). This may possibly be directly correlated with the smaller sizes of their cheliceral digits and of their reduced armature, whereby it may become more difficult to cut through the superficial tissues of the skin (Arthur, 1953b). On the contrary, observations show that once the tick is attached, actively secreting saliva, the tissues are liquefied; e.g. the mouth parts of both larvae of *I. trianguliceps* and females of *Haemaphysalis bispinosa* can penetrate the cartilage of the pinnae of mice (Arthur, 1962).

To what extent the source of blood limits the host range has never been thoroughly investigated. Rodhain (1920, 1922) found that the blood of lizards, geckos and snakes could be digested by *O. moubata*, but that adults fed as nymphs on snakes showed a high mortality. Similarly chameleon blood was digested only very slowly and resulted in a high initial mortality of ticks and very few of them became adapted to this diet. The cause may be attributed to a deficiency of certain accessory substances in the blood of the host, because it has been established that *O. moubata* will not grow by feeding on rats showing thiamine deficiency. That some blood factor may in part regulate the intake of blood by a tick species is also suggested by the fact that *Argas brumpti* will feed to repletion on mouse blood, but other *Argas* species only become partially replete (Hoogstraal, 1956). Attempts to feed larvae of *I. hexagonus* on day-old rats failed, whereas larvae of *I. ricinus* feed successfully on the same host under precisely similar environmental conditions (Arthur and Sutton, unpublished). Likewise nymphae of *I. rubicundus* will feed to repletion on elephant shrews—the normal host of larvae in the field—but only become partially replete on rabbits under experimental conditions (Theiler, 1959). The blood meals imbibed by *Argas persicus* (Nuttall *et al.*, 1908) and by *Ornithodoros hermsi* (Gregson, 1956) do not always appear to be agreeable to the tick and not uncommonly engorged adults turn purple and die. No adequate explanation has been propounded for this phenomenon, although Gregson (1956) suggested that some form of sensitization may be set up within the tick and a change of hosts may be necessary for its survival. Observations on *Ixodes rubicundus* are also of interest in this respect. Not all individuals of this species are capable of producing paralysis in sheep and the assessment of the incidence of infection in ticks or of the disease itself is complicated by the development of immunity in these hosts. There is firstly an immunity of short duration, about 5 weeks, to the toxic agent itself, and secondly an immunity to the engorgement of ticks. In the former the immunity developed is specific in character and associated only with certain individual ticks; these presumably produce either the disease or an immunity response to the toxin. In the latter all ticks can produce an immune response, which manifests itself by preventing ticks, attaching subsequently, from becoming fully engorged and materially retarding the rate of feeding. These ticks are brown in colour in contrast to the blue colour of those which engorge on susceptible sheep (Stampa and du Toit, 1958). Comparable observations have been made by Enigk (1953) on *I. ricinus* in Europe.

XIII. FOOD SOURCES AVAILABLE TO TICKS

The rapid feeding of argasid ticks is reflected in their ecology, as they effect more certain life histories by infesting the resting places of their hosts. Argasid ticks, having imbibed blood meals rapidly, secrete themselves in crevices usually in the nesting places of their hosts to digest their meals before attacking the same hosts on subsequent occasions (see, for example, Hoogstraal, 1956). Because ixodid ticks feed continuously for a number of days on their hosts, they are less economic in their life histories and may show a diffuse spatial pattern by dropping indiscriminately during the peregrinations of the hosts. This behaviour pattern opens up a variety of feeding sources for ticks infesting the grazing or hunting areas of their hosts, when compared with those ticks which are restricted to the nesting quarters of their hosts. The dynamic community relationships between such ticks and their hosts have been shown by MacLeod (1962), using a mechanical analogue to illustrate the complex interactions which may take place (Fig. 8). In Fig. 8 the disks represent factors: clockwise turn means increase. The central pulleys are the drive wheels and the peripheral pulleys the pick up. The whole line belt drives indicate ecological action, the interrupted lines coaction and the dotted line reaction. As "good grass" cover increases, the proportion of rough grass must decrease because the drive is toothed. Increase of the rough cover proportion, acting through the increased moisture of the microclimate (= toothed idler wheel B) will increase the survival of fully fed ticks. A second type of drive is optional, e.g. the grass factor to the cattle stock. Increase of cattle tends to reduce the rough cover, i.e. to reverse the direction of rotation of the rough cover disk. This non-toothed or friction contact represents a third type of power linkage, i.e. the transmission of turning movement will not necessarily take place, e.g. the cattle could be increased without decreasing the sheep stock. The good grass factor could be linked directly to the sheep numbers. Here, because of the selective grazing habits of the sheep—represented by friction wheel A—the tendency is to increase the amount of rough cover. Increase of the sheep and/or cattle will tend to increase the numbers of ticks.

Increase of the good grass proportion increases the density of wild herbivores; increase of rough cover produces more suitable conditions for microfaunal elements, e.g. rodents. Increase of either or both of these faunal components results in greater carnivore populations, all of which contribute to increasing tick density.

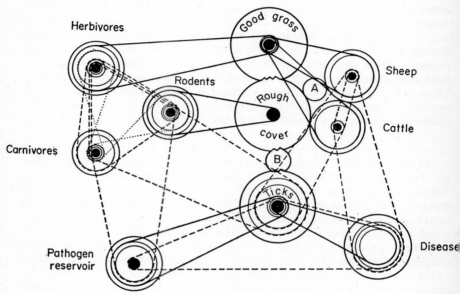

Fig. 8. Diagram of some dynamic community relations. Clockwise rotation indicates increase. A, Selective grazing habit of sheep; B, microclimatic humidity. (From MacLeod, 1962.) For further details, see text.

Doubtless the concepts indicated by this mechanical analogue are applicable to the host relations of other ticks which occupy similar habitats and parasitize a wide range of hosts. On the basis of the classification of ticks and their host preferences, such ticks are regarded as non-specific (Theiler, 1959; Arthur, 1962) and would include such species as *I. persulcatus* (see Pomerantzev, 1950), *I. ricinus* (see Milne, 1949; Arthur, 1963), *R. tricuspis*, *R. sanguineus* and *R. simus* (see Theiler, 1959). Group specific forms are associated with (a) birds, e.g. *Haemaphysalis hoodi hoodi*, *I. theilerae*, *I. daveyi*, *I. brunneus*, *I. frontalis*, *Argas persicus*, *A. reflexus* (see Arthur, 1962); (b) tortoises, e.g. *Amblyomma sylvaticum*, *A. marmoreum*, *A. falso-marmoreum*, *A. nuttalli*, *A. sparsum* (see Theiler, 1959); (c) snakes, e.g. *Aponomma latum* (see Theiler, 1959); (d) bats, e.g. *I. vespertilionis*, *I. simplex*, *A. (Chiropterargas) boueti*, *A. (C.) confusus*, *A. (C.) vespertilionis* (see Arthur, 1962); (e) carnivores, e.g. *"Haemaphysalis" leachi* group (Theiler, 1959); and

(f) herbivores, e.g. *R. appendiculatus, R. ayrei* (= *compositus*), *R. evertsi evertsi, R. kochi, R. pravus,* etc. (see Theiler, 1959).

Species which are host specific are relatively few in number among well-established forms and include *I. trianguliceps, I. alluaudi, Aponomma transversale, Amblyomma tholloni, A. rhinocerotis, A. cuneatum, Haemaphysalis calcarata, H. houyi, Rhipicephalus arnoldi, R. complanatus, R. cuspidatus, R. distinctus, R. simpsoni, Dermacentor rhinocerinos* and *D. circumguttatus* (see Arthur, 1962; Theiler, 1959). Theiler (1959) considered that representatives of the most primitive genera appear to show the greatest specificity. Immature stages of ticks may be found either in association with adults on their hosts, e.g. *R. appendiculatus* and *R. evertsi,* avian and small mammal Haemaphysalids, all the *Aponommas* and the chelonian *Amblyomma* (see Theiler, 1959) and *I. hexagonus* (see Arthur, 1953c) or on different, and usually smaller hosts than are parasitized by the adults, as in certain *Dermacentor* species (see Arthur, 1960). Theiler (1959) stated that the selection of hosts by larvae and nymphs may not be haphazard; the larvae of *R. simus* and *R. tricuspis* for example, are found on representatives of Muridae and Cricetidae. Macroscelidae and *Pronolagus* (Leporidae) play an important part in maintaining the immature stages of *I. rubicundus* (see Stampa, 1959) as also do Macroscelidae in the life cycles of *I. pilosus, H. leachii* and some *Rhipicephalus* sp. In species where adults and immatures occur on the same hosts the immatures may frequently parasitize a wide range of small mammals and birds, as in *I. ricinus* (see Milne, 1949). The few adults collected from small hosts and their distribution in areas out of reach of the beaks in birds and of the mouths in small mammals are suggestive of active de-ticking and removal of large excrescences in the form of gorging females (see Alfeev, 1935; Shcheglova, 1939; Milne, 1949; Černý and Balat, 1960; Arthur, 1963).

XIV. HOST–TICK NUTRITIONAL RELATIONSHIPS IN DISEASE TRANSMISSION

Many facets of the tick-host-vegetation complex, and accordingly of tick-borne diseases, remain obscure, and as far as British species are concerned these gaps are clearly exposed by MacLeod (1962). The role of vertebrate and tick hosts for the continued survival of tick-borne viruses in nature has been summarized by Gordon Smith (1962). The long-term natural maintenance of such viruses depends on geographical and behavioural associations between the tick vector and the host in whose bloodstream the virus, inoculated by the biting tick, can circulate adequately to infect further ticks. Because tick populations are adequate only where suitable vegetation provides the appropriate microclimates, infection occurs only in restricted foci. Vertebrate maintenance hosts are, in general, wild species and presumably because of mutually interacting selection during long symbiosis with the virus do not normally exhibit symptoms of infection. They circulate virus once only because of antibody formation, and hence their population turnovers must therefore supply sufficient new susceptibles annually. Incidental vertebrate hosts may or may not show symptoms, and with severe infections die. This condition is described in terms of overt disease in man or domestic animals which are usually incidental hosts, and as far as the virus is concerned represent culs-de-sac. The passage of viruses to new areas is effected by movements of infected ticks carried by large mammals or by birds, so that a stable enzootic state may be transformed to that of an epizootic or epidemic status by population changes in ticks or vertebrates or to the introduction of a virus into new areas and its perpetuation by the prevailing tick-vertebrate complex. Similar principles appear to be valid in considering the transmission of rickettsial infections by ticks (Bertram, 1962) and hence the need for more intensive work on the relationships of the host and the tick in all its stages, as a necessary foundation for further studies.

The role of the tick as a reservoir for pathogenic organisms, as well as their vertebrate hosts, has been reviewed and discussed by Philip and Burgdorfer (1961) and Philip (1961), who considered that the reservoir function is often a dual one involving in varying degrees both the vertebrate and invertebrate hosts, supplementing or complementing one another in the total reservoir system for many of the arthropod-borne zoonoses. Acarines, qualify more readily as reservoirs than do biting flies because of their longevity and their ability to transmit infectious agents transovarially to succeeding generations, although this is not an invariable prerequisite, as shown by its absence in the transmission of louping ill (MacLeod and Gordon, 1932; Neitz, 1948), Colorado tick-fever (Eklund *et al.*, 1960) and in *Cowdria ruminantium* (see Neitz, 1956). The great majority of infectious agents are also adapted to residence in ticks without producing inimical effects on them, and indeed proliferate in the customary vector. The Kyasanur forest virus, transmitted to man, monkeys and domestic stock in India by *Haemaphysalis spinigera* is, according to Philip (1961), an example of a widely adapted agent of a virus group having a probable reservoir in ticks. All the isolations from ticks were made from the Kyasanur forest or the forests adjacent to Holekatte Hosur and Kannur where both men and monkeys had been affected by the disease. Haemaphysalid ticks from localities outside the epidemic area do not carry the virus, and this is true of other genera of ticks within the epidemic area or from adjacent areas (Work *et al.*, 1957).

The intensity of transmission of virulent agents in relation to the reservoir mechanism in ticks is also affected by the degradation of infection resident in vectors due to subsequent feeding on immune hosts (MacLeod and Gordon, 1932) with circulating antibodies as shown by Benda (1958) in Czechoslovakia.

The questions of how and when pathogenic organisms reach the blood circulation, whether they undergo a tissue stage before reaching the circulation and how and when pathogens are taken up by vectors from blood and/or extravascular tissue still remain fields for active research. Equally important too are the biochemical and biophysical factors which determine the changing forms and the migrations of the infectious agents through the arthropod tissues, whereby they reach the trophi for inoculation into new vertebrate hosts.

References

Alfeev, N. I. (1935). *In* "Cattle Pests" (E. N. Pavlovsky, ed.), pp. 111–136. Izd. Akad. Nauk SSSR.
André, M. (1927). *Bull. Mus. Hist. nat., Paris* 33, 509.
Arthur, D. R. (1947). *Ent. mon. Mag.* 83, 69.
Arthur, D. R. (1951). *Parasitology* 41, 66.
Arthur, D. R. (1953a). *Parasitology* 42, 161.
Arthur, D. R. (1953b). *Parasitology* 42, 187.
Arthur, D. R. (1953c). *Parasitology* 43, 227.
Arthur, D. R. (1956). *Parasitology* 46, 261.
Arthur, D. R. (1957). *Parasitology* 47, 169.
Arthur, D. R. (1960). "Ticks: A Monograph of the Ixodoidea," Pt. V. Cambridge University Press, London.
Arthur, D. R. (1962). "Ticks and Disease." Pergamon Press, Oxford.
Arthur, D. R. (1963). "British Ticks." Butterworth, London.
Arthur, D. R. (1965). "Ticks of the Genus *Ixodes* in Africa." Athlone Press, London.
Audy, J. R. (1951). *Aust. J. Sci.* 14, 94.
Audy, J. R. (1952). *Trans. R. Soc. trop. Med. Hyg.* 46, 459.
Balashov, Y. S. (1954). *Dokl. Akad. SSSR.* (N.S.), 98, 317.
Balashov, Y. S. (1957). *Zool. Akad. Sci. SSSR* 36, 870.
Balashov, Y. S. (1958). *Parazit. Sbol. Zool. Inst. Akad. Nauk. USSR* 18, 78.
Balashov, Y. S. (1961). *Mag. Parasit., Moscow* 20, 185.
Benda, R. (1958). *J. Hyg. Epidem. Microbiol. Immun.* 2, 314.
Bertkau, P. (1881). *S.B. niederrhain. Ges. Nat.-u. Heilk.* 38, 1.
Bertram, D. S. (1939). *Ann. trop. Med. Parasit.* 33, 229.
Bertram, D. S. (1962). *In* "Aspects of Disease Transmission by Ticks" (D. R. Arthur, ed.). Symposium of the Zoological Society of London, No. 6.
Blagoveshchensky, D. I. and Pomerantzev, B. I. (1930). *Pract. Vet. Sci., Moscow* 8.
Brandes, G. (1908). *Z. naturwiss.* 80, 302.
Brandis, F. (1897). Uber *Leptus autumnalis.* Festschr. 50 jähr. Best. Provinz. Irrenanst. Nietleben, Leipzig.
Brethes, J. (1909). *An. Mus. nac. B. Aires* 12, 211.
Carrick, A. and Bullough, W. S. (1940). *Parasitology* 32, 313.
Černý, V. and Balat, F. (1960). *Zool. Listy* 9, 217.
Christophers, S. R. (1906). *Sci. Mem. med. Sanit. Dep. India* (N.S.), 23, 1.
Cowdry, E. V. and Danks, W. B. C. (1933). *Parasitology* 25, 1.
Cross, H. F. (1962). *J. econ. Ent.* 55, 22.
Dickerson, G. and Lavoipierre, M. M. J. (1959). *Ann. trop. Med. Parasit.* 53, 347.
Douglas, J. K. (1943). *Univ. Calif. Publ. Ent.* 7, 207.
Edwards, E. E. and Arthur, D. R. (1947). *Parasitology* 38, 72.
Eklund, C. M., Kohls, G. M. and Kennedy, R. C. (1960). "Symposium: Biology of Viruses." Czechoslovakia. (Abstract.)
El Ziady, S. (1958). *Ann. ent. Soc. Amer.* 51, 317.
Enigk, K. (1953). *Z. Parasitenk.* 7, 56.
Evans, G. O. (1950). *Bull. ent. Res.* 40, 459.
Ewing, H. E. (1944). *J. Parasit.* 30, 339.
Feng, L. C. and Hoeppli, R. (1933). *Chinese Med. J.* 47, 1191.
Foggie, A. (1959). *Ann. trop. Med. Parasit.* 53, 27.
Foggie, A. (1962). *In* "Aspects of Disease Transmission by Ticks" (D. R. Arthur, ed.). Symposium of the Zoological Society of London, No. 6.
Galuzo, I. G. (1943). *Izv. kazakh. Fil. Akad. Nauk, SSSR* (Ser. Zool.), 2, 85.

Gordon, R. M. (1958). *E. Afr. med. J.* **35**, 393.
Gordon, R. M. and Crewe, W. (1948). *Ann. trop. Med. Parasit.* **42**, 334.
Gordon, R. M. and Crewe, W. (1953). *Ann. trop. Med. Parasit.* **47**, 74.
Gordon, R. M. and Duke, B. O. L. (1955). *Trans. R. Soc. trop. Med. Hyg.* **49**, 29ℂ
Gordon, R. M. and Lumsden, W. H. R. (1939). *Ann. trop. Med. Parasit.* **33**, 25ℂ
Gordon, R. M. and Willett, K. C. (1958). *Ann. trop. Med. Parasit.* **52**, 346.
Gordon, R. M., Crewe, W. and Willett, K. C. (1956). *Ann. trop. Med. Parasit.* **5ℂ
    426.
Gordon Smith, C. E. (1962). *In* "Aspects of Disease Transmission by Ticks
    (D. R. Arthur, ed.). Symposium of the Zoological Society of London, No. ℂ
Gorirossi, F. E. (1950). *J. Parasit.* **36**, 301.
Gregson, J. D. (1935). *Proc. ent. Soc. Brit. Colomb.* **31**, 17.
Gregson, J. D. (1937). *Proc. ent. Soc. Brit. Colomb.* **33**, 15.
Gregson, J. D. (1938). *J. Path. Bact.* **47**, 143.
Gregson, J. D. (1955). *Mon. Rep. Can. Div. Ent. Kamloops.*
Gregson, J. D. (1956). "The Ixodoidea of Canada." Sci. Serv. Ent. Div., Canadℂ
    Department of Agriculture.
Gregson, J. D. (1960a). *Acta trop. Basel* **17**, 48.
Gregson, J. D. (1960b). *Acta trop. Basel* **17**, 72.
Griffiths, R. B. and Gordon, R. M. (1952). *Ann. trop. Med. Parasit.* **46**, 311.
Gudden, B. A. (1871). *Virchows Arch. path. Anat.* **52**, 255.
Hindle, E. and Merriman, G. (1912). *Parasitology* **5**, 203.
Hoeppli, R. and Feng, L. C. (1931). *Nat. med. J. China* **17**, 541.
Hoeppli, R. and Feng, L. C. (1933). *China med. J.* **47**, 29.
Hoeppli, R. and Schumacher, H. H. (1962). *Z. Tropenmed.* **13**, 419.
Hoogstraal, H. (1956). "African Ixodoidea. Ticks of the Sudan." Vol. 1, pp
    1–1101. Bur. Med. Surg. U.S. Navy.
Hughes, T. E. (1954). *Ann. trop. Med. Parasit.* **48**, 397.
Jellison, W. L. and Kohls, G. M. (1938). *J. Parasitol.* **24**, 143.
Jones, B. M. (1950). *Parasitology* **40**, 247.
Jourdain, S. (1899). *Arch. Parasit.* **2**, 28.
Keilin, D. and Wang, Y. L. (1947). *Biochem. J.* **41**, 491.
Kheisin, E. M. (1953). Scientific records of the Karelo-Finnish State University,
    Vol. 4, Part 3.
Kheisin, E. M. and Lavrenenko, L. E. (1956). *Zool. Zhur.* **35**, 379.
Kitaoka, S. (1961a). *Nat. Inst. Anim. Hlth Quart.* **1**, 85.
Kitaoka, S. (1961b). *Nat. Inst. Anim. Hlth Quart.* **1**, 96.
Kitaoka, S. (1962). *Nat. Inst. Anim. Hlth Quart.* **2**, 106.
Kitaoka, S. and Yajima, A. (1958). *Bull. nat. Inst. Anim. Hlth.* **34**, 135.
Kossel, H., Weber, A., Schulze, P. and Miessner, A. (1903). *Arb. K. GesundhAmt.*
    20, 1–77.
Lavoipierre, M. M. J. (1958). *Ann. trop. Med. Parasit.* **52**, 103.
Lavoipierre, M. M. J. and Riek, R. F. (1955). *Ann. trop. Med. Parasit.* **49**, 96.
Lavoipierre, M. M. J., Dickerson, G. and Gordon, R. M. (1959). *Ann. trop. Med.
    Parasit.* **53**, 235.
Lees, A. D. (1946). *Parasitology* **37**, 172.
Lees, A. D. (1947). *J. exp. Biol.* **23**, 379.
Lees, A. D. (1948). *J. exp. Biol.* **25**, 145.
Lees, A. D. (1952). *Proc. zool. Soc. Lond.* **121**, 759.
MacLeod, J. (1962). *In* "Aspects of Disease Transmission by Ticks" (D. R. Arthur,
    ed.). Symposium of the Zoological Society of London, No. 6.
MacLeod, J. and Gordon, W. S. (1932). *J. comp. Path.* **45**, 240.

Milne, A. (1947). *Parasitology* **38**, 34.
Milne, A. (1949). *Parasitology* **39**, 173.
Mironov, V. S. and Baldina, A. I. (1942). *Med. Parasit. Moscow* **11**, 51.
Neitz, W. O. (1948). *S. Afr. J. Sci.* **1**, 133.
Neitz, W. O. (1956). *Onderstepoort J. vet. Res.* **27**, 115.
Nordenskiöld, E. (1908). *Zool. Jber.* Alt. 2, **25**, 637.
Nuttall, G. H. F. (1914). *Parasitology* **7**, 258.
Nuttall, G. H. F. and Strickland, C. (1908). *Parasitology* **1**, 302.
Nuttall, G. H. F. and Warburton, C. (1911). "Ticks: A Monograph of the Ixodoidea.
    Pt. II: the Genus *Ixodes*," pp. 105–348. Cambridge University Press, London.
Nuttall, G. H. F., Warburton, C., Cooper, W. F. and Robinson, L. E. (1908).
    "Ticks: A Monograph of the Ixodoidea. Pt. I: Argasidae," pp. 1–104. Cam-
    bridge University Press, London.
Nuttall, G. H. F., Warburton, C., Cooper, W. F. and Robinson, L. E. (1915).
    "Ticks: A Monograph of the Ixodoidea. Pt. III: The Genus *Haemaphysalis*,"
    pp. 349–550. Cambridge University Press, London.
O'Rourke, F. J. (1956). *Nature, Lond.* **177**, 1087.
Olsuf'ev, N. G. and Kagramanov, S. V. (1947). *Ent. Oboz. Mosk.* **29**, 256.
Pavlovsky, E. N. and Alfeeva, S. P. (1949). *Izv. Akad. Nauk. SSSR* **6**, 709.
Pavlovsky, E. N. and Chodukin, N. I. (1928). *Pensee med. Usbéquist.* **2**, 8.
Pavlovsky, E. N. and Chodukin, N. I. (1929). *Z. Parasitenk.* **2**, 90.
Philip, C. B. (1961). *Acta trop. Basel* **18**, 257.
Philip, C. B. and Burgdorfer, W. (1961). *Annu. Rev. Ent.* **6**, 391.
Pomerantzev, B. I. (1950). *Ixodidae. In* "Fauna of the USSR", Vol. 4, pt. 2. Acad-
    emy of Sciences of the USSR.
Pomerantzev, B. I. and Alfeev, N. (1935). "Pests of Breeding Farms." Akad. Nauk.
    SSSR M.-L.
Riek, R. F. (1957). *Aust. J. Agric. Res.* **8**, 209.
Robinson, L. E. and Davidson, J. (1914). *Parasitology* **6**, 217.
Rodhain, J. (1920). *Ann. Soc. belge. Med. trop.* **1**, 133.
Rodhain, J. (1922) *Bull. Soc. Path. exot.* **15**, 560.
Roesler, R. (1934). *Z. morph. Ökol Tiere* **28**, 297.
Roubaud, E. (1916). *Bull. Soc. Pat. exot.* **9**, 768.
Sabbatani, L. (1898–9). *G. Accad. Med. Torino* **4**, 380.
Saito, Y. and Ohara, S. (1961). *Acta Med. Biol.* **9**, 1.
Saito, Y., Ohara, S. and Unagami, T. (1960). *Acta Med. Biol.* **7**, 323.
Samson, K. (1909). *Z. wiss. Zool.* **93**, 185.
Shcheglova, A. I. (1939). *Probl. Ecol. Biocenol.* **5–6**, 83–101. Dept. Vert. Zool.,
    Leningrad State University.
Schulze, P. (1943). *Z. Morph. Ökol. Tiere* **39**, 320.
Schumacher, H. H. and Hoeppli, R. (1963). *Z. tropenmed.* **13**, 192.
Serdyukova, V. G. (1954). *Tadj. Fill. Akad. Nauk. SSSR*, No. 6. (Cited by Balashov,
    1954.)
Shortt, H. E. and Swaminath, C. S. (1928). *Indian J. med. Res.* **15**, 827.
Stampa, S. (1959). *Onderstepoort J. vet. Res.* **28**, 170.
Stampa, S. and du Toit, R. (1958). *S. Afr. J. Sci.* **54**, 241.
Sutton, E. and Arthur, D. R. (1962). *In* "Aspects of Disease Transmission by Ticks"
    (D. R. Arthur, ed.). Symposium of the Zoological Society of London, No. 6.
Talice, R. V. (1929). *Ann. Parasit. hum. comp.* **7**, 483.
Talice, R. V. (1930). *Ann, Parasit. hum. comp.* **8**, 173.
Tatchell, R. J. (1964). *Parasitology* **54**, 423.
Tchij, A. N. (1949). "Babesiellosis of Large Horned Cattle." Sclhozgiz, M., Moscow.

Theiler, G. (1959). *S. Afr. J. Sci.* **55**, 67–71.

Thor, S. (1904). Cited by Jones (1950).

Till, W. M. (1959). *Nature, Lond.* **184**, 1078.

Till, W. M. (1961). *Mem. ent. Soc. S. Afr.* **6**, 1.

Toldt, K. (1923). *Wien. klin. Wschr.* **6**, 108.

Totze, R. (1933). *Z. vergl. Physiol.* **19**, 110.

Vitzhum, H. Graf (1930). *Z. Parasitenk.* **2**, 223.

Volodina, Z. V. (1942). *Zool. Zh.* **21**, 179.

Weitz, B. and Buxton, P. A. (1953). *Bull. ent. Res*, **44**, 445.

Wharton, G. W. and Fuller, H. S. (1952). A manual of the chiggers. *Mem. ent. Soc Wash.*, No. 4.

Wigglesworth, V. B. (1943). *Proc. R. Soc.* B, **131**, 313.

Wilkinson, P. R. (1953). *Aust. J. Zool.* **1**, 345.

Willman, C. (1955). *Z. Parasitenk.* **17**, 175.

Winkler, A. (1953). *Hantarzt.* **4**, 135.

Work, T. H., Trapido, H., Narasimba Murthy, D. P., Laxmana Rao, R., Bhatt D. N. and Kulkarni, H. G. (1957). *Indian J. med. Sci.* **11**, 619.

Yonge, C. M. (1928). *Biol. Rev.* **3**, 21.

Author Index

Numbers in italics refer to pages in the References at the end of each article.

A

Abbott, R. T., 107, *153*
Abe, Y., 133, *153*
Ackert, J E., 184, *218*
Agersborg, H. P. K., 87, *95*
Ajisaka, S., 147, 148, *154*
Akaiwa, H., 133, *153*
Akane, S., 62, *96*
Alfeev, N., 283, *297*
Alfeev, N. I., 293, *295*
Alfeeva, S. P., 265, *297*
Alicata, J. E., 70, 93, *95*, 173, *219*, 223, 224, 225, 227, 228, 230, 231, 232, 233, 234, 235, 236, 237, 239, 240, 242, 243, 244, 245, *246, 247*
Allen, G. M., 2, *49*
Allison, M. E., 240, 244, *247*
Amagishi, T., 138, 140, 147, *157*
Ameel, D. J., 102, 104, 108, 109, 111, 112, 124, *153*
Anantaraman, M., 174, *218*
Ando, A., 113, 121, 123, 141, 142, *153*
André, M., 251, 252, 253, *295*
Andrewartha, H. G., 21, *49*
Apostol, R., 240, *248*
Applebaum, I. L., 240, *247*
Apted, F. I. C., 23, 43, 46, 47, *49*
Araki, K., 120, *158*
Armitage, P., 10, *55*
Arthur, D. R., 253, 255, 256, 259, 260, 261, 262, 264, 265, 266, 268, 270, 272, 273, 280, 281, 285, 286, 288, 289, 290, 292, 293, *295, 297*
Ash, L. R., 231, 232, 236, *247*
Ashcroft, M. T., 28, 29, 30, 40, 42, *49, 50*
Audy, J. R., 254, *295*
Awano, R., 141, *157*
Azavedo, J. F. de, 16, *50*

B

Baer, J. G., 163, 165, 190, *218*
Bailey, C. A., 239, 240, 242, 244, 245, 247
Baker, J. A., 161, *218*
Baker, J. R., 45, *55*
Balashov, Y. S., 255, 273, 276, 278, 280, 281, 283, 284, 285, *295*
Balat, F., 293, *295*
Baldina, A. I., 264, *297*
Balducci, D., 163, *220*
Ball, G. H., 184, 185, *220*
Barbosa, C., 244
Barnes, G., 240, *248*
Basch, P. F., 108, *153*
Bauman, P. M., 90, *95*
Beadle, L. C., 186, *219*
Beaver, P. C., 112, *153*, 241, *247*
Becker, E. R., 8, *50*
Bell, E. J., 204, 205, *218*
Benda, R., 294, *295*
Bennett, H. J., 90, *95*
Berntzen, A. K., 192, 193, 194, 195, 196, 200, 216, 217, *218*
Bertkau, P., 280, *295*
Bertram, D. S., 254, 262, 294, *295*
Bhalerao, G. D., 61, *95*
Bhatt, D. N., 294, *298*
Birch, L. C., 21, 49
Blagoveshchensky, D. I., 280, *295*
Blair, D. M., 43, *55*
Boray, J. C., 77, 80, 84, *95*
Bordes, F. P., 240, *248*
Bories, S., 239, 240, 241, 242, 243, *247, 248*
Boycott, A. E., 75, *95*
Bozicevich, J., 141, *153*
Brand, T. von, 77, 88, *97*
Brandes, G., 251, *295*

299

P

Subject Index

S

Saliva, secretion, in ticks, 256–62
Salivaria, taxonomy, 5
Sampling, of *Glossina* spp., 16–7
Schistocephalus solidus, cultivation, 190, 191–2
Schistosoma japonicum, cultivation, 209, 210–1
mansoni, cultivation, 209–10, 211, 216
Schistosomatidae, cultivation, adults, 209–11
immature forms, 212–4
Sero-immunological diagnosis, in paragonimiasis, 137–42
Slugs, as *A. cantonensis* hosts, 227, 228–34
Snails,
as *A. cantonensis* hosts, 227, 228–34
development of *Fasciola* spp. in, 68
factors affecting, 79–85
pathogenicity, 87–9
Snail, *see also Lymnaea* spp.
Spirometra mansonoides, cultivation, 192–3
Steilocheilus longicaudus, 232
Stephanurus dentatus, cultivation, 175
Stercoraria, taxonomy, 5
Sterilization, and cultivation of helminths, 216
Strigeidae, cultivation, 202–6
Strongyloides papillosus, cultivation, 217
Subulina octona, as *A. cantonensis* host, 227, 231, 234, 238
Sulphonamides, in treatment of paragonimiasis, 144
Sulpha drugs, in treatment of paragonimiasis, 144–5

T

Tabanus taeniola, 22
Taenia crassiceps, cultivation, 194, 216
taeniaeformis, cultivation, 193–4
Taxonomy, of *Paragonimus* spp., 100–2
of *Trypanosoma* spp., 4–9
Temperature
effect on development of *Fasciola* spp., cercariae, 90
eggs, 64
in snail, 79–82
metacercariae, 92–3

Thiara granifera, 232
Ticks, attachment, 285–7
detachment, 283–5
digestion, 273
removal of residue, 280
engorgement, 280–3
feeding, 254–73
anatomy, 254–5
cement substance, 259–60
haemorrhage, 263, 264–5
mechanics, 256
non-blood tissue, 270–2
oedema, 264
salivary glands, 256–62
rate of secretion, 257–8
feeding sites, 287–91
feeding times, 255–6
food sources, 291–3
haemolysis, 276–7
conditions for, 275
host-tick nutrition relationship, 293–4
Tilapia, 232
Tinde experiment, 40–1
T. M. test, for paragonimiasis, 141
Trematodes, cultivation, 202–14
Fasciolidae, 206–9
P. westermani, 214
Philophthalmus, 214
Schistosomatidae, 209–14
Strigeidae, 202–6
Triatomine bugs, feeding, 249
Trichinella, cultivation, 179–81
Trichostrongylus axei, cultivation, 172–3, 217
Trombicula, larvae, feeding, 249, 250–4
akamushi, as vector of rat typhus, 254
larvae, feeding, 250
autumnalis, larvae, feeding, 251, 252, 253
deliensis, as vector of rat typhus, 254
larvae, feeding, 250
Trypanosoma spp.,
counting of organisms, 10
culture, 13–4
host infection,
distribution of, 29–30
early development, 25–6
established, 26–8
immunology of, 30–40
susceptibility to, 28–9
identification, 9